WORKING PAPERS
CHAPTERS 12-26

ACCOUNTING

WORKING PAPERS
CHAPTERS 12-26
Ellen Sweatt *Georgia Perimeter College*
William L. Sweatt, C.P.A.

ACCOUNTING
Sixth Edition

Charles T. Horngren
Walter T. Harrison
Linda S. Bamber

PEARSON

Prentice
Hall

Upper Saddle River, New Jersey 07458

VP/Editorial Director: Jeff Shelstad
Assistant Editor: Sam Goffinet
Manager, Print Production: Christy Mahon
Production Editor & Buyer: Carol O'Rourke
Printer/Binder: Courier, Stoughton

Pearson Prentice Hall™ is a trademark of Pearson Education, Inc.

10   9   8   7   6   5   4
ISBN 0-13-143612-0

Contents

Req. 1

Req. 2

Journal

DATE	ACCOUNTS AND EXPLANATIONS	POST. REF.	DEBIT	CREDIT

Req. 1

Req. 2

		Journal			
DATE		ACCOUNTS AND EXPLANATIONS	POST. REF.	DEBIT	CREDIT

Req. 1

Req. 2

Req. 1

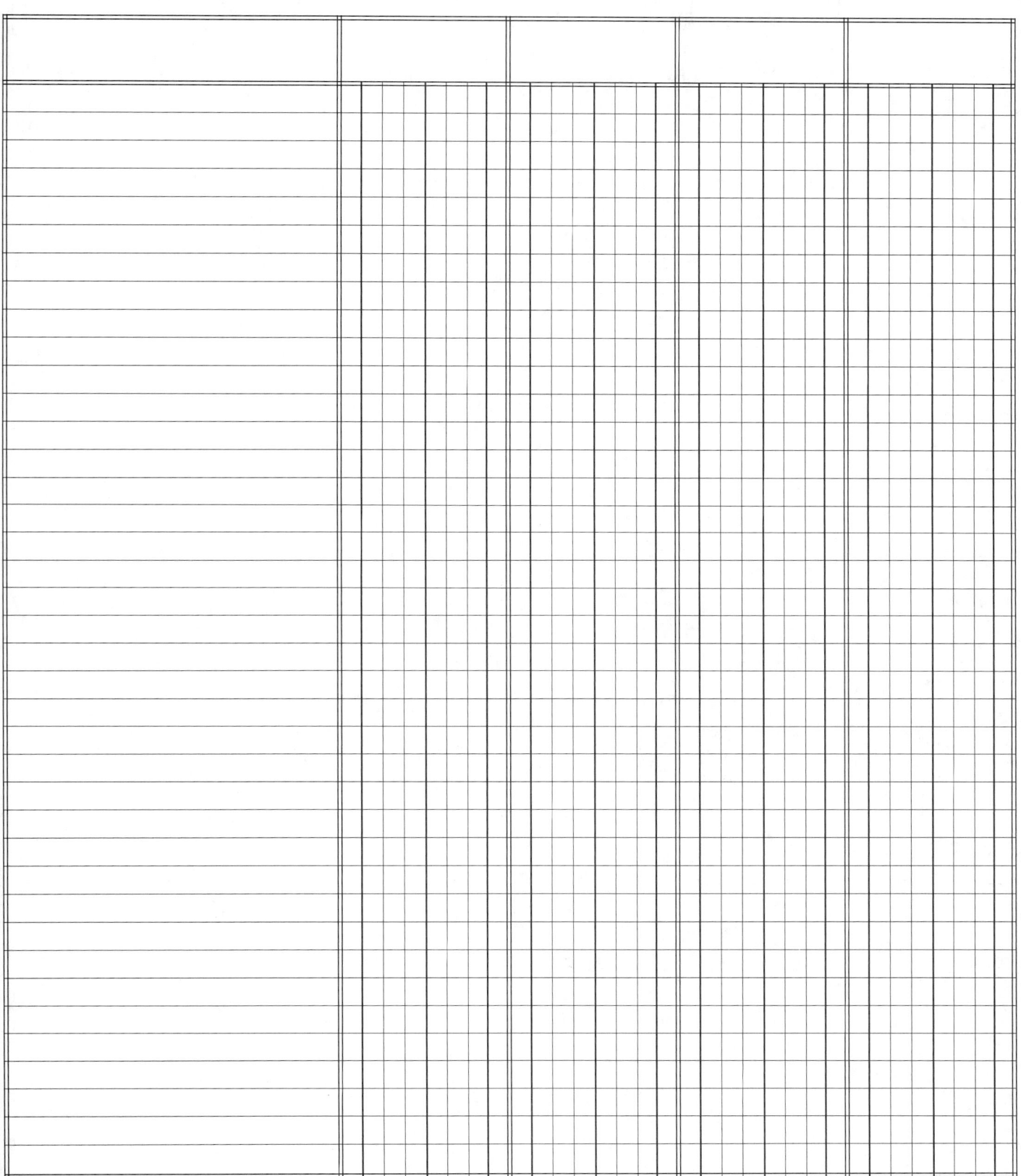

Req. 1

		Journal			
DATE		ACCOUNTS AND EXPLANATIONS	POST. REF.	DEBIT	CREDIT

Req. 2

Req. 1

S12-7

Req. 2

		Journal			
DATE		ACCOUNTS AND EXPLANATIONS	POST. REF.	DEBIT	CREDIT

Journal

DATE	ACCOUNTS AND EXPLANATIONS	POST. REF.	DEBIT	CREDIT

S12-9

Journal

DATE	ACCOUNTS AND EXPLANATIONS	POST. REF.	DEBIT	CREDIT

Chapter 12

NAME
SECTION
DATE

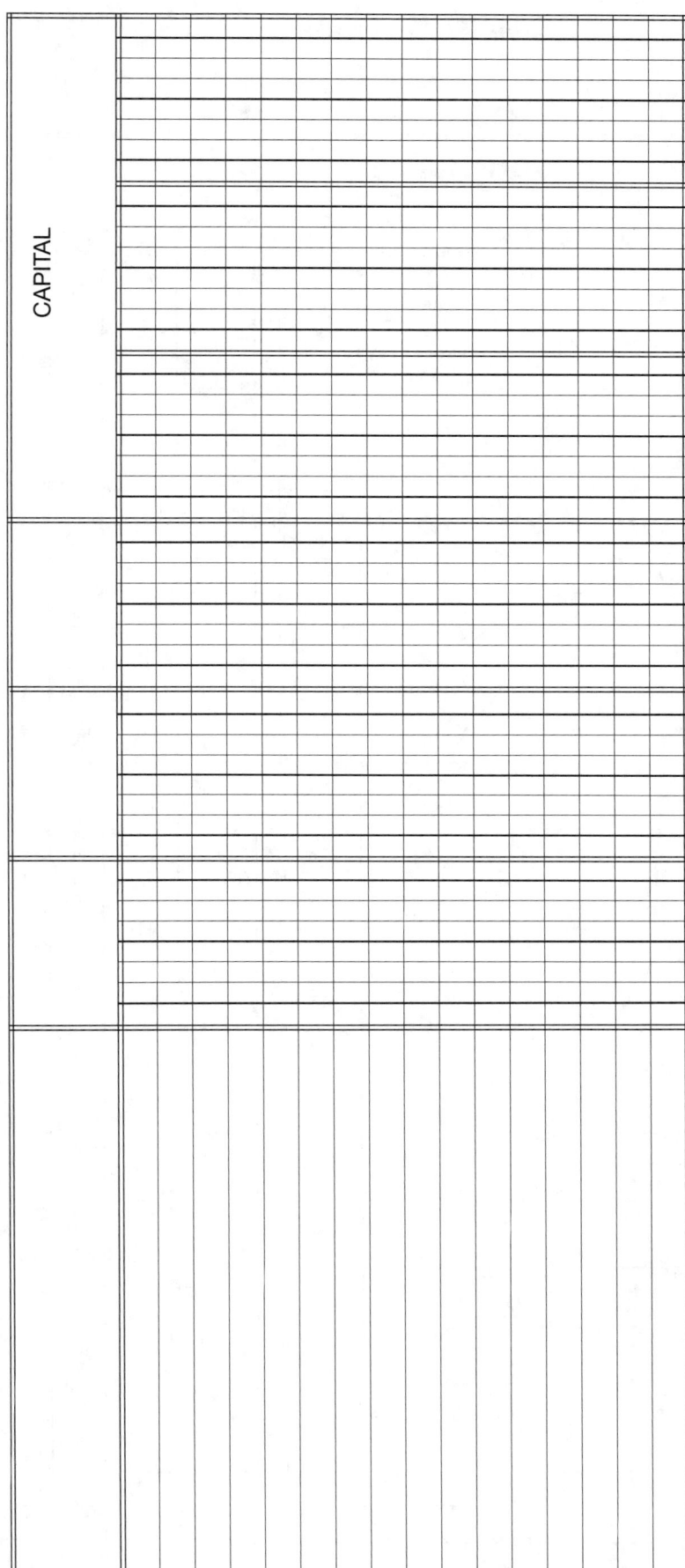

CAPITAL

			Journal															
DATE		ACCOUNTS AND EXPLANATIONS		POST. REF.	DEBIT						CREDIT							

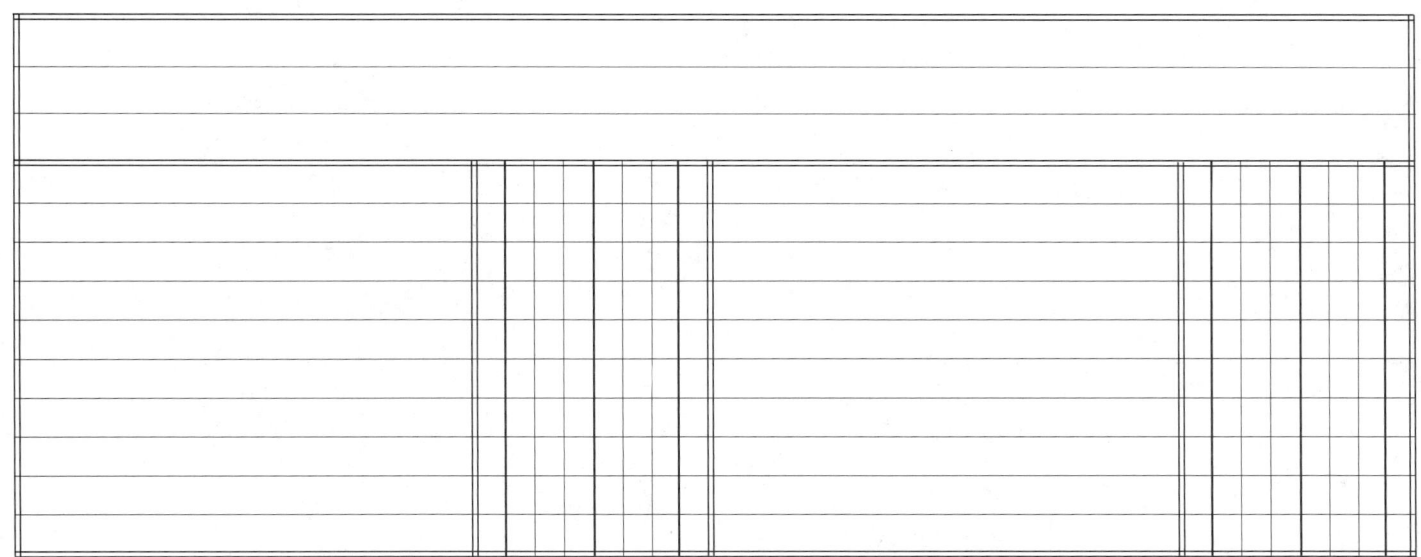

S12-14

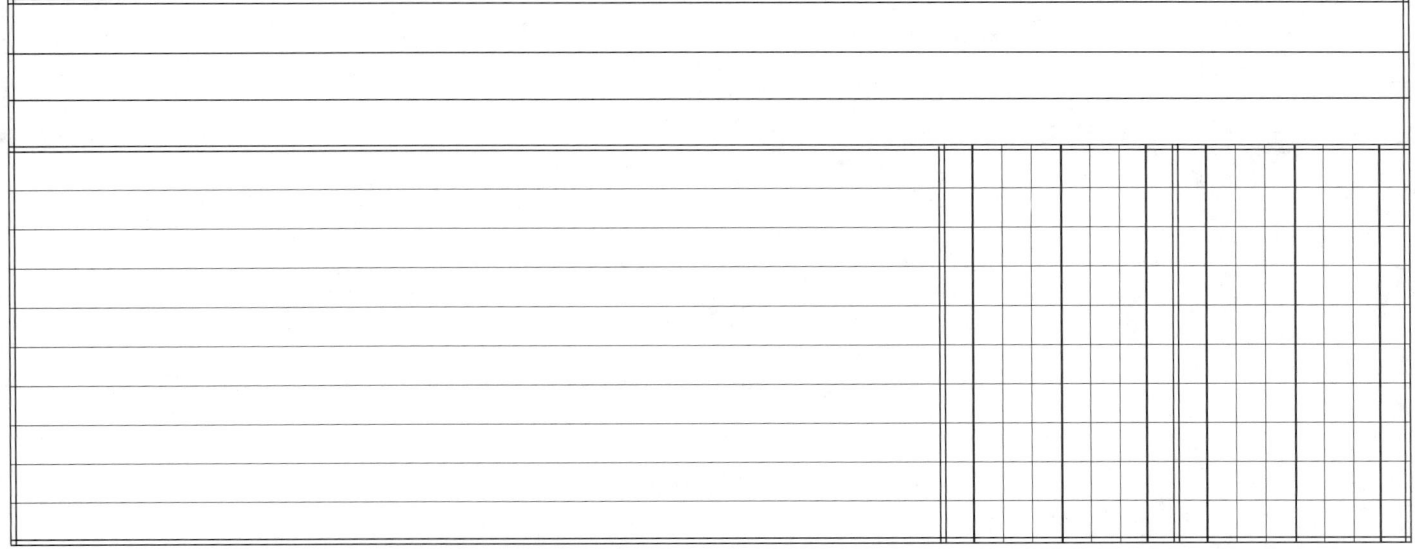

_____

_____

_____

_____

_____

_____

E12-2

		Journal			
DATE		ACCOUNTS AND EXPLANATIONS	POST. REF.	DEBIT	CREDIT

Journal

DATE	ACCOUNTS AND EXPLANATIONS	POST. REF.	DEBIT	CREDIT

Journal

DATE	ACCOUNTS AND EXPLANATIONS	POST. REF.	DEBIT	CREDIT

Journal

DATE	ACCOUNTS AND EXPLANATIONS	POST. REF.	DEBIT	CREDIT

Req. 1

Req. 2

NAME
SECTION
DATE

CAPITAL

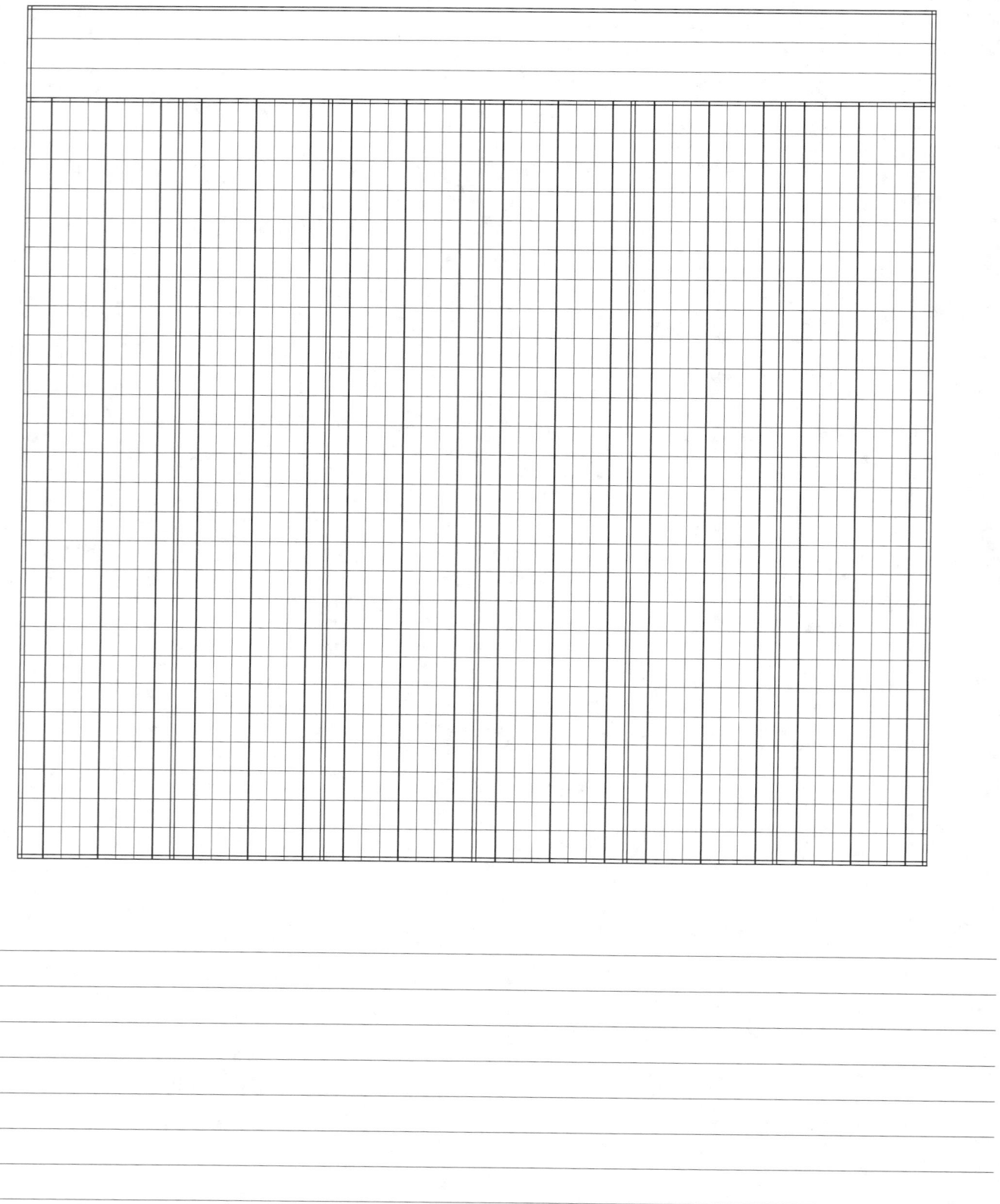

Reqs. 1 & 3

		Journal			
DATE		ACCOUNTS AND EXPLANATIONS	POST. REF.	DEBIT	CREDIT

Req. 2

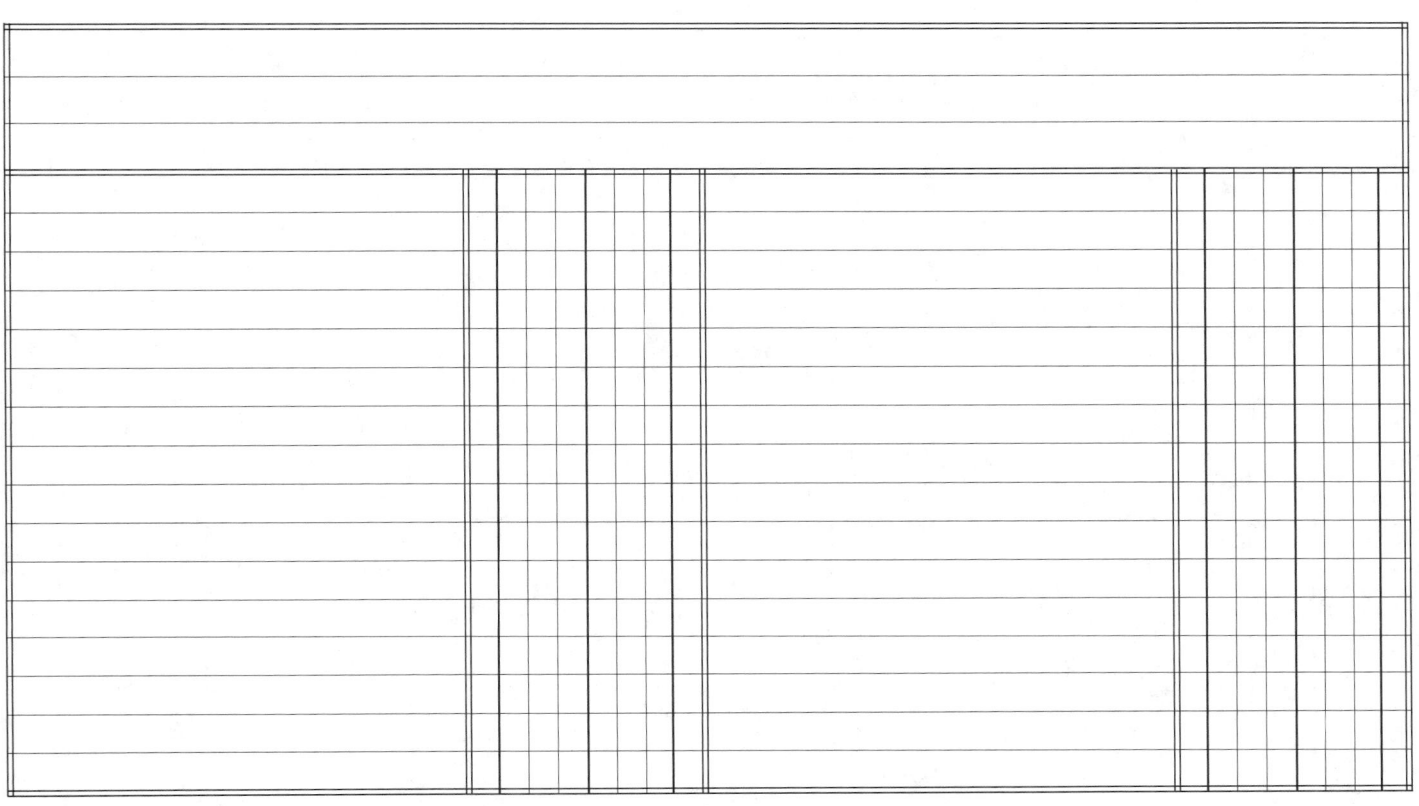

Reqs. 1 & 2

		Journal			
DATE		ACCOUNTS AND EXPLANATIONS	POST. REF.	DEBIT	CREDIT

Req. 3

			Journal					
DATE		ACCOUNTS AND EXPLANATIONS		POST. REF.		DEBIT		CREDIT

Req. 1

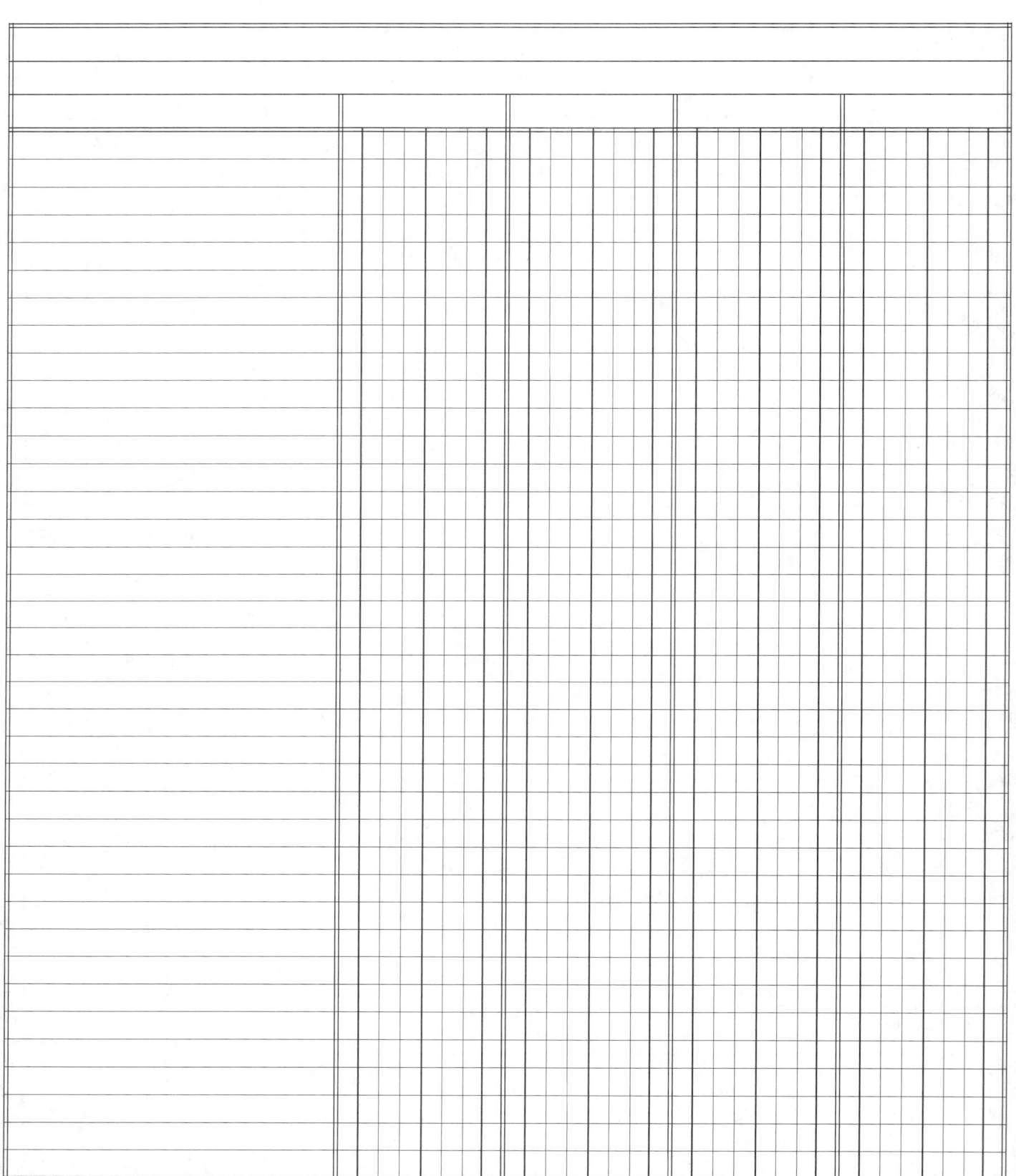

Req. 1 (Continued)

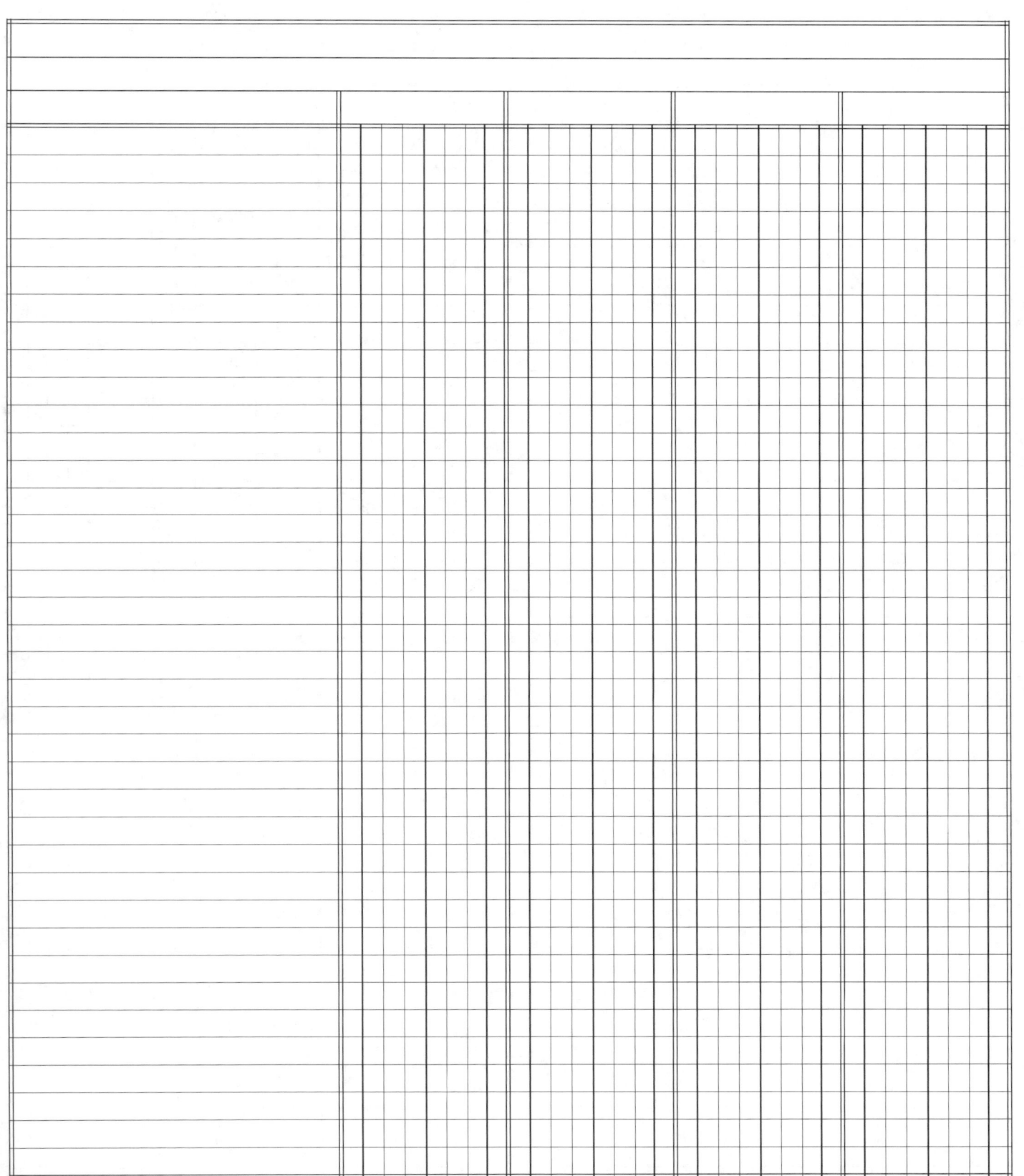

Req. 1 (Continued)

Req. 2

Reqs. 1–4

		Journal				
DATE		ACCOUNTS AND EXPLANATIONS	POST. REF.	DEBIT		CREDIT

Reqs. 1–4 (Continued)

		Journal				
DATE		ACCOUNTS AND EXPLANATIONS	POST. REF.	DEBIT		CREDIT

Req. 1

CAPITAL

Req. 2

Journal

DATE	ACCOUNTS AND EXPLANATIONS	POST. REF.	DEBIT	CREDIT

Req. 1

		Journal				
DATE		ACCOUNTS AND EXPLANATIONS	POST. REF.	DEBIT		CREDIT

Req. 2

Reqs. 1 & 3

		Journal			
DATE		ACCOUNTS AND EXPLANATIONS	POST. REF.	DEBIT	CREDIT

Req. 2

Reqs. 1–3

		Journal																			
DATE		ACCOUNTS AND EXPLANATIONS	POST. REF.		DEBIT						CREDIT										

Reqs. 1–3 (Continued)

DATE	ACCOUNTS AND EXPLANATIONS	POST. REF.	DEBIT	CREDIT

Req. 1

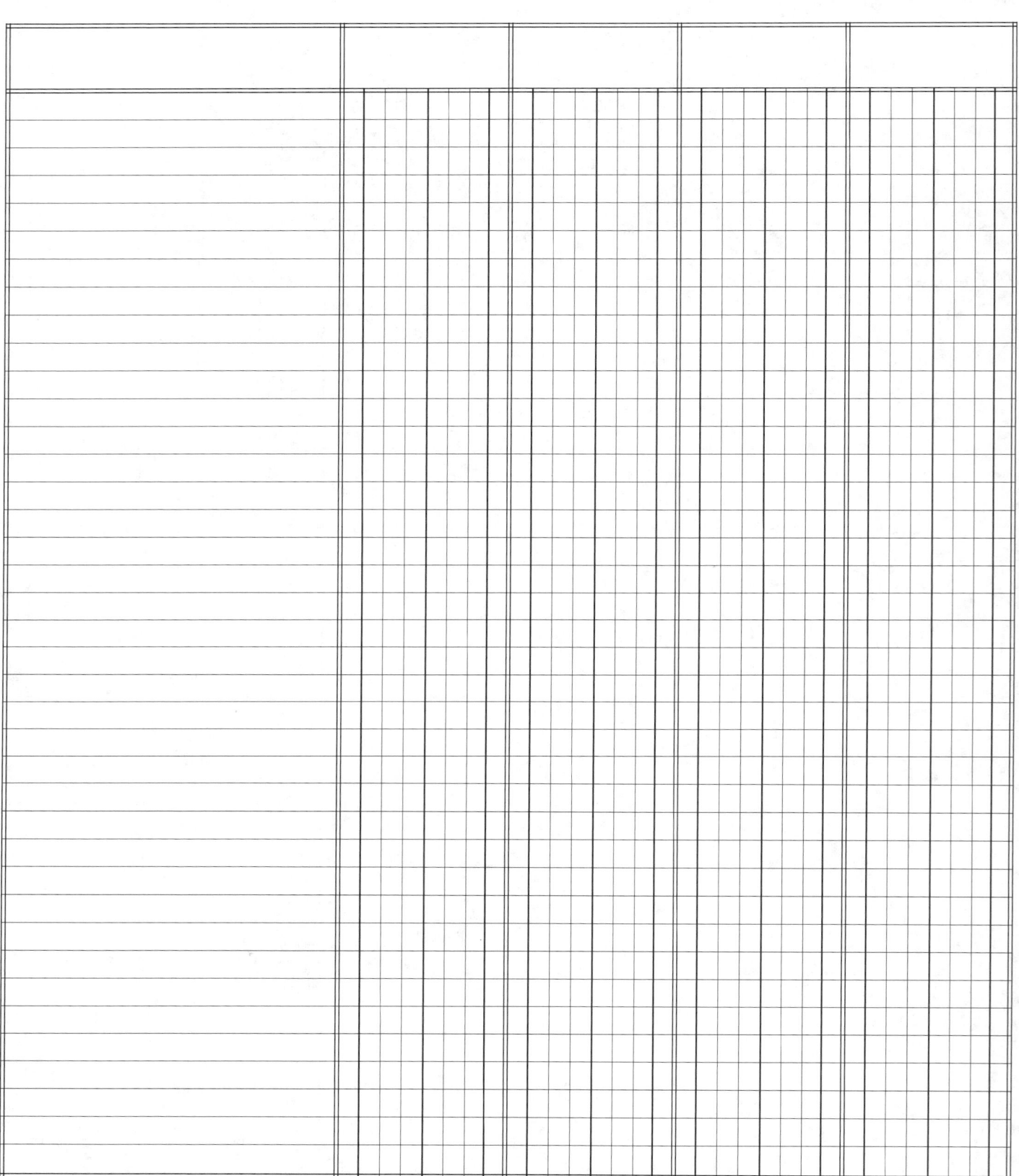

Req. 1 (Continued)

Req. 2

Reqs. 1–4

		Journal			
DATE		ACCOUNTS AND EXPLANATIONS	POST. REF.	DEBIT	CREDIT

Reqs. 1–4 (Continued)

		Journal			
DATE		ACCOUNTS AND EXPLANATIONS	POST. REF.	DEBIT	CREDIT

Chapter 12

Req. 1

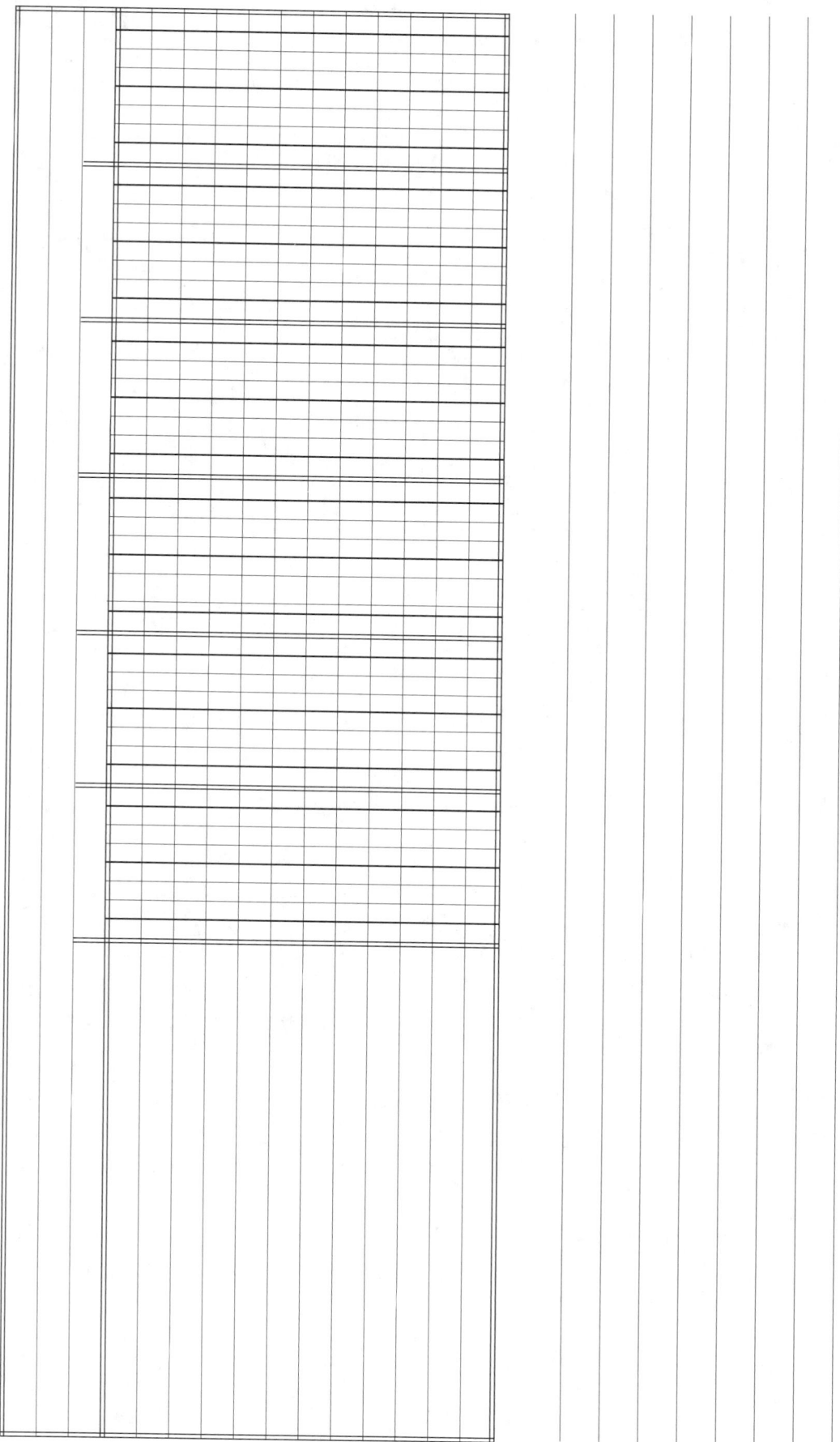

Req. 2

		Journal			
DATE		ACCOUNTS AND EXPLANATIONS	POST. REF.	DEBIT	CREDIT

Req. 1

		Journal				
DATE		ACCOUNTS AND EXPLANATIONS	POST. REF.	DEBIT		CREDIT

Req. 2

Reqs. 1–4

Reqs. 1–3

Chapter 12

Ethical Issue

Req. 1

		Journal				
DATE		ACCOUNTS AND EXPLANATIONS	POST. REF.	DEBIT		CREDIT

Req. 2

S13-2

Case A

Journal

DATE		ACCOUNTS AND EXPLANATIONS	POST. REF.	DEBIT	CREDIT

Case B

Journal

DATE		ACCOUNTS AND EXPLANATIONS	POST. REF.	DEBIT	CREDIT

Journal

DATE	ACCOUNTS AND EXPLANATIONS	POST. REF.	DEBIT	CREDIT

		Journal				
DATE		ACCOUNTS AND EXPLANATIONS	POST. REF.	DEBIT	CREDIT	

S13-8

Journal

DATE	ACCOUNTS AND EXPLANATIONS	POST. REF.	DEBIT	CREDIT

S13-12

		Journal				
DATE		ACCOUNTS AND EXPLANATIONS	POST. REF.	DEBIT		CREDIT

Req. 1

DATE	ACCOUNTS AND EXPLANATIONS	POST. REF.	DEBIT	CREDIT
	Journal			

Req. 2

Req. 1

		Journal			
DATE		ACCOUNTS AND EXPLANATIONS	POST. REF.	DEBIT	CREDIT

Req. 2

Journal

DATE	ACCOUNTS AND EXPLANATIONS	POST. REF.	DEBIT	CREDIT

E13-6

NAME
SECTION
DATE

E13-11

Req. 1

Journal

DATE	ACCOUNTS AND EXPLANATIONS	POST. REF.	DEBIT	CREDIT

Req. 2

Journal

DATE	ACCOUNTS AND EXPLANATIONS	POST. REF.	DEBIT	CREDIT

Req. 1

		Journal	POST. REF.	DEBIT	CREDIT
DATE		ACCOUNTS AND EXPLANATIONS			

Req. 2

Stockholders' Equity	

Reqs. 1–3

Req. 4

		Journal			
DATE	ACCOUNTS AND EXPLANATIONS	POST. REF.	DEBIT	CREDIT

Req. 5

Req. 1

Req. 2

		Journal			
DATE		ACCOUNTS AND EXPLANATIONS	POST. REF.	DEBIT	CREDIT

Req. 3

		Journal						
DATE		ACCOUNTS AND EXPLANATIONS	POST. REF.	DEBIT			CREDIT	

Req. 1

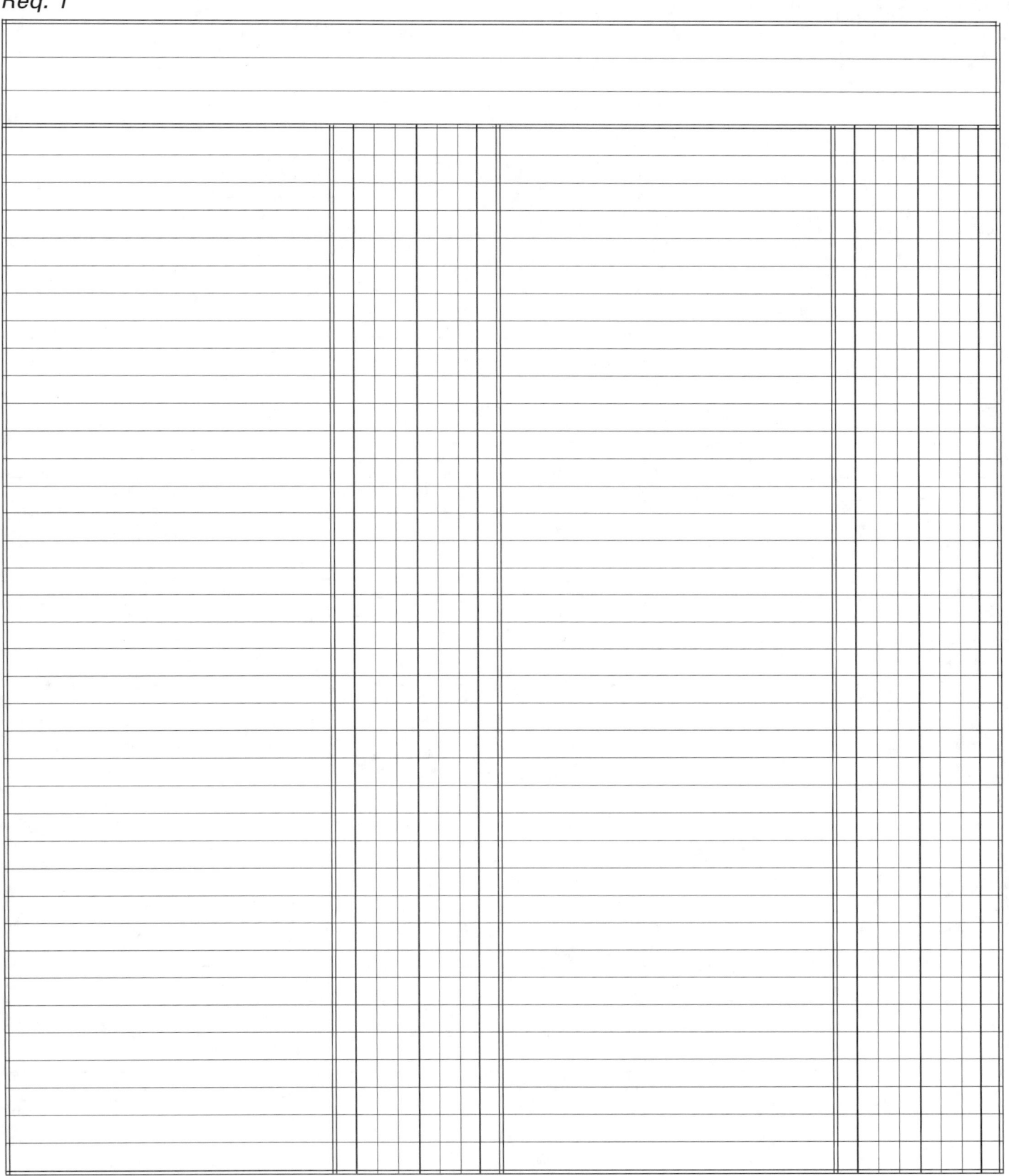

Reqs. 2 & 3

Req. 1a

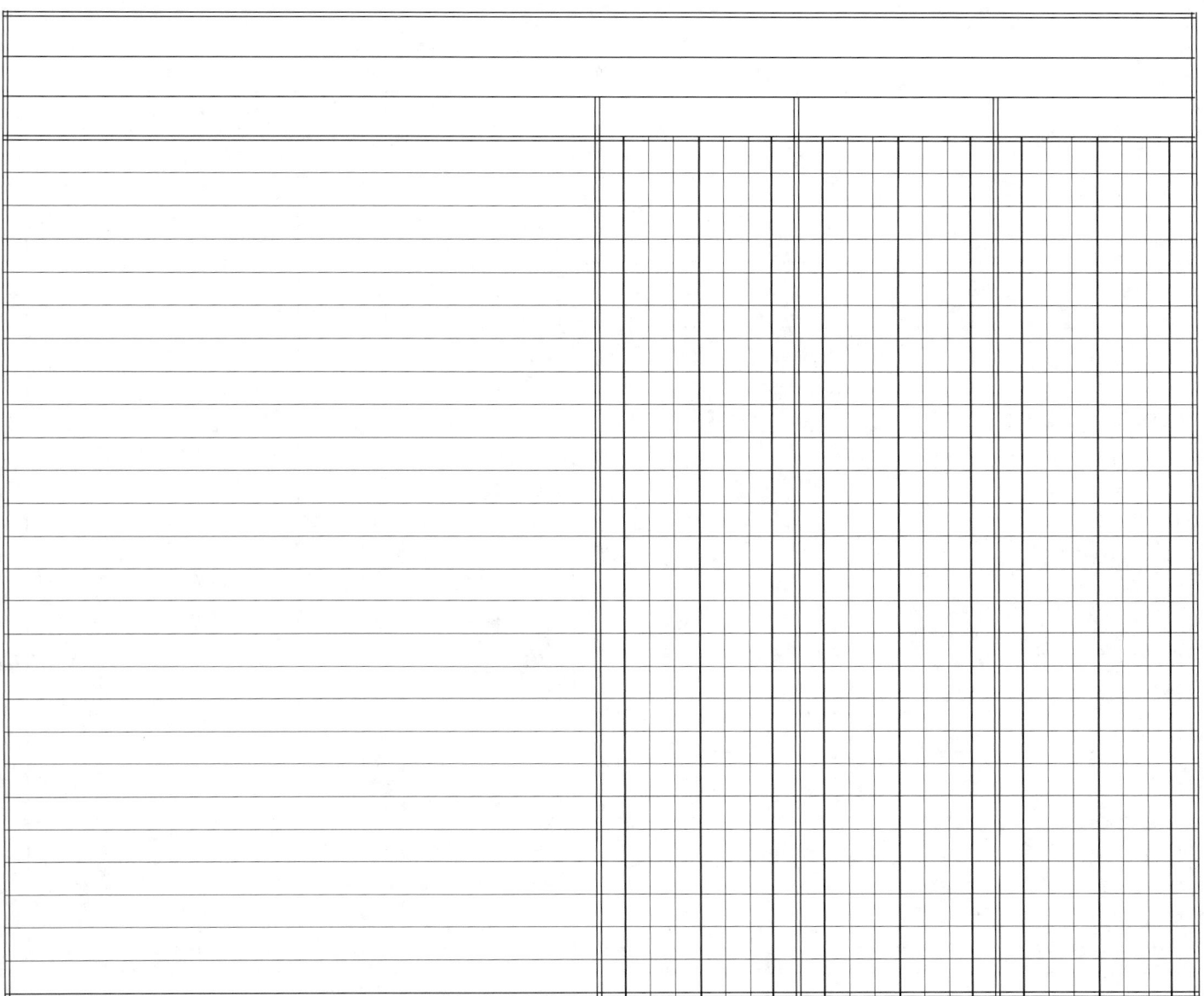

NAME
SECTION
DATE

Chapter 13

P13-7A(Continued)

Req. 1b

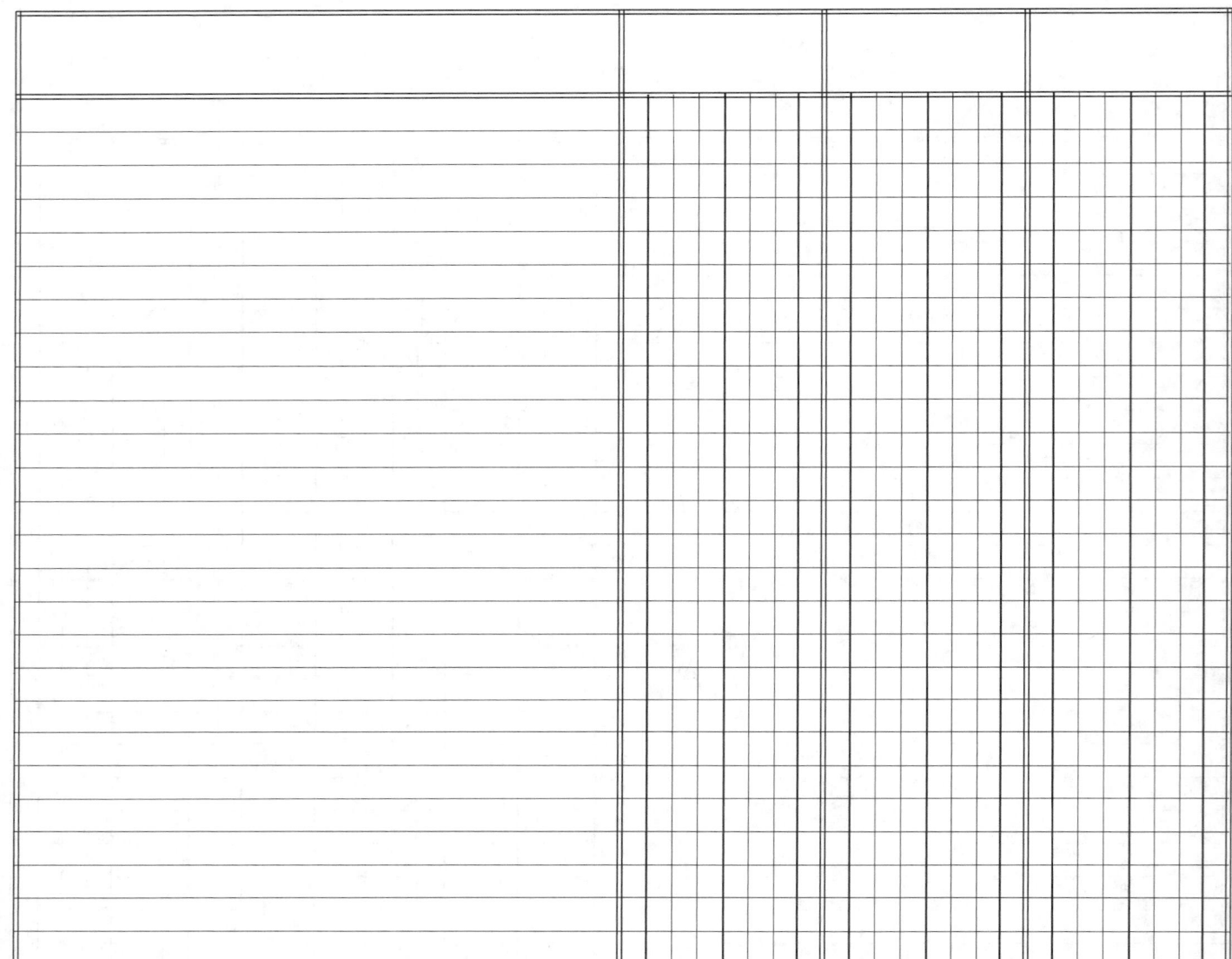

Req. 2

		Journal			
DATE		ACCOUNTS AND EXPLANATIONS	POST. REF.	DEBIT	CREDIT

Reqs. 1–5

Req. 6

Req. 1

Req. 2

		Journal			
DATE		ACCOUNTS AND EXPLANATIONS	POST. REF.	DEBIT	CREDIT

Req. 3

Req. 1

	Journal			
DATE	ACCOUNTS AND EXPLANATIONS	POST. REF.	DEBIT	CREDIT

Req. 2

Req. 1–3

Req. 4

Journal

DATE		ACCOUNTS AND EXPLANATIONS	POST. REF.	DEBIT	CREDIT

Req. 5

Computation:

Computation:

Req. 1

_____

_____

_____

_____

Req. 2

DATE	ACCOUNTS AND EXPLANATIONS	POST. REF.	DEBIT	CREDIT

Journal

Req. 3

		Journal				
DATE		ACCOUNTS AND EXPLANATIONS	POST. REF.	DEBIT		CREDIT

Req. 1

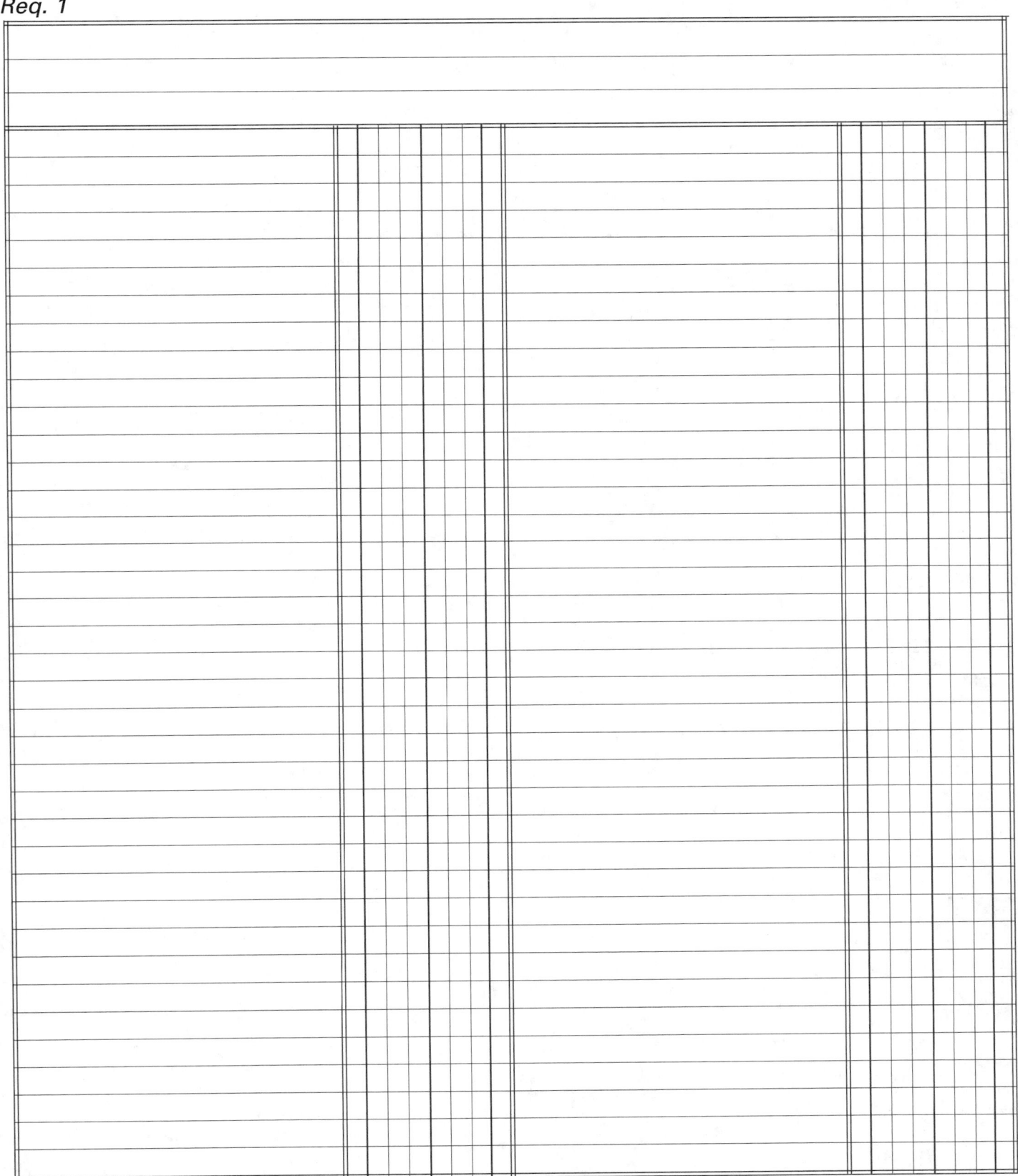

Reqs. 2 & 3

Req. 1a

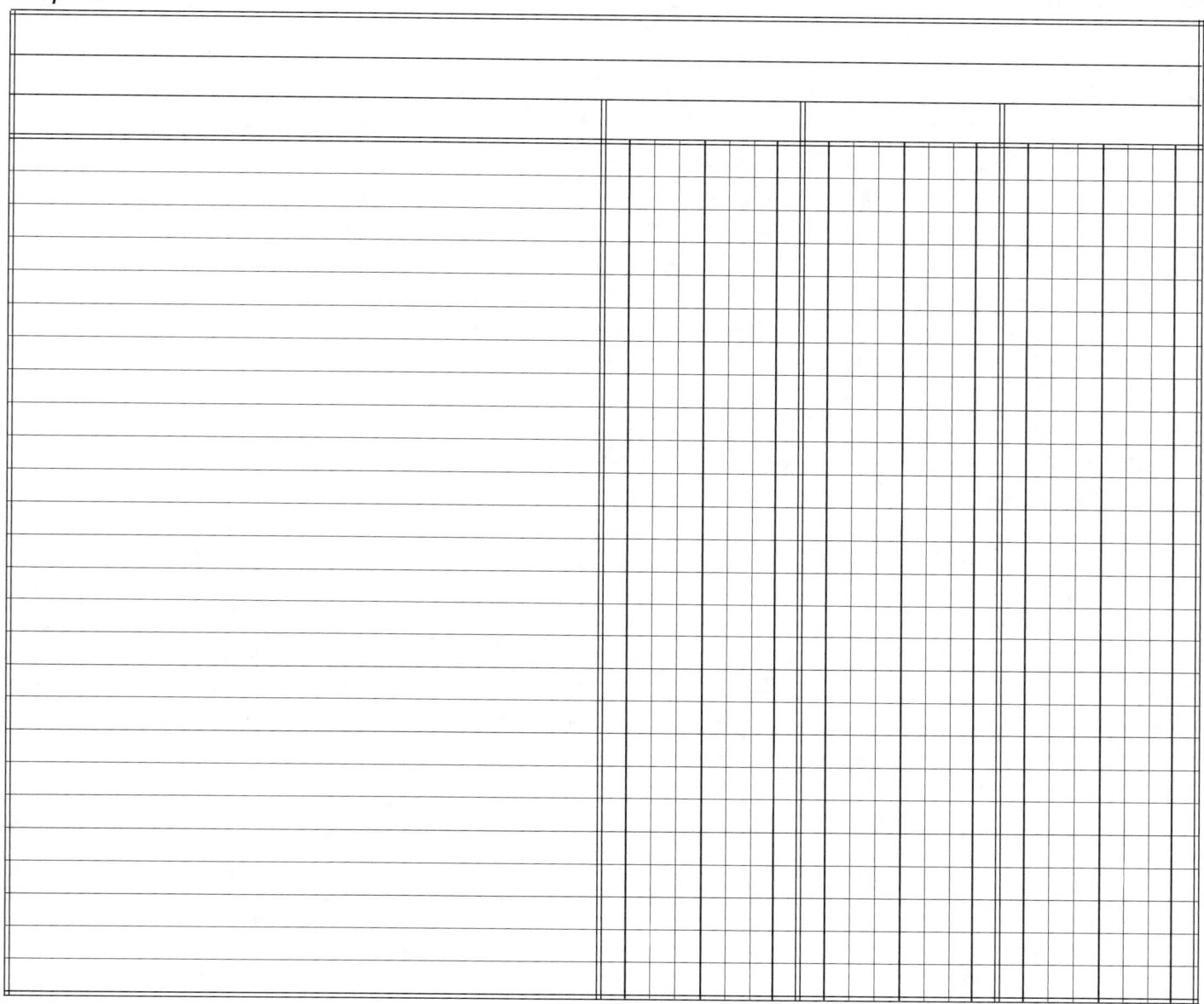

Req. 1b

Req. 2

		Journal																
DATE		ACCOUNTS AND EXPLANATIONS	POST. REF.		DEBIT						CREDIT					

Req. 1–4

Req. 5

Req. 1

Req. 2

Journal

DATE	ACCOUNTS AND EXPLANATIONS	POST. REF.	DEBIT	CREDIT

Req. 3

Reqs. 1 & 2

Journal

DATE	ACCOUNTS AND EXPLANATIONS	POST. REF.	DEBIT	CREDIT

NAME
SECTION
DATE

Chapter 13

Decision Case 1
(Continued)

Req. 3
Plan 1:

Plan 2:

NAME
SECTION
DATE

Chapter 13

Decision Case 1
(Continued)

Req. 4

Decision Case 2

Reqs. 1–4

Reqs. 1 & 2

Financial Statement Case

Reqs. 1–4

Reqs. 1–3

NAME
SECTION
DATE

Chapter 13

Team Project
(Continued)

Reqs. 1–3 (continued)

Team Project

(Continued)

Reqs. 1–3 (continued)

Chapter 14

Excel Application Exercise

Req. 1

		General Journal				
DATE		ACCOUNTS AND EXPLANATIONS	POST. REF.	DEBIT	CREDIT	

Req. 2

S14-2

Req. 1

Req. 2

General Journal

DATE	ACCOUNTS AND EXPLANATIONS	POST. REF.	DEBIT	CREDIT

Reqs. 1–3

NAME
SECTION
DATE

Reqs. 1 & 2

Req. 1

	Journal						
DATE	ACCOUNTS AND EXPLANATIONS	POST. REF.	DEBIT		CREDIT		

Req. 2

Req. 3

Req. 1

General Journal

DATE		ACCOUNTS AND EXPLANATIONS	DEBIT	CREDIT

Req. 2

Reqs. 1 & 2

General Journal

DATE	ACCOUNTS AND EXPLANATIONS	POST. REF.	DEBIT	CREDIT

General Journal

DATE	ACCOUNTS AND EXPLANATIONS	POST. REF.	DEBIT	CREDIT

General Journal

DATE	ACCOUNTS AND EXPLANATIONS	POST. REF.	DEBIT	CREDIT

Req. a

Req. b

Req. c

Computations:

E14-12

Req. 1

Req. 2

Chapter 14

NAME
SECTION
DATE

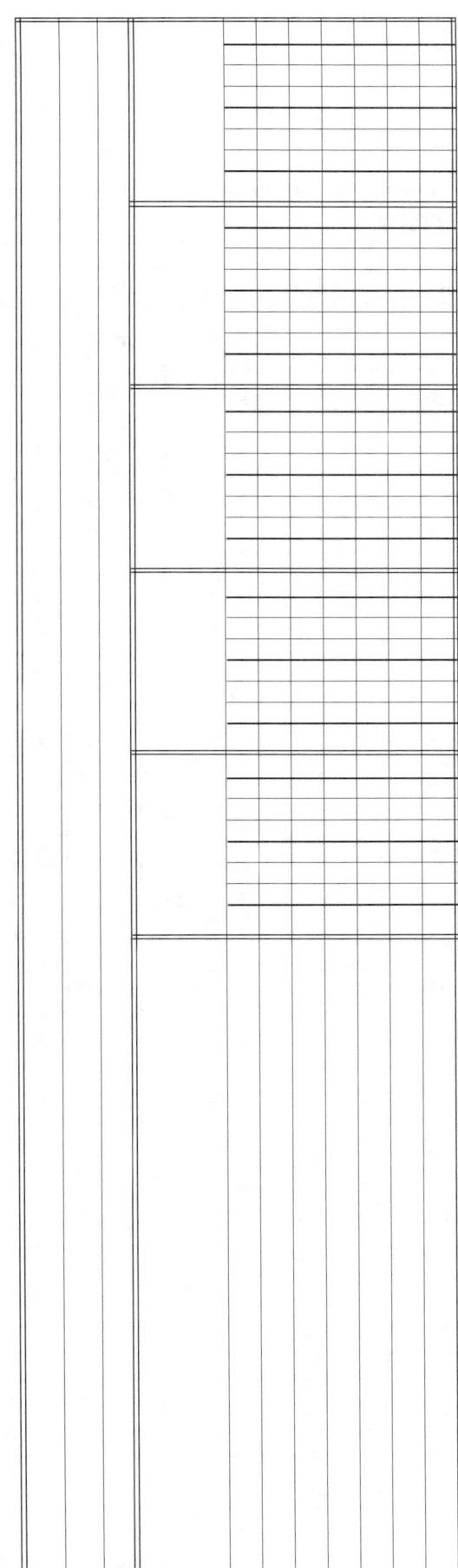

Req. 1

Journal

DATE	ACCOUNTS AND EXPLANATIONS	POST. REF.	DEBIT	CREDIT

Req. 2

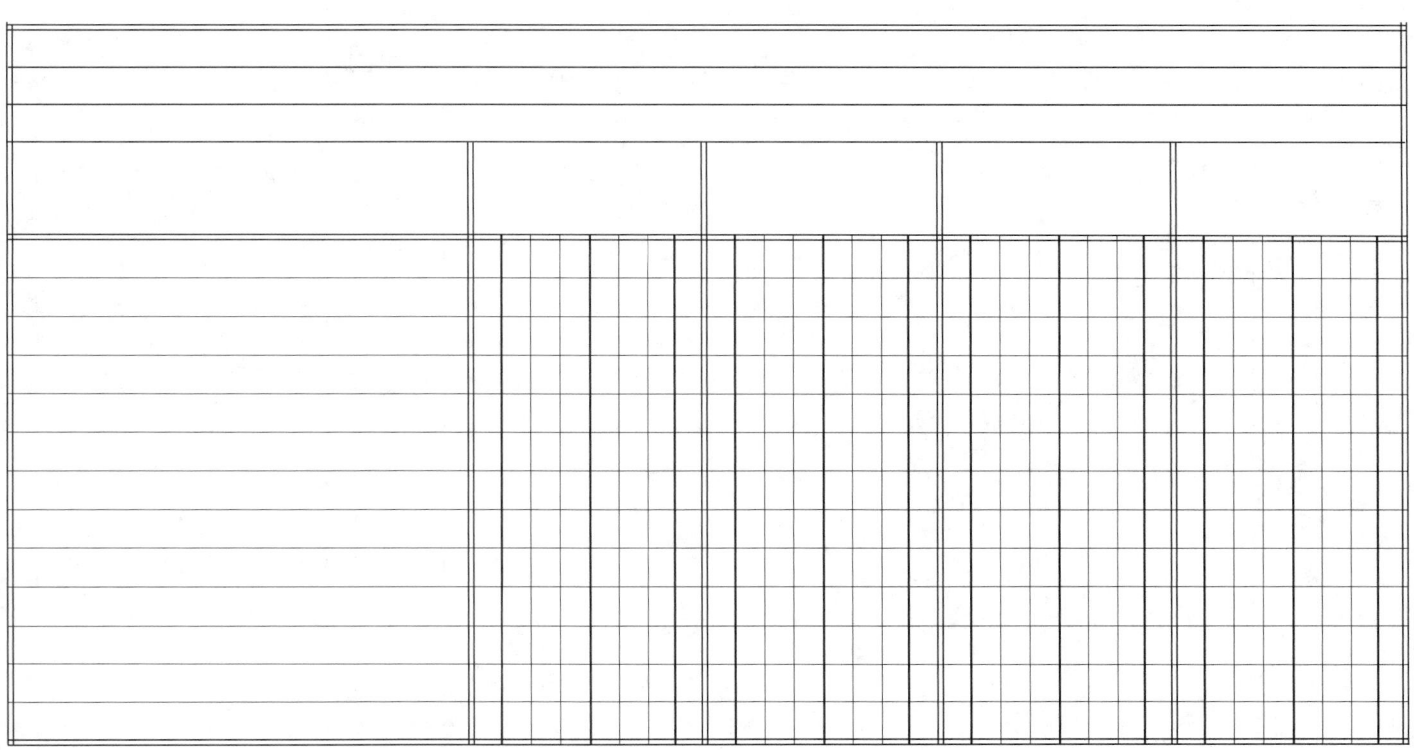

Computations:

General Journal

DATE	ACCOUNTS AND EXPLANATIONS	POST. REF.	DEBIT	CREDIT

General Journal

DATE		ACCOUNTS AND EXPLANATIONS	POST. REF.	DEBIT	CREDIT

Req. 1

General Journal

DATE	ACCOUNTS AND EXPLANATIONS	POST. REF.	DEBIT	CREDIT

Req. 2

Reqs. 1 & 2

Req. 1

		General Journal			
DATE		ACCOUNTS AND EXPLANATIONS	POST. REF.	DEBIT	CREDIT

Req. 2

Req. 3

Req. 1

Computations

Req. 2

Reqs. 1–4

		General Journal				
DATE		ACCOUNTS AND EXPLANATIONS	POST. REF.	DEBIT		CREDIT

General Journal

DATE	ACCOUNTS AND EXPLANATIONS	POST. REF.	DEBIT	CREDIT

Req. 1

General Journal						
DATE	ACCOUNTS AND EXPLANATIONS	POST. REF.	DEBIT		CREDIT	

Req. 2

Req. 1

General Journal					
DATE	ACCOUNTS AND EXPLANATIONS	POST. REF.	DEBIT		CREDIT

Req. 2

Req. 3

Computation:

Req. 1

Computations

Req. 2

Reqs. 1–4

Reqs. 1–3

NAME
SECTION
DATE

Chapter 14

Decision Case 1
(Continued)

Reqs. 1–3 (Continued)

Reqs. 1–3

NAME
SECTION
DATE

Chapter 14

Decision Case 2
(Continued)

Reqs. 1–3 (Continued)

Reqs. 1–3

NAME
SECTION
DATE

Chapter 14

Financial
Statement Case

Reqs. 1–3

S15-2

S15-3

General Journal

DATE	ACCOUNTS AND EXPLANATIONS	POST. REF.	DEBIT	CREDIT

General Journal

DATE		ACCOUNTS AND EXPLANATIONS	POST. REF.	DEBIT	CREDIT

General Journal

DATE	ACCOUNTS AND EXPLANATIONS	POST. REF.	DEBIT	CREDIT

General Journal

DATE		ACCOUNTS AND EXPLANATIONS	POST. REF.	DEBIT	CREDIT

1.

2.

3.

General Journal					
DATE	ACCOUNTS AND EXPLANATIONS	POST. REF.	DEBIT		CREDIT

General Journal

DATE		ACCOUNTS AND EXPLANATIONS	POST. REF.	DEBIT	CREDIT

1. – 3.

4.

		General Journal			
DATE		ACCOUNTS AND EXPLANATIONS	POST. REF.	DEBIT	CREDIT

1.

_____

_____

_____

2.

	General Journal			
DATE	ACCOUNTS AND EXPLANATIONS	POST. REF.	DEBIT	CREDIT

3.

General Journal

DATE	ACCOUNTS AND EXPLANATIONS	POST. REF.	DEBIT	CREDIT

General Journal

DATE	ACCOUNTS AND EXPLANATIONS	POST. REF.	DEBIT	CREDIT

Reqs. a – c

General Journal

DATE		ACCOUNTS AND EXPLANATIONS	POST. REF.	DEBIT	CREDIT

Req. 2

_____

_____

_____

_____

_____

_____

E15-4

_____

a. _____

b. _____

c. _____

d. _____

e. _____

Req. 1

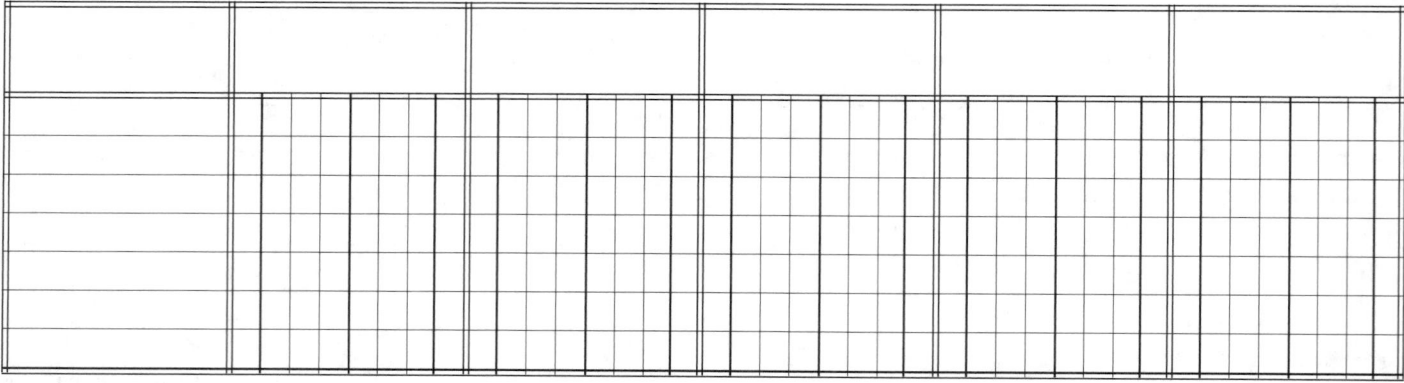

Req. 2

		General Journal			
DATE		ACCOUNTS AND EXPLANATIONS	POST. REF.	DEBIT	CREDIT

Req. 1

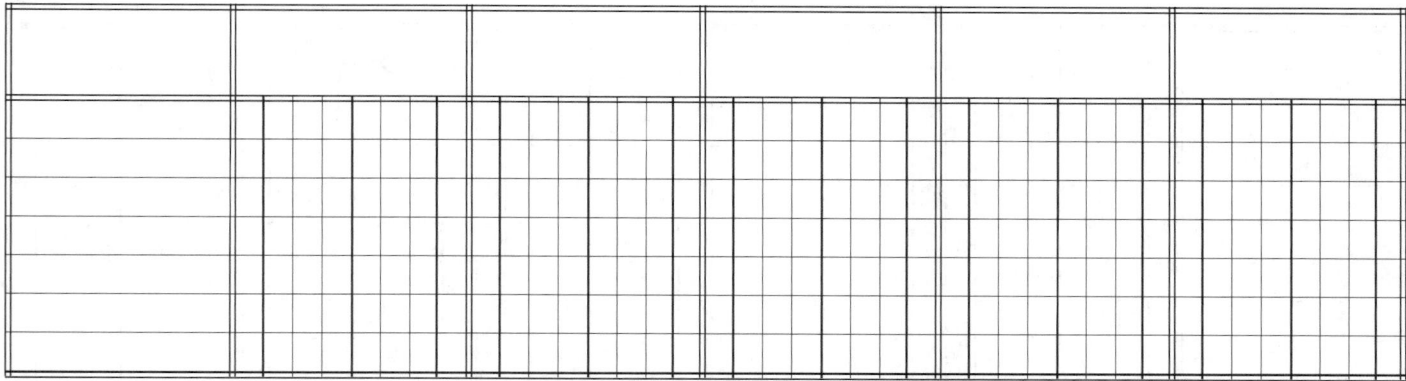

Req. 2

		General Journal			
DATE		ACCOUNTS AND EXPLANATIONS	POST. REF.	DEBIT	CREDIT

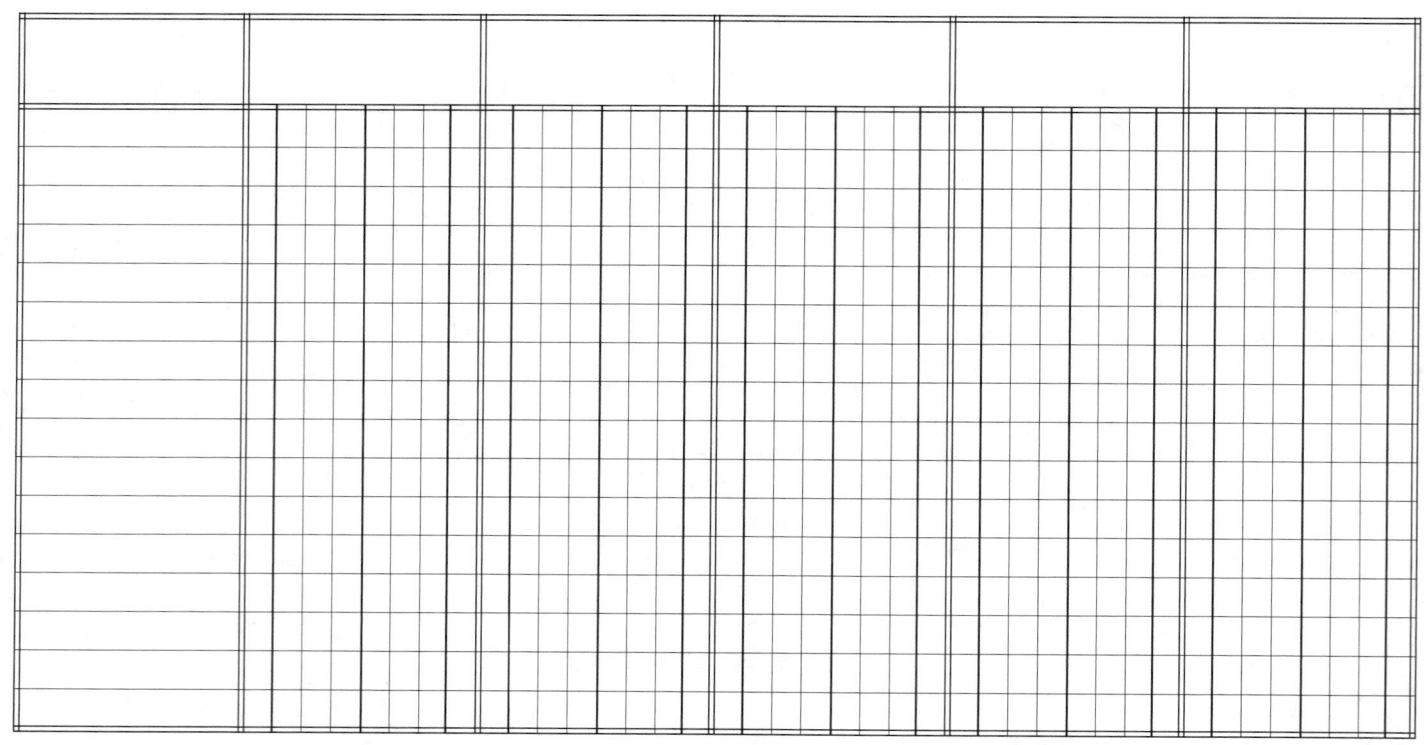

E15-8

General Journal

DATE	ACCOUNTS AND EXPLANATIONS	POST. REF.	DEBIT	CREDIT

General Journal

DATE		ACCOUNTS AND EXPLANATIONS	POST. REF.	DEBIT	CREDIT

Reqs. 1 and 2

Req. 3

General Journal

DATE		ACCOUNTS AND EXPLANATIONS	POST. REF.	DEBIT	CREDIT

General Journal

DATE	ACCOUNTS AND EXPLANATIONS	POST. REF.	DEBIT	CREDIT

Reqs. 1–4

5.

6.

Req. 1

		General Journal				
DATE		ACCOUNTS AND EXPLANATIONS	POST. REF.	DEBIT	CREDIT

Req. 2

Req. 1

Req. 3

Req. 2

		General Journal				
DATE		ACCOUNTS AND EXPLANATIONS	POST. REF.	DEBIT	CREDIT	

Reqs. 1 & 2

General Journal

DATE	ACCOUNTS AND EXPLANATIONS	POST. REF.	DEBIT	CREDIT

General Journal

DATE		ACCOUNTS AND EXPLANATIONS	POST. REF.	DEBIT	CREDIT

1.

2.

3.

	General Journal			
DATE	ACCOUNTS AND EXPLANATIONS	POST. REF.	DEBIT	CREDIT

4.

Req. 1

General Journal				
DATE	ACCOUNTS AND EXPLANATIONS	POST. REF.	DEBIT	CREDIT

Req. 2

Req. 1

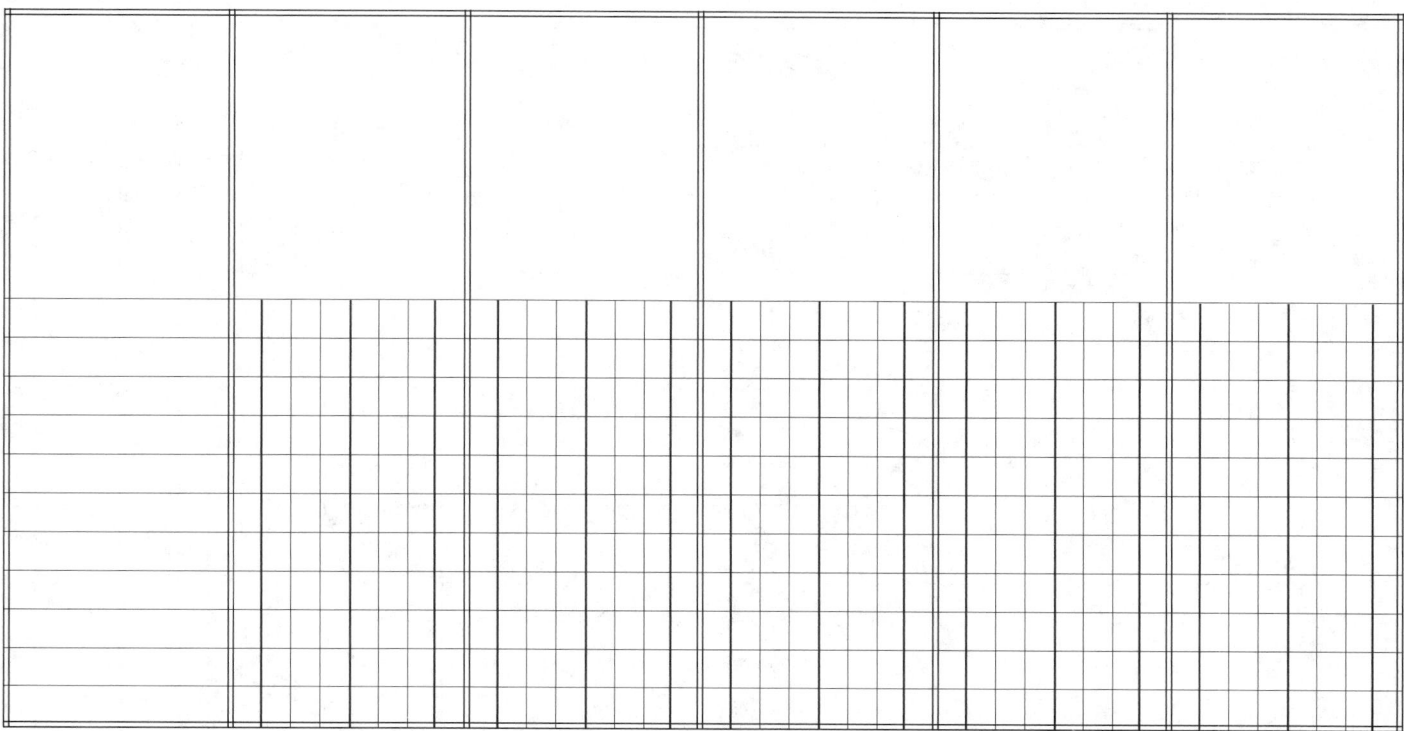

Req. 2

General Journal

DATE		ACCOUNTS AND EXPLANATIONS	POST. REF.	DEBIT	CREDIT

Req. 2 (Continued)

General Journal

DATE	ACCOUNTS AND EXPLANATIONS	POST. REF.	DEBIT	CREDIT

Req. 3

Reqs. 1 & 2

Reqs. 1 & 2 (Continued)

Req. 1

Req. 3

Req. 2

General Journal							
DATE	ACCOUNTS AND EXPLANATIONS	POST. REF.	DEBIT			CREDIT	

Reqs. 1 & 2

Req. 3

General Journal

DATE	ACCOUNTS AND EXPLANATIONS	POST. REF.	DEBIT	CREDIT

		Journal			
DATE		ACCOUNTS AND EXPLANATIONS	POST. REF.	DEBIT	CREDIT

1.

2.

3.

General Journal

DATE	ACCOUNTS AND EXPLANATIONS	POST. REF.	DEBIT	CREDIT

4.

Req. 1

General Journal					
DATE	ACCOUNTS AND EXPLANATIONS	POST. REF.	DEBIT	CREDIT	

Req. 2

Req. 1

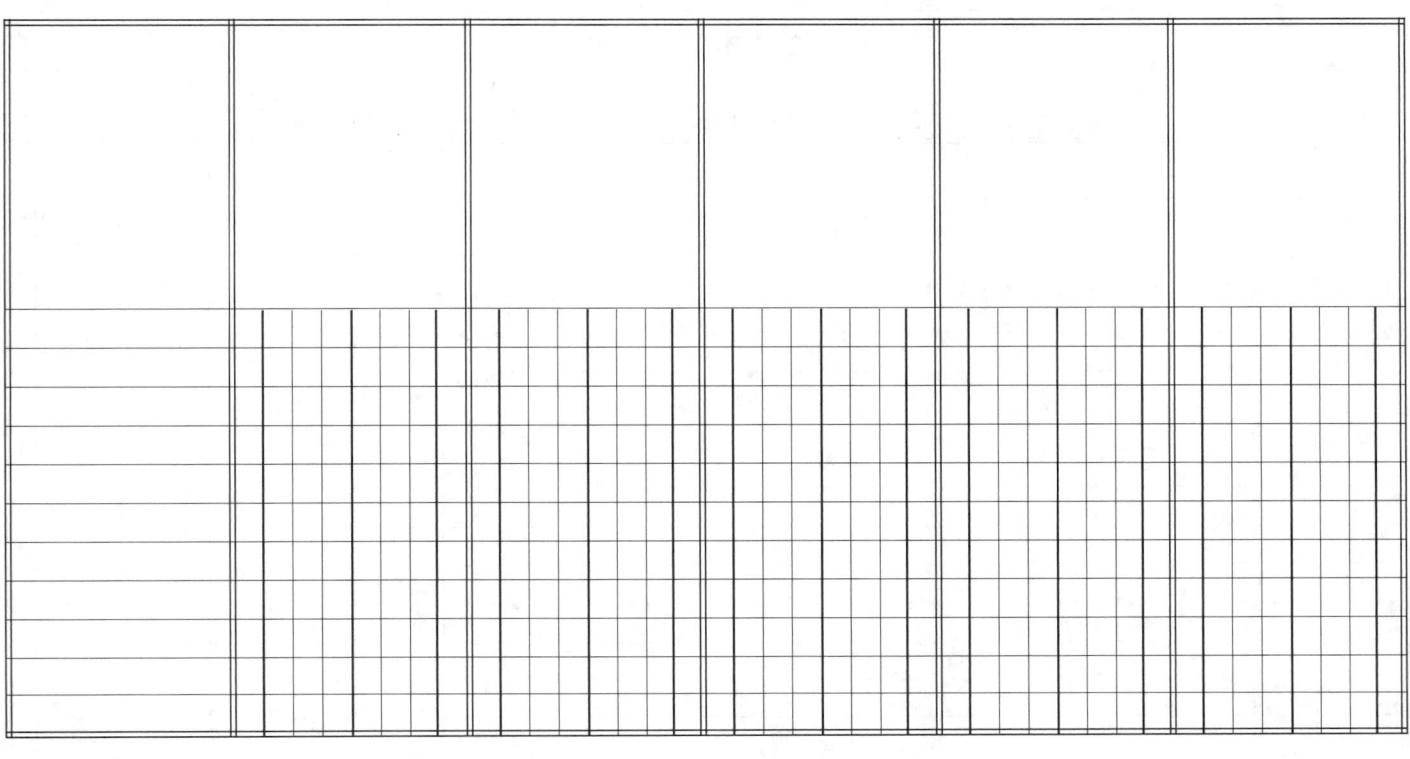

Req. 3

Req. 2

General Journal

DATE	ACCOUNTS AND EXPLANATIONS	POST. REF.	DEBIT	CREDIT

Req. 1

Reqs. 1 (Continued) & 2

Req. 1

NAME
SECTION
DATE

Chapter 15

Decision Case 1
(Continued)

Req. 2

Ethical Issue

NAME
SECTION
DATE

Chapter 15

Financial Statement Case

Reqs. 1–3

Team Project

Req. 1

Req. 2

Req. a

Req. b

Req. c

Req. 1

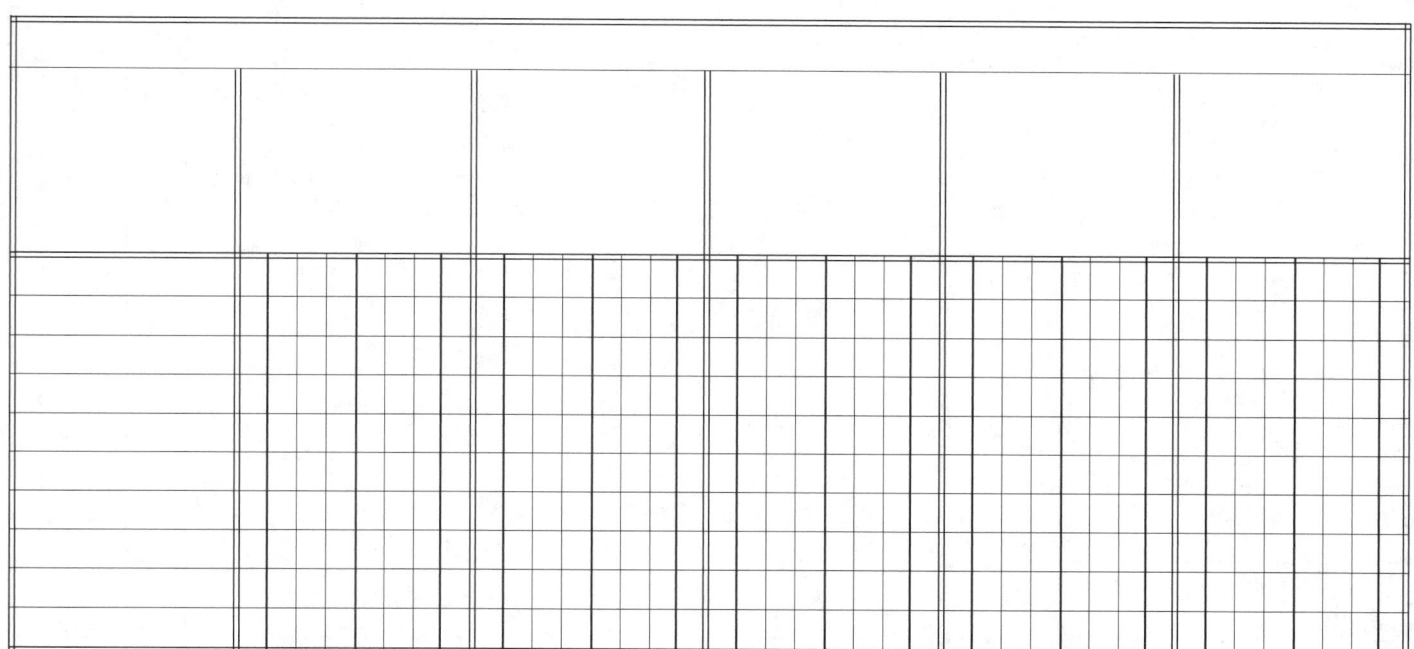

Req. 2

Req. 3

		General Journal			
DATE		ACCOUNTS AND EXPLANATIONS	POST. REF.	DEBIT	CREDIT

S16-2

General Journal

DATE	ACCOUNTS AND EXPLANATIONS	POST. REF.	DEBIT	CREDIT

1.

_____

2.

		General Journal																				
DATE		ACCOUNTS AND EXPLANATIONS	POST. REF.		DEBIT						CREDIT					

1.

		General Journal																				
DATE		ACCOUNTS AND TITLES	POST. REF.		DEBIT							CREDIT					

2.

1.

DATE	ACCOUNTS AND EXPLANATIONS	DEBIT	CREDIT

General Journal

2.

1.

_____

_____

_____

2.

	General Journal			
DATE	ACCOUNTS AND EXPLANATIONS	POST. REF.	DEBIT	CREDIT

3.

General Journal

DATE	ACCOUNTS AND EXPLANATIONS	POST REF.	DEBIT	CREDIT

General Journal

DATE	ACCOUNTS AND EXPLANATIONS	POST. REF.	DEBIT	CREDIT

Req. 1

General Journal

DATE		ACCOUNTS AND EXPLANATIONS	POST. REF.	DEBIT	CREDIT

Req. 2

General Journal

DATE	ACCOUNTS AND EXPLANATIONS	POST. REF.	DEBIT	CREDIT

General Journal

DATE	ACCOUNTS AND EXPLANATIONS	POST. REF.	DEBIT	CREDIT

Req. 1

Req. 2

General Journal

DATE	ACCOUNTS AND EXPLANATIONS	POST. REF.	DEBIT	CREDIT

Req. 3

General Journal

DATE	ACCOUNTS AND EXPLANATIONS	POST. REF.	DEBIT	CREDIT

Reqs. 1–3

Req. 1 _____

Req. 2

		General Journal				
DATE		ACCOUNTS AND EXPLANATIONS	POST. REF.	DEBIT	CREDIT	

Req. 3

General Journal

DATE	ACCOUNTS AND EXPLANATIONS	POST. REF.	DEBIT	CREDIT

Req. 1

Req. 2

Req. 1

General Journal

DATE	ACCOUNTS AND EXPLANATIONS	POST. REF.	DEBIT	CREDIT

Req. 2

Req. 1

		General Journal				
DATE		ACCOUNTS AND EXPLANATIONS	POST. REF.	DEBIT	CREDIT	

Req. 2

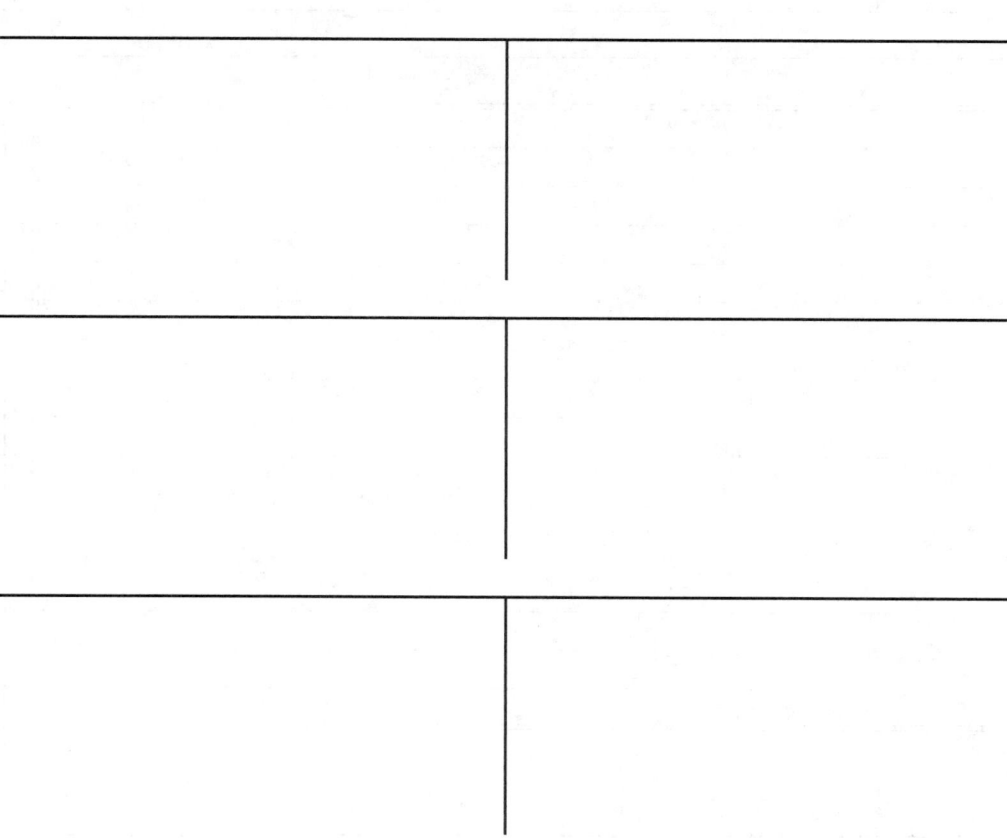

Req. 3

Req. 1

General Journal				
DATE	ACCOUNTS AND EXPLANATIONS	POST. REF.	DEBIT	CREDIT

Req. 2

	General Journal			
DATE	ACCOUNTS AND EXPLANATIONS	POST. REF.	DEBIT	CREDIT

Req. 1

General Journal

DATE		ACCOUNTS AND EXPLANATIONS	POST. REF.	DEBIT	CREDIT

Req. 2

Req. 1

	General Journal			
DATE	ACCOUNTS AND EXPLANATIONS	POST. REF.	DEBIT	CREDIT

Req. 2

Req. 1

General Journal

DATE		ACCOUNTS AND EXPLANATIONS	POST. REF.	DEBIT	CREDIT

_____
                            |
                            |
                            |
                            |
                            |

_____
                            |
                            |
                            |
                            |

_____
                            |
                            |
                            |

Req. 2

_____

_____

_____

_____

_____

_____

Req. 1

		General Journal				
DATE		ACCOUNTS AND EXPLANATIONS	POST. REF.	DEBIT		CREDIT

Req. 2

General Journal

DATE	ACCOUNTS AND EXPLANATIONS	POST. REF.	DEBIT	CREDIT

Req. 1

		General Journal			
DATE		ACCOUNTS AND EXPLANATIONS	POST. REF.	DEBIT	CREDIT

Req. 2

NAME

SECTION

DATE

Chapter 16

Decision Case 1

(Continued)

Ethical Issue

Reqs. 1 and 2

NAME
SECTION
DATE

Chapter 16

Ethical Issue
(Continued)

Reqs. 1 & 2 (Continued)

Req. 1

a. _____

_____

b.

General Journal

DATE	ACCOUNTS AND EXPLANATIONS	POST. REF.	DEBIT	CREDIT

Req. 2

_____

_____

_____

_____

NAME
SECTION
DATE

Chapter 16

Team Project

Req. 1

NAME
SECTION
DATE

Chapter 16

Team Project
(Continued)

Req. 2

General Journal

DATE		ACCOUNTS AND EXPLANATIONS	POST. REF.	DEBIT	CREDIT

NAME
SECTION
DATE

Chapter 16

Team Project
(Continued)

Req. 2

Excel Application Exercise

S17-3

_____

_____

_____

_____

_____

_____

_____

_____

_____

_____

_____

S17-5

a–c.

_____

_____

_____

_____

_____

_____

_____

_____

_____

_____

_____

_____

a. _____

b. _____

c. _____

d. _____

e. _____

f. _____

g. _____

h. _____

i. _____

j. _____

k. _____

l. _____

m. _____

n. _____

o. _____

p. _____

q. _____

a. _____   h. _____

b. _____   i. _____

c. _____   j. _____

d. _____   k. _____

e. _____

f. _____

g. _____

E17-4

E17-5

Req. 1

Req. 2

a.

b.

c.

d.

e.

f.

g.

h.

i.

j.

k.

l.

m.

n.

o.

p.

a. _____

b. _____

c. _____

d. _____

e. _____

f. _____

g. _____

h. _____

i. _____

j. _____

k. _____

l. _____

E17-11

Req. 1

Req. 2

Req. 1

Req. 2

Req. 3

Req. 1

Req. 2

Req. 1

Req. 2

Req. 1

Req. 2

Req. 3

Req. 1

Req. 2

Req. 1

Req. 2

Req. 3

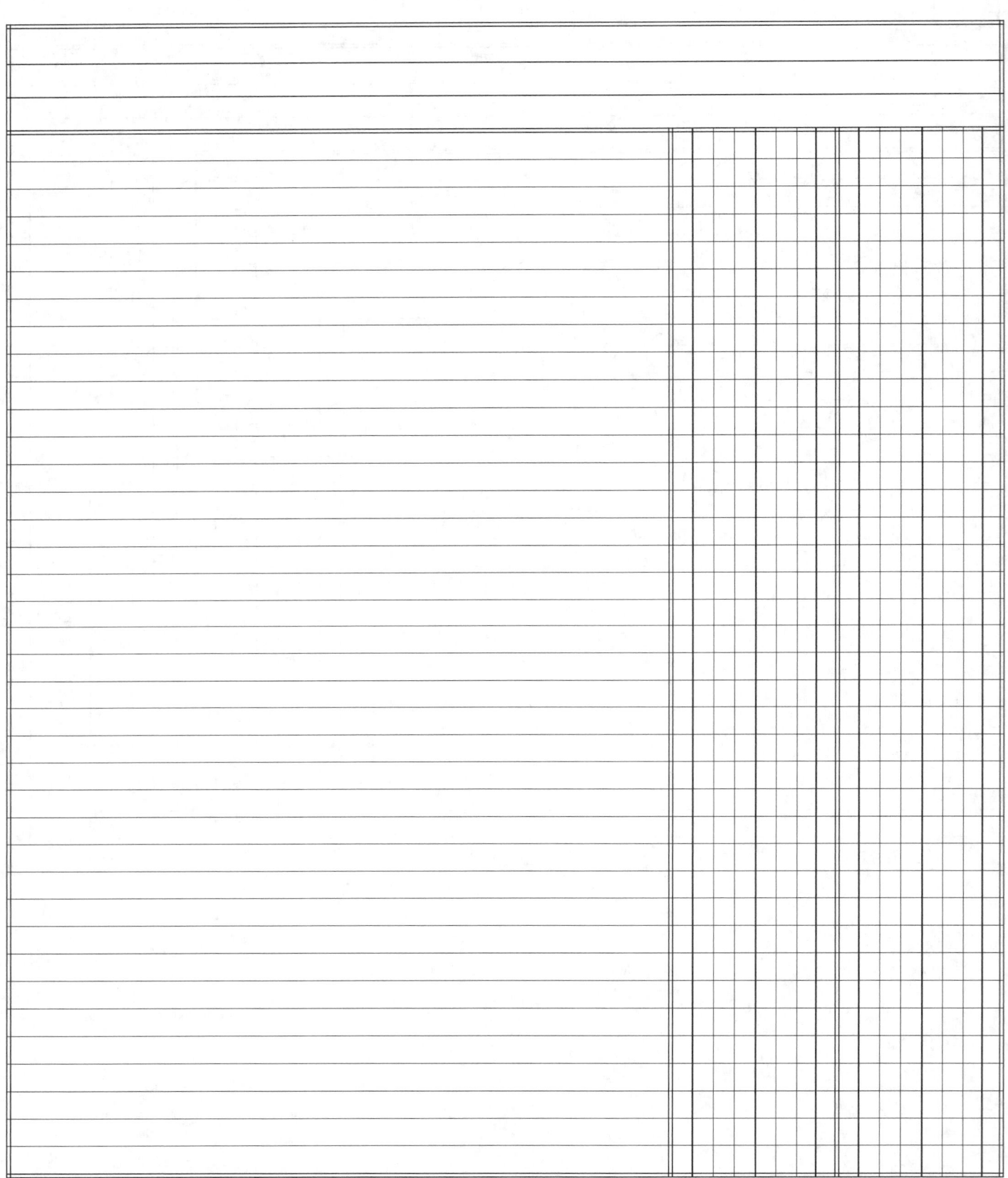

Req. 1

Req. 2

Req. 1

Req. 2

Req. 1

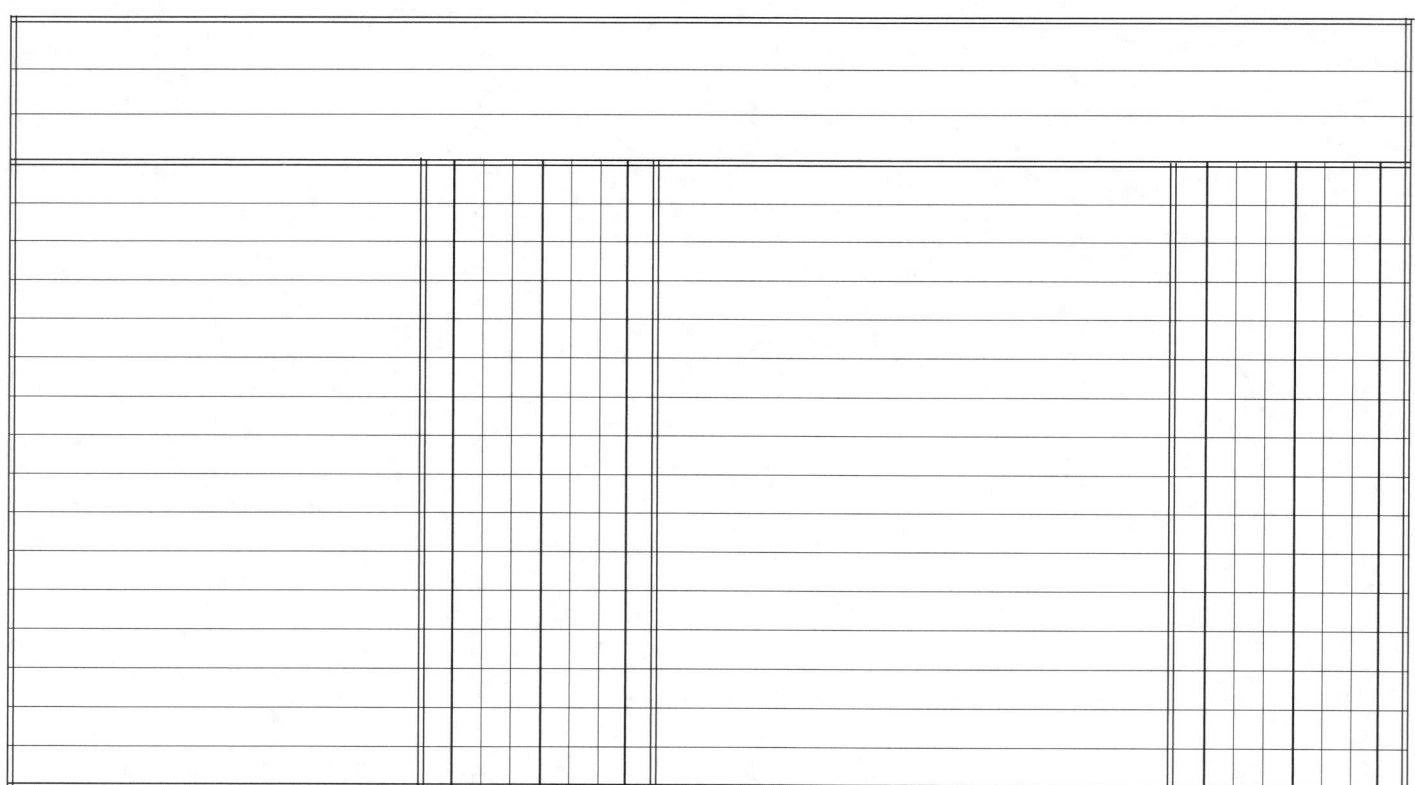

Req. 2

Req. 3

Req. 1

Req. 2

Req. 1

NAME
SECTION
DATE

Chapter 17

Decision Case 1
(Continued)

Req. 2

Req. 3

Decision Case 2

Ethical Issue

Reqs. 1–2

NAME
SECTION
DATE

Reqs. 1–4

Chapter 17

Financial Statement Case

NAME
SECTION
DATE

Chapter 17

Financial
Statement Case
(Continued)

Reqs. 1–4 (Continued)

Excel Application Exercise

NAME

SECTION

DATE

Chapter 18

**Excel Application
Exercise***(Continued)*

	Amount in Millions			Increase (Decrease)				
	2002	2001	2000	2002		2001	
				Amount	Percent	Amount	Percent

NAME
SECTION
DATE

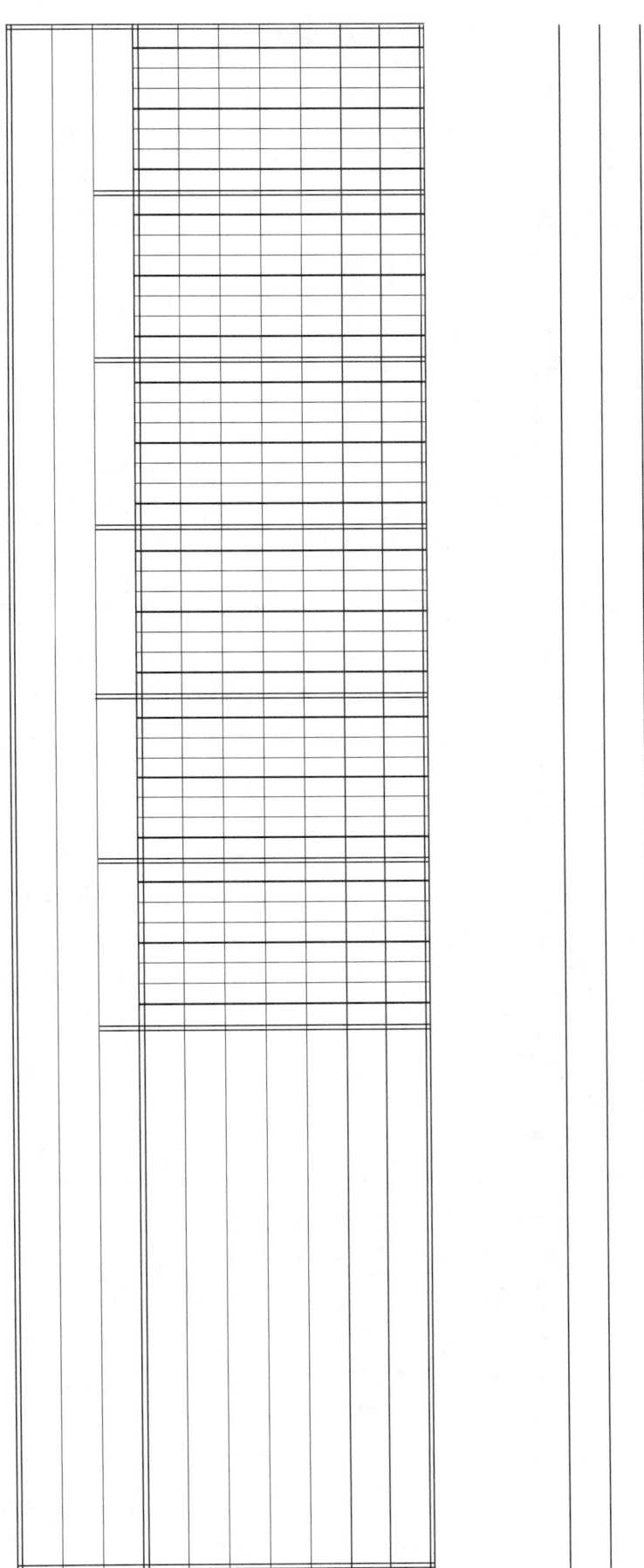

S18-10

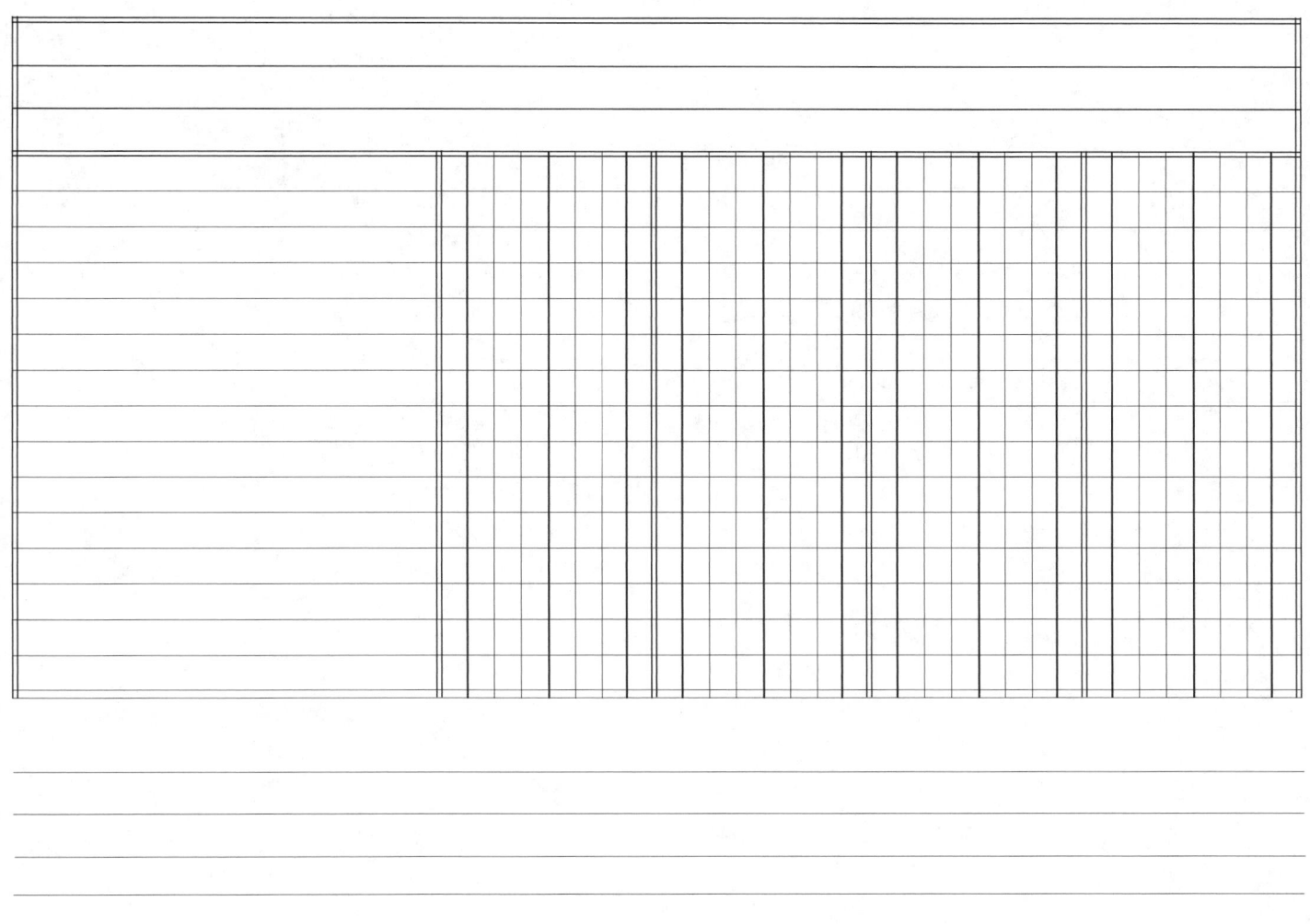

Req. 1

a. Current ratio:

b. Acid-test ratio:

c. Inventory turnover:

**d. Days' sales in
average Receivables**

E18-11

Reqs. 1–3

Req. 1

Reqs. 2 & 3

Reqs. 1 & 2

Req. 1

	20 × 6	**20 × 5**

a. Current ratio:

b. Inventory turnover:

c. Times-interest earned Ratio:

d. Return on common stockholders' equity:

e. Earnings per share of common stock:

f. Price/Earnings Ratio:

Reqs. 2 & 3

_____   _____

a. Acid-Test Ratio:

b. Inventory turnover:

**c. Days' sales in
average
Receivables:**

d. Debit Ratio:

**e. Earnings per share of
common stock:**

**f. Price/earnings
Ratio:**

Reqs. 1,2 & 3

Reqs. 2 & 3

Req. 1

Reqs. 2 & 3

Reqs. 1 and 2

Req. 1

	20 × 9	**20 × 8**

a. **Current ratio:**

b. **Inventory turnover:**

c. **Times-interest-earned ratio:**

d. **Return on common stockholders' equity:**

e. **Earnings per share of common stock:**

f. **Price/earnings Ratio:**

Reqs. 2 & 3

Req. 1

a. **Acid-test ratio:**

b. **Inventory turnover:**

c. **Days' sales in average Receivables:**

d. **Debt Ratio:**

e. **Earnings per share of common stock:**

f. **Price/earnings Ratio:**

Decision:

_____

_____

_____

_____

_____

Req . 2

_____

_____

_____

_____

_____

_____

_____

_____

_____

_____

_____

_____

_____

_____

_____

_____

_____

_____

Ethical Issue

NAME
SECTION
DATE

Chapter 18

Financial
Statement Case

Reqs. 1–3

a. _____

b. _____

c. _____

d. _____

e. _____

f. _____

g. _____

h. _____

i. _____

j. _____

_____
_____
_____
_____
_____
_____
_____
_____
_____
_____
_____
_____
_____
_____
_____
_____

S19-5

a. _____
b. _____
c. _____
d. _____
e. _____
f. _____
g. _____
h. _____
i. _____

S19-10

Chapter 19

E19-2

Reqs. 1 and 2

Samsung Electronics

Cost Classification

	R&D	Design of Products, Services, or Processes	Production			Marketing	Distribution	Customer Service
			Direct Materials	Direct Labor	Manufacturing Overhead			

Req. 3

Reqs. 1 and 2

Radio Shack

Cost Classification

R&D	Design of Products, Services, or Processes	Purchases of Merchandise inventory	Marketing	Distribution	Customer Service

Req. 3

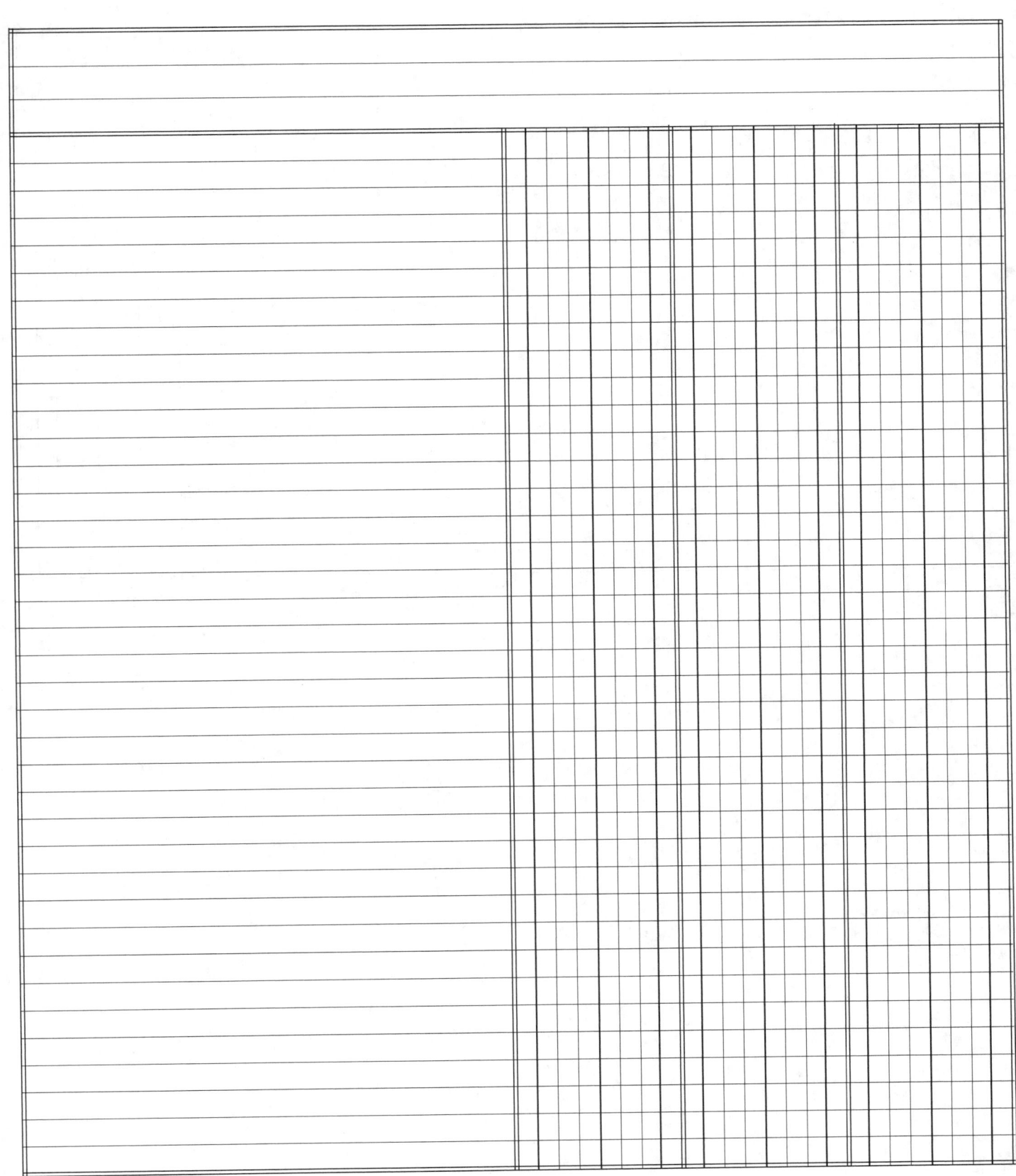

a.

b.

c.

d.

Reqs. 1–3

Reqs. 1 and 2

NAME
SECTION
DATE

Chapter 19

Reqs. 1 and 2

Shazam Cola
Value Chain Cost Classification

Cost	R&D	Design of Products, Services, or Processes	Production			Marketing	Distribution	Customer Service
			Direct Materials	Direct Labor	Manufacturing Overhead			

Reqs. 3 and 4

Part One:

Part Two:

Req. 1

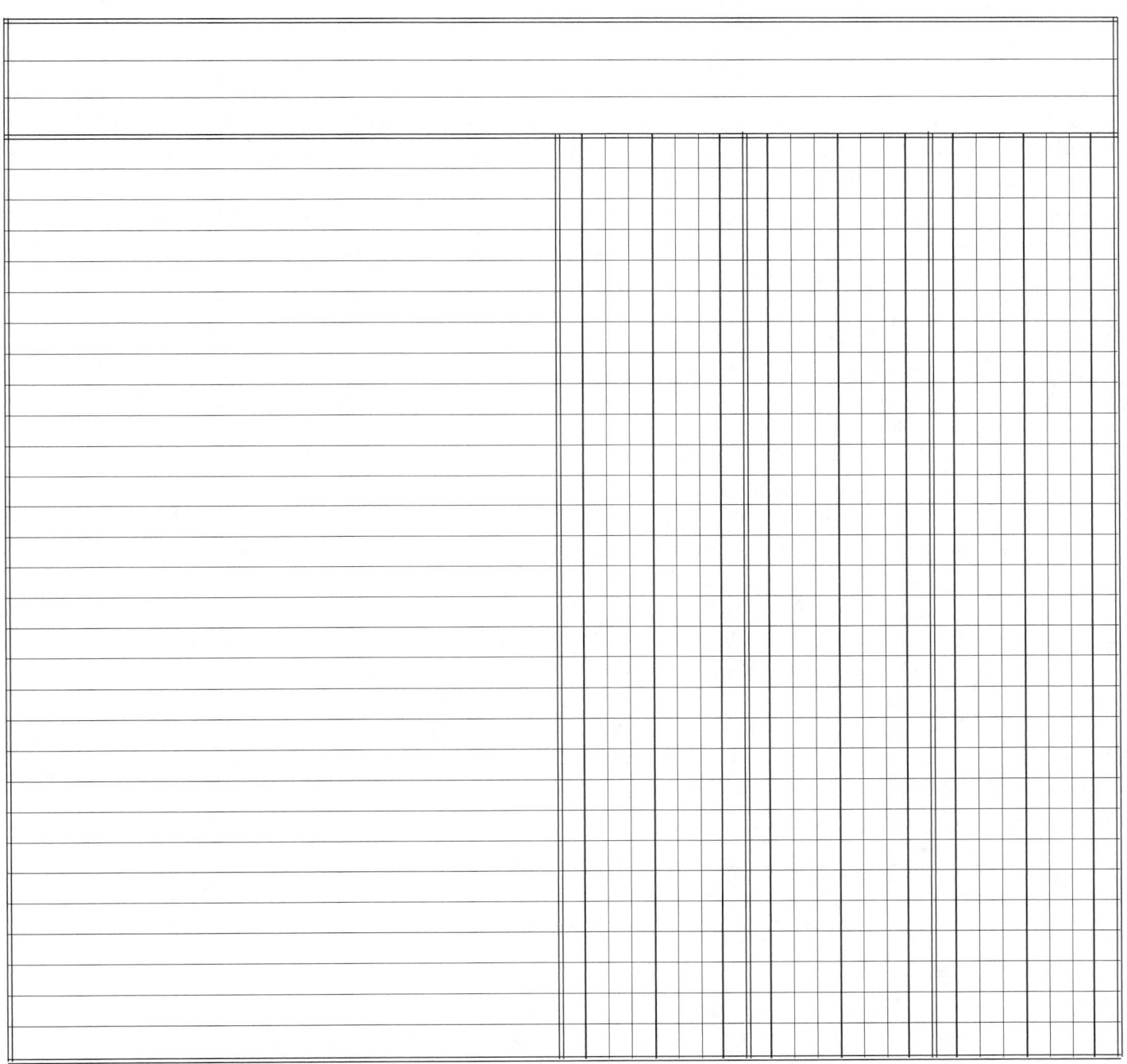

Req. 2

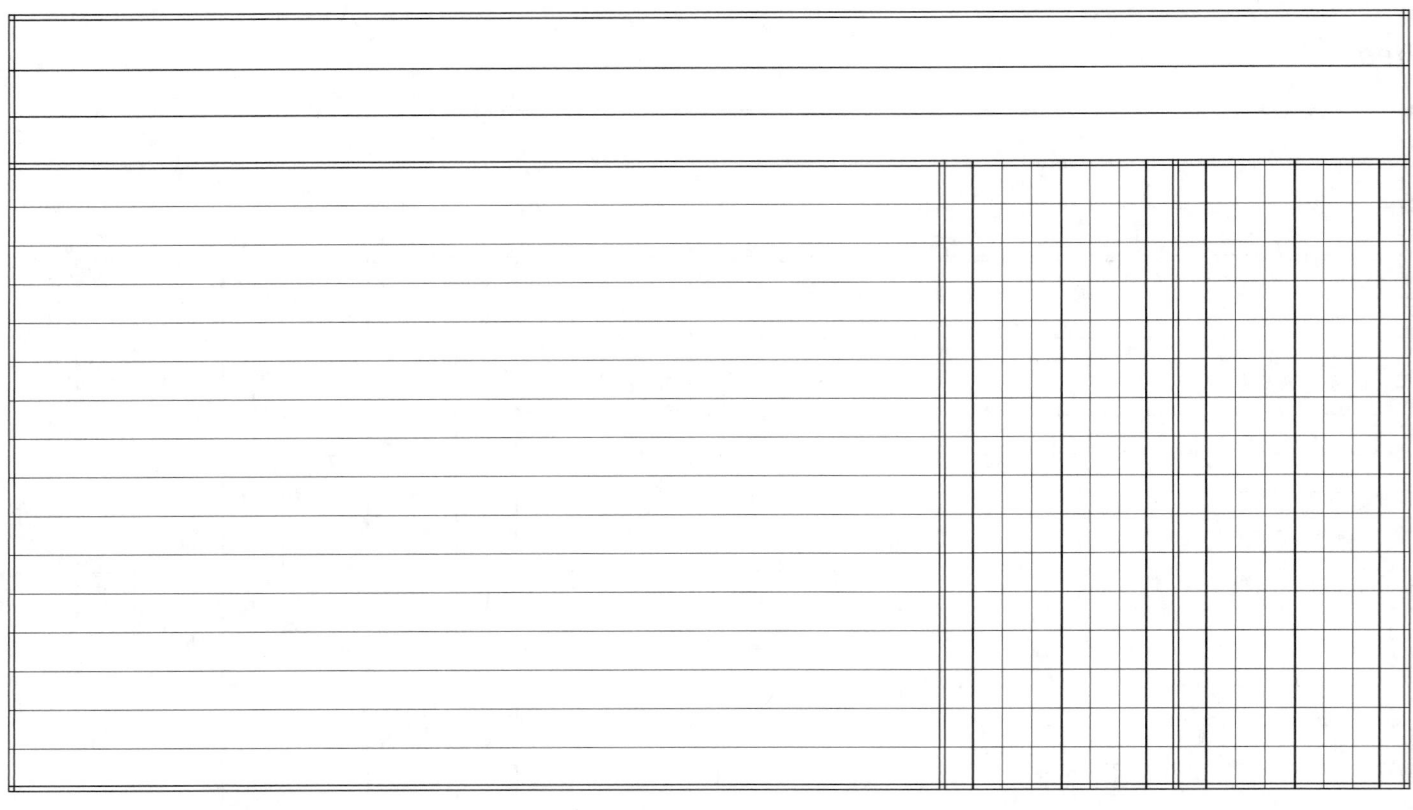

Req. 3

Req. 3

Reqs. 1–2

Req. 1

Req. 2

Reqs. 1 & 2

Req. 3

Chapter 19

NAME
SECTION
DATE

Reqs. 1 and 2

Apple Computer

Value Chain Cost Classification

		Production					
R&D	Design of Products, Services, or Processes	Direct Materials	Direct Labor	Manufacturing Overhead	Marketing	Distribution	Customer Service

Reqs. 3 and 4

Part One:

Part Two:

Req. 1

Req. 2

Req. 3

Part Three:

Reqs. 1–2

Reqs. 1–3

Reqs. 1–3 (Continued)

Reqs. 1 & 2

Req. 3

Chapter 19

Decision Case 1

Req. 1

Power Box

Inventory Reconstruction Schedule

Direct Materials Inventory		Work in Process Inventory		Finished Goals Inventory	
Beginning Inventory		Beginning Inventory		Beginning Inventory	

NAME
SECTION
DATE

Chapter 19

Decision Case 1
(Continued)

NAME
SECTION
DATE

Chapter 19

Decision Case 1
(Continued)

Req. 2

Ethical Issue

NAME
SECTION
DATE

Chapter 19

Ethical Issue
(Continued)

Financial Statement Case

Reqs. 1–4

NAME
SECTION
DATE

Chapter 19

**Financial
Statement Case**
(Continued)

Reqs. 1–4 (Continued)

NAME
SECTION
DATE

Chapter 19

Financial Statement Case
(Continued)

Reqs. 1–4 (Continued)

Team Project

NAME
SECTION
DATE

Chapter 19

Team Project
(Continued)

Journal

DATE		ACCOUNTS AND EXPLANATIONS	POST. REF.	DEBIT	CREDIT

S20-5

		Journal				
DATE		ACCOUNTS AND EXPLANATIONS	POST. REF.	DEBIT		CREDIT

S20-7

S20-9

Reqs. 1–3

General Journal

DATE	ACCOUNTS AND EXPLANATIONS	POST. REF.	DEBIT	CREDIT

S20-12

Reqs. 1 & 2

Reqs. 1 & 2

General Journal

DATE	ACCOUNTS AND EXPLANATIONS	POST. REF.	DEBIT	CREDIT

General Journal

DATE		ACCOUNTS AND EXPLANATIONS	POST. REF.	DEBIT	CREDIT

Req. 1

Reqs. 2 & 3

		General Journal				
DATE		ACCOUNTS AND EXPLANATIONS	POST REF.	DEBIT		CREDIT

Req. 4

Req. 1

Req. 2

		General Journal				
DATE		ACCOUNTS AND EXPLANATIONS	POST. REF.	DEBIT		CREDIT

Req. 3

Req. 4

		General Journal				
DATE		ACCOUNTS AND EXPLANATIONS	POST. REF.	DEBIT		CREDIT

Req. 1

Req. 2

General Journal

DATE		ACCOUNTS AND EXPLANATIONS	DEBIT	CREDIT

Req. 3

Req. 4

General Journal

DATE		ACCOUNTS AND EXPLANATIONS	POST. REF.	DEBIT	CREDIT

Req. 1

Req. 2

General Journal

DATE		ACCOUNTS AND EXPLANATIONS	POST. REF.	DEBIT	CREDIT

Req. 3

Reqs. 1–3

Reqs. 1–3 (Continued)

Reqs. 1 & 2

Req. 3

		General Journal				
DATE		ACCOUNTS AND EXPLANATIONS	POST. REF.	DEBIT	CREDIT	

Req. 1

	WORK IN PROCESS INVENTORY	FINISHED GOODS INVENTORY	COST OF GOODS SOLD

Req. 2

	General Journal			
DATE	ACCOUNTS AND EXPLANATIONS	POST. REF.	DEBIT	CREDIT

Req. 3

General Journal				
DATE	ACCOUNTS AND EXPLANATIONS	POST. REF.	DEBIT	CREDIT

Req. 4

NAME
SECTION
DATE

Req. 1

		Journal			
DATE		ACCOUNTS AND EXPLANATIONS	POST. REF.	DEBIT	CREDIT

Req. 2

Req. 3

Req. 4

Req. 5

Chapter 20

P20-3A

Req. 1

Job Cost Record

JOB NO. _____
CUSTOMER NAME AND ADDRESS _____
JOB DESCRIPTION _____

DATE PROMISED		DATE STARTED		DATE COMPLETED		

	DIRECT MATERIALS		TIME RECORD NO.	DIRECT LABOR	MANUFACTURED OVERHEAD ALLOCATED		
DATE	REQUISITION NO.	AMOUNT		AMOUNT	DATE	RATE	AMOUNT
TOTAL							

OVERALL COST SUMMARY
MATERIALS . . . . $
LABOR . . . .
OVERHEAD . . . .

TOTAL JOB COST . . . . . . $

Reqs. 2 & 3

		General Journal			
DATE		ACCOUNTS AND EXPLANATIONS	POST. REF.	DEBIT	CREDIT

Reqs. 1 & 2

Req. 3

		General Journal			
DATE		ACCOUNTS AND EXPLANATIONS	POST. REF.	DEBIT	CREDIT

Req. 4

Reqs. 1 & 2

General Ledger:

Reqs. 1 & 2 (Continued)

Material Ledger:

Total balances = $_____

Work in Process Ledger:

Total balances = $_____

Finished Goods Ledger:

Total balances = $_____

Req. 3

ACCOUNT	DEBIT	CREDIT

Req. 4

Req. 5

Req. 1

Req. 2

Reqs. 3 & 4

Req. 1

	WORK IN PROCESS INVENTORY			FINISHED GOODS INVENTORY			COST OF GOODS SOLD		

Req. 2

		General Journal			
DATE		ACCOUNTS AND EXPLANATIONS	POST. REF.	DEBIT	CREDIT

Req. 3

General Journal

DATE	ACCOUNTS AND EXPLANATIONS	POST. REF.	DEBIT	CREDIT

Req. 4

Req. 1

		General Journal			
DATE		ACCOUNTS AND EXPLANATIONS	POST. REF.	DEBIT	CREDIT

Req. 1 (Continued)

General Journal

DATE		ACCOUNTS AND EXPLANATIONS	POST. REF.	DEBIT	CREDIT

Req. 2

Req. 3

Req. 4

Req. 5

P20-3B

Req. 1

Job Cost Record

JOB NO. _____
CUSTOMER NAME AND ADDRESS _____
JOB DESCRIPTION _____

DATE PROMISED _____   DATE STARTED _____   DATE COMPLETED _____

DATE	DIRECT MATERIALS		DIRECT LABOR		MANUFACTURED OVERHEAD ALLOCATED		
	REQUISITION NO.	AMOUNT	TIME RECORD NO.	AMOUNT	DATE	RATE	AMOUNT
TOTAL							

OVERALL COST SUMMARY
MATERIALS . . . . $
LABOR . . . .
OVERHEAD . . . .

TOTAL JOB COST . . . . . . $

Reqs. 2 & 3

General Journal

DATE	ACCOUNTS AND EXPLANATIONS	POST. REF.	DEBIT	CREDIT

Req. 1

Req. 2

Req. 3

		General Journal			
DATE		ACCOUNTS AND EXPLANATIONS	POST. REF.	DEBIT	CREDIT

Req. 4

Reqs. 1 & 2

General Ledger:

Reqs. 1 & 2

Material Ledger:

Total balances = $_____

Work in Process Ledger:

Total balances = $_____

Finished Goods Ledger:

Total balances = $_____

Req. 3

ACCOUNT	DEBIT	CREDIT

Req. 4

Req. 5

Req. 1

Req. 2

Reqs. 3 & 4

Reqs. 1–3

Reqs. 1 & 2

NAME
SECTION
DATE

Chapter 20

Decision Case 2

(Continued)

Reqs. 1 & 2 (Continued)

Chapter 20

Ethical Issue

Reqs. 1 & 2

NAME
SECTION
DATE

Chapter 20

Ethical Issue
(Continued)

Reqs. 1 & 2 (Continued)

Req. 1

Req. 2

Req. 3

Req. 1

Req. 2

S21-6

Reqs. 1 and 2

	DIRECT MATERIALS	CONVERSION COST	TOTAL

Req. 1

General Journal

DATE	ACCOUNTS AND EXPLANATIONS	POST. REF.	DEBIT	CREDIT

Req. 2

Req. 1

Req. 2

Flow of Production	Flow of Physical Units	Equivalent Units of Production		
		Transferred In	Direct Materials	Conversion Costs

	Cost per Equivalent Units			
	Transferred In	Direct Materials	Conversion Costs	Total Costs

	Assignment of Costs (Weighted Average)			
	Transferred In	Direct Materials	Conversion Costs	Total

Req. 1

General Journal

DATE	DESCRIPTION	POST. REF.	DEBIT	CREDIT

Req. 2

General Journal

DATE	ACCOUNTS AND EXPLANATIONS	POST. REF.	DEBIT	CREDIT

Req. 1

Req. 2

FLOW OF PRODUCTION	FLOW OF PHYSICAL UNITS	EQUIVALENT UNITS	
		DIRECT MATERIALS	CONVERSION COSTS

Req. 3

COST PER EQUIVALENT UNIT	DIRECT MATERIALS	CONVERSION COSTS

Assign Costs:	Direct Materials	Conversion Costs	Total

Req. 1

General Journal

DATE	ACCOUNTS AND EXPLANATIONS	POST. REF.	DEBIT	CREDIT

Req. 2

Req. 3

E21-5

NAME
SECTION
DATE

Req. 1

	FLOW OF PHYSICAL UNITS	EQUIVALENT UNITS	
		DIRECT MATERIALS	CONVERSION COSTS

Req. 2

COST PER EQUIVALENT UNIT

	DIRECT MATERIALS	CONVERSION COSTS

Req. 3

Costs Assigned	Direct Materials	Conversion Costs	Total

Req. 4

General Journal

DATE	ACCOUNTS AND EXPLANATIONS	POST. REF.	DEBIT	CREDIT

Req. 5

Req. 1

Req. 2

Req. 3

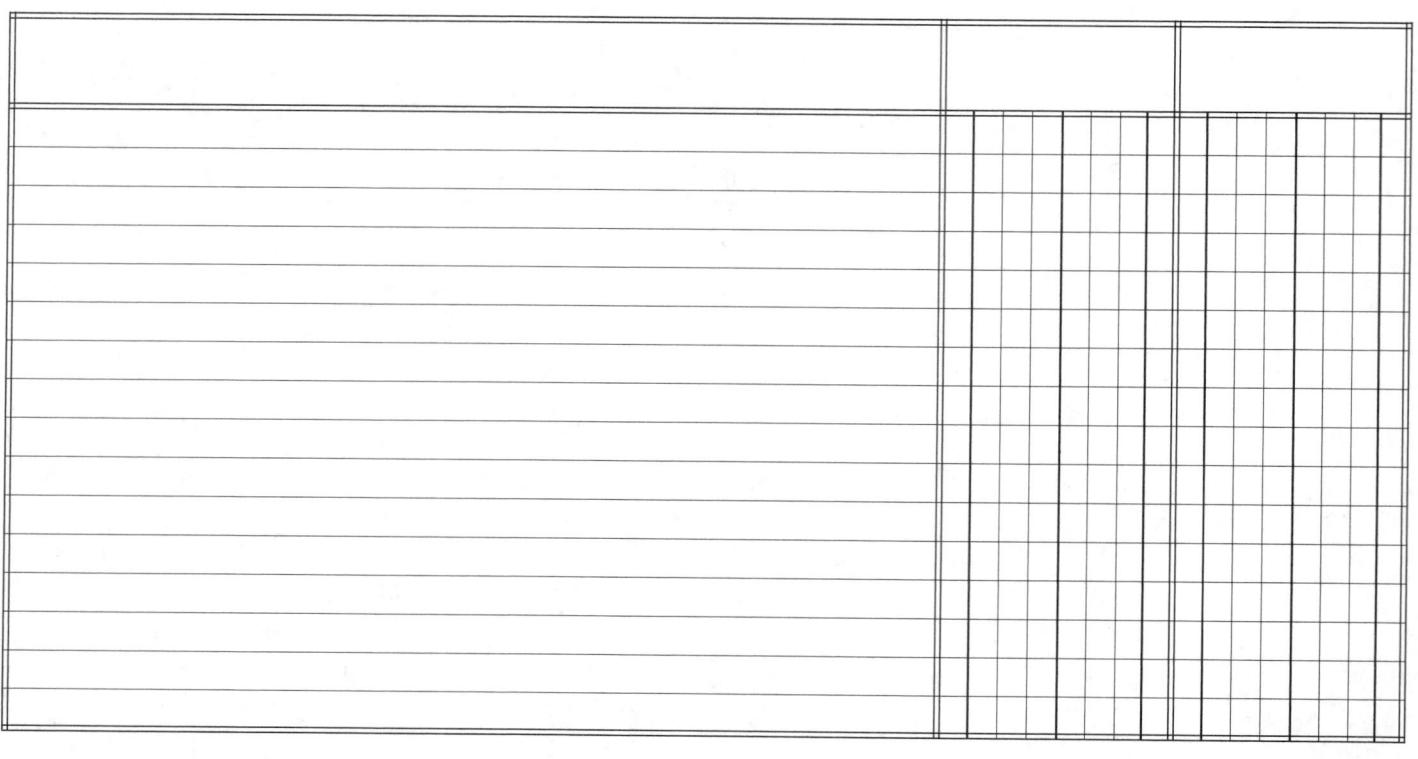

Req. 1

		General Journal				
DATE		ACCOUNTS AND EXPLANATIONS	POST. REF.	DEBIT		CREDIT

Req. 2

Req. 3

	Flow of Physical Units	Equivalent Units of Production	
		Direct Materials	Conversion Costs

COST PER EQUIVALENT UNIT	Direct Materials	Conversion Costs

Cost Assigned	Conversion Costs		
	Direct Materials	Conversion Costs	Total

General Journal

DATE	ACCOUNTS AND EXPLANATIONS	POST. REF.	DEBIT	CREDIT

Req. 1

	Materials	Conversion Costs
a.	_____	_____
b.	_____	_____

	Flow of Physical Units	Equivalent Units of Production	
		Direct Materials	Conversion Costs

Flow of Production	Flow of Physical Units	Equivalent Units		
		Transferred In	Direct Materials	Conversion Costs

Req. 1

Req. 2

Flow of Production	Flow of Physical Units	Equivalent Units of Production		
		Transferred In	Direct Materials	Conversion Costs

Req. 3

| | Cost per Equivalent Units | | | |
	Transferred In	Direct Materials	Conversion Costs	Total Costs

| | Assignment of Costs (Weighted Average) | | | |
	Transferred In Costs	Direct Materials	Conversion Costs	Total

Req. 1

NAME
SECTION
DATE

P21-1A(Continued)

Req. 2

FLOW OF PRODUCTION	FLOW OF PHYSICAL UNITS	EQUIVALENT UNITS	
		DIRECT MATERIALS	CONVERSION COSTS

Req. 2 (Continued)

COST PER EQUIVALENT UNIT	DIRECT MATERIALS	CONVERSION COSTS

Req. 3

Req. 4

Req. 1

NAME
SECTION
DATE

Req. 2

P21-2A*(Continued)*

FLOW OF PRODUCTION	FLOW OF PHYSICAL UNITS	EQUIVALENT UNITS	
		DIRECT MATERIALS	CONVERSION COSTS

COST PER EQUIVALENT UNIT	DIRECT MATERIALS	CONVERSION COSTS

Req. 3

Req. 4

General Journal

DATE		ACCOUNTS AND EXPLANATIONS	POST. REF.	DEBIT	CREDIT

Req. 1

Req. 2

		EQUIVALENT UNITS		

Req. 3

Req. 3 (Continued)

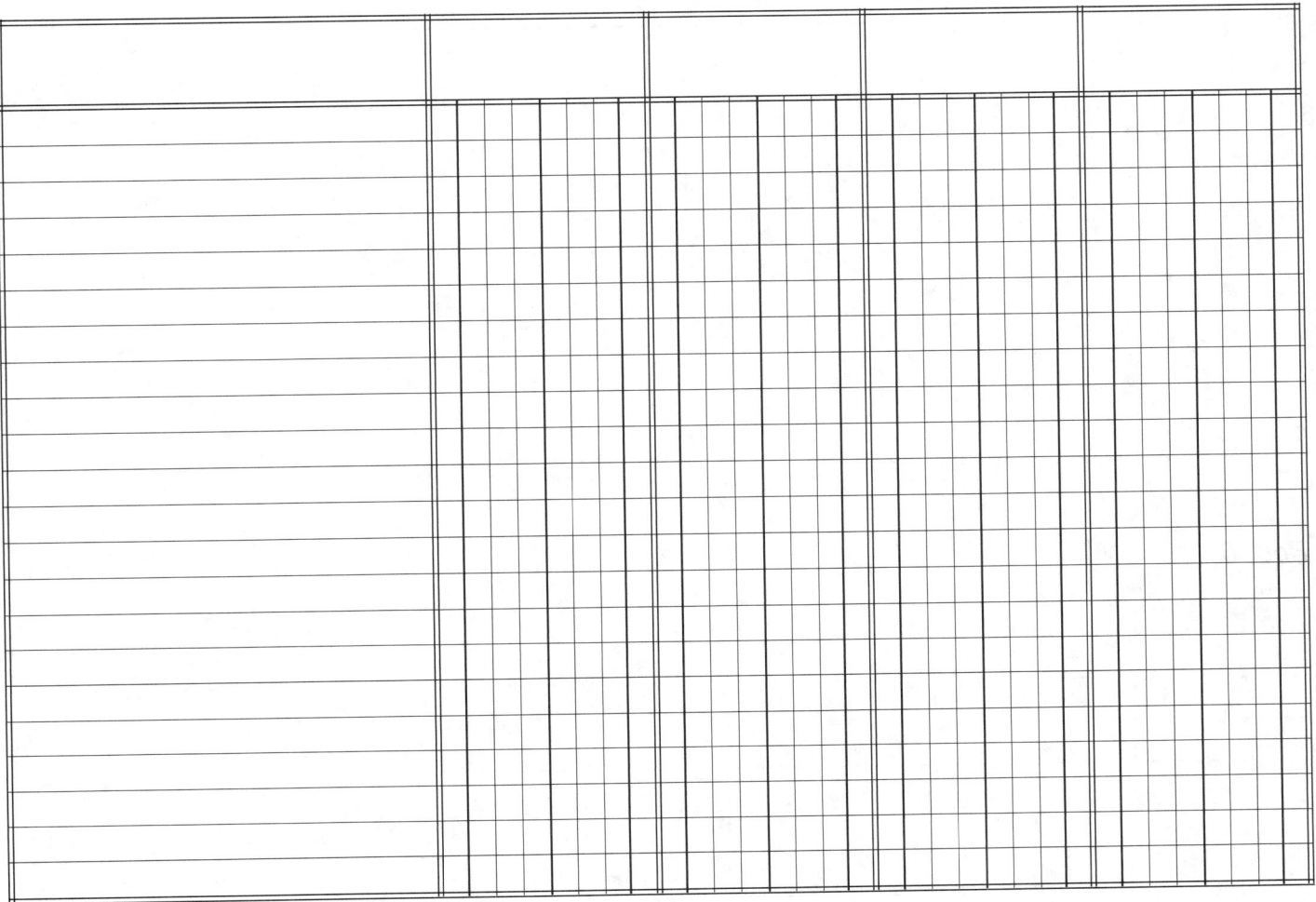

Req. 4

General Journal

DATE	ACCOUNTS AND EXPLANATIONS	POST. REF.	DEBIT	CREDIT

Req. 5

Req. 6

Req. 1

Req. 2

Flow of Production	Flow of Physical Units	Equivalent Units of Production		
		Transferred In	Direct Materials	Conversion Costs

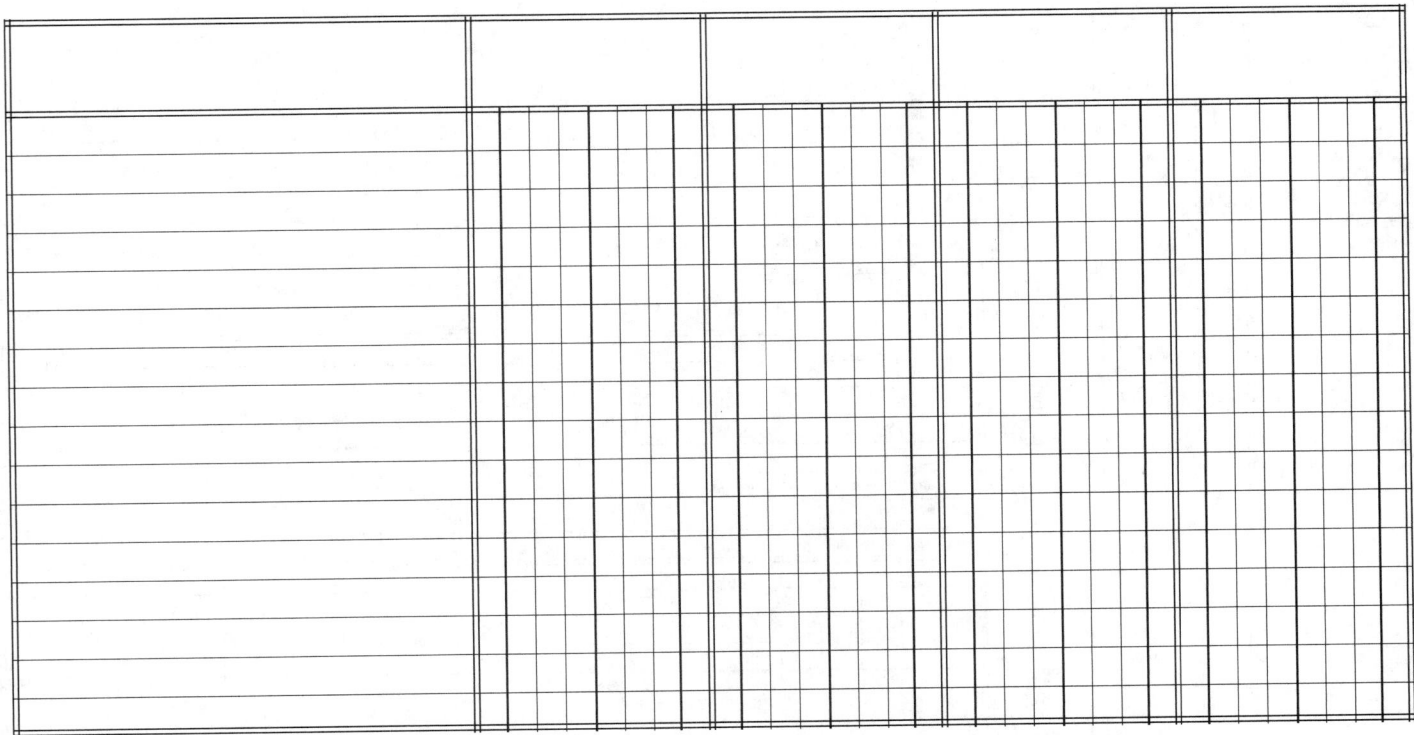

Chapter 21

P21-4A(Continued)

Req. 3

		TRANSFERRED IN	DIRECT MATERIALS	CONVERSION COSTS	TOTAL

Req. 4

		General Journal			
DATE		DESCRIPTION	POST. REF.	DEBIT	CREDIT

Req. 1

Chapter 21

P21-5A(Continued)

Req. 2

FLOW OF PRODUCTION	FLOW OF PHYSICAL UNITS	EQUIVALENT UNITS	
		TRANSFERRED IN	CONVERSION COSTS

Req. 3

Req. 1

NAME
SECTION
DATE

P21-1B(Continued)

Req. 2

FLOW OF PRODUCTION	FLOW OF PHYSICAL UNITS	EQUIVALENT UNITS	
		DIRECT MATERIALS	CONVERSION COSTS

COST PER EQUIVALENT UNIT	DIRECT MATERIALS	CONVERSION COSTS

Req. 3

Req. 4

Req. 1

NAME
SECTION
DATE

P21-2B(Continued)

Req. 2

FLOW OF PRODUCTION	FLOW OF PHYSICAL UNITS	EQUIVALENT UNITS	
		DIRECT MATERIALS	CONVERSION COSTS

COST PER EQUIVALENT UNIT	DIRECT MATERIALS	CONVERSION COSTS

Req. 3

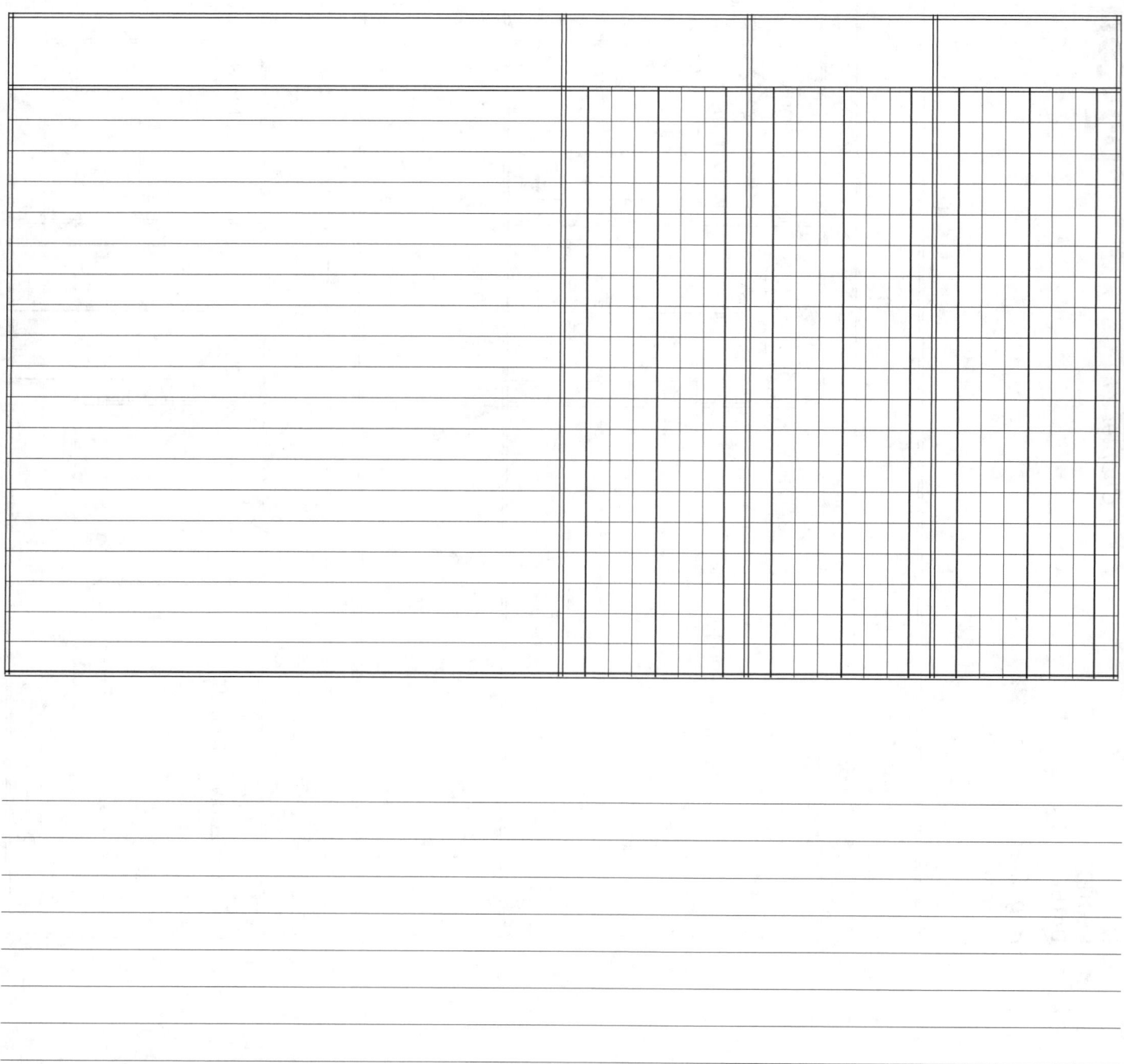

Req. 4

	General Journal			
DATE	ACCOUNTS AND EXPLANATIONS	POST. REF.	DEBIT	CREDIT

Req. 1

Req. 2

		EQUIVALENT UNITS		

Req. 3

Req. 3(Continued)

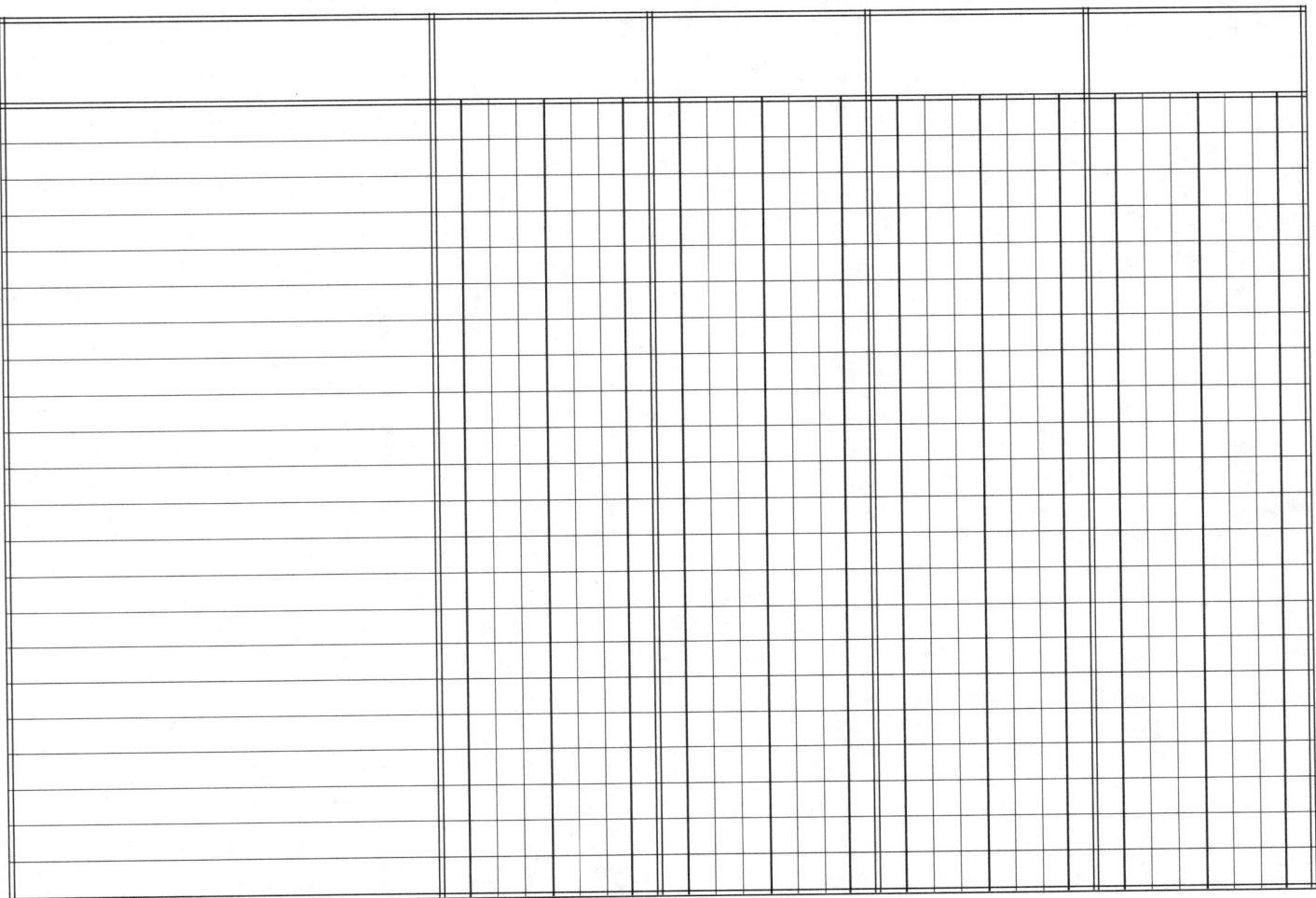

Req. 4

General Journal

DATE		ACCOUNTS AND EXPLANATIONS	POST. REF.	DEBIT	CREDIT

Req. 5

Req. 1

Req. 2

	Flow of Physical Units	Equivalent Units of Production		
Flow of Production		Transferred In	Direct Materials	Conversion Costs

NAME
SECTION
DATE
Req. 3

							TRANSFERRED IN	DIRECT MATERIALS	CONVERSION COSTS	TOTAL

Req. 4

		General Journal				
DATE		DESCRIPTION	POST. REF.	DEBIT	CREDIT	

Req. 1

NAME
SECTION
DATE

P21-5B *(Continued)*

Req. 2

FLOW OF PRODUCTION	FLOW OF PHYSICAL UNITS	EQUIVALENT UNITS	
		TRANSFERRED IN	CONVERSION COSTS

Req. 3

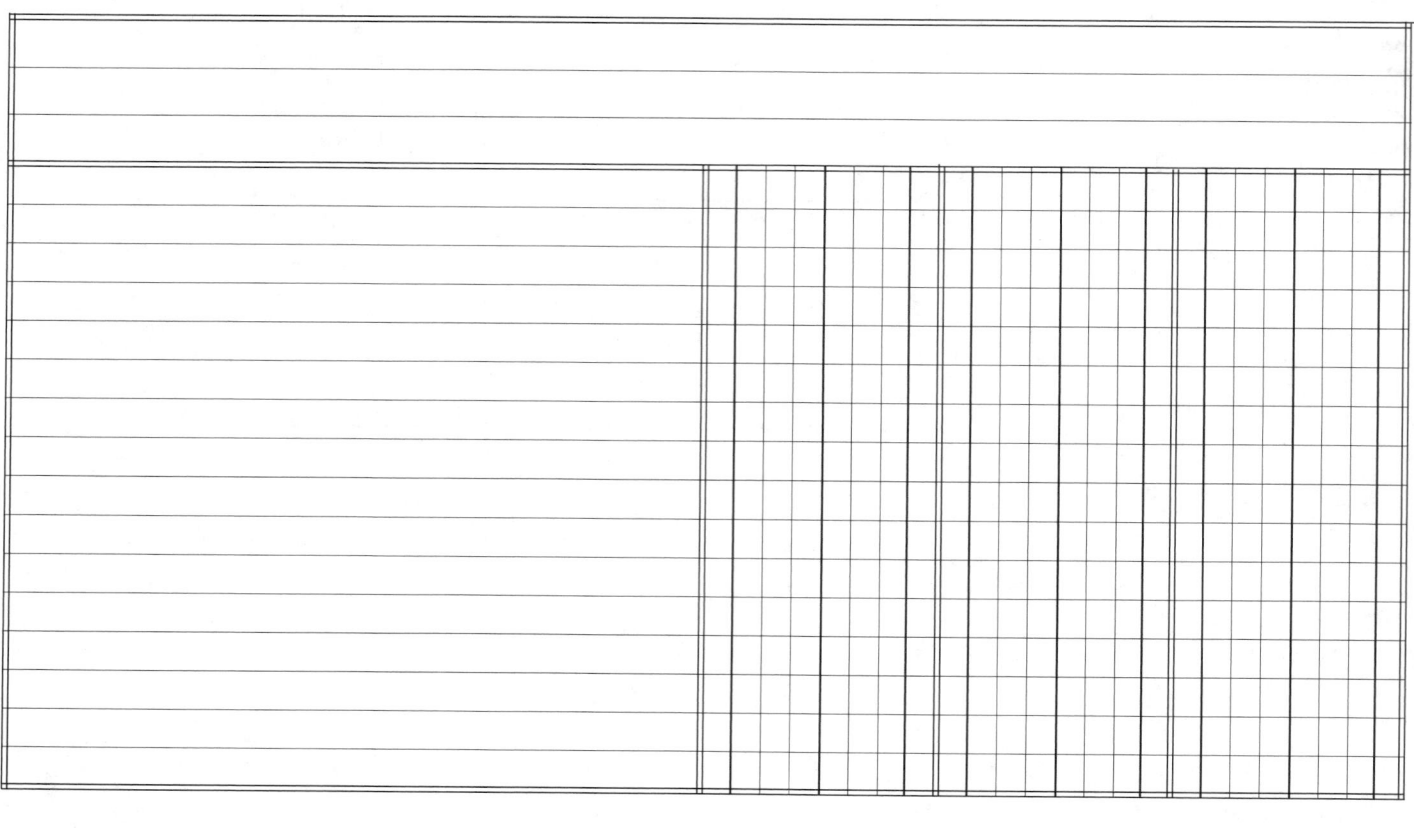

Req. 4

Req. 4(Continued)

Decision Case 1

Reqs. 1–5

NAME

SECTION

DATE

Chapter 21

Decision Case 1

(Continued)

Reqs. 1–5(Continued)

NAME
SECTION
DATE

Chapter 21

Decision Case 1
(Continued)

Reqs. 1–5(Continued)

Ethical Issue

Reqs. 1–4

Ethical Issue
(Continued)

Reqs. 1–4(Continued)

NAME
SECTION
DATE

Chapter 21

Ethical Issue
(Continued)

Reqs. 1–4(Continued)

Ethical Issue
(Continued)

Reqs. 1–4(Continued)

NAME
SECTION
DATE

Chapter 21

Ethical Issue
(Continued)

Reqs. 1–4(Continued)

Chapter 21

Team Project

Req. 1

NAME
SECTION
DATE

Team Project
(Continued)

Req. 1(Continued)

NAME
SECTION
DATE

Chapter 21

Team Project
(Continued)

Req. 1(Continued)

NAME
SECTION
DATE

Chapter 21

Team Project
(Continued)

Req. 2

NAME
SECTION
DATE

Chapter 21

Team Project
(Continued)

Req. 2(Continued)

Team Project
(Continued)

Req. 2(Continued)

Req. 3

Req. 1

Req. 2

Flow of Production	Flow of Physical Units	Equivalent Units of Production		
		Transferred In	Direct Materials	Conversion Costs

	Transferred In	Direct Materials	Conversion Costs	Total Costs

Flow of Production	Transferred In	Direct Materials	Conversion Costs	Total

Req. 1

Req. 2

Flow of Production	Flow of Physical Units	Equivalent Units of Production		
		Transferred In	Direct Materials	Conversion Costs

Flow of Production	Flow of Physical Units	Equivalent Units of Production		
		Transferred In	Direct Materials	Conversion Costs

Req. 1

Req. 2

Flow of Production	Flow of Physical Units	Equivalent Units of Production		
		Transferred In	Direct Materials	Conversion Costs

Req. 3

	Equivalent Units of Production			
	Transferred In	Direct Materials	Conversion Costs	Total

NAME
SECTION
DATE

Req. 3 (Continued)

E21A-2 *(Continued)*

	TRANSFERRED IN	DIRECT MATERIALS	CONVERSION COSTS	TOTAL

Req. 1

Req. 2

FLOW OF PRODUCTION	FLOW OF PHYSICAL UNITS	EQUIVALENT UNITS		
		TRANSFERRED IN	DIRECT MATERIALS	CONVERSION COSTS

Footnotes

	Transferred In Costs	Direct Materials	Conversion Costs	Total Costs

Req. 3

	Transferred In Costs	Direct Materials	Conversion Costs	Total

NAME
SECTION
DATE

Req. 1

	TRANSFERRED IN	DIRECT MATERIALS	CONVERSION COSTS	TOTAL

Req. 2

General Journal

DATE	ACCOUNTS AND EXPLANATIONS	POST. REF.	DEBIT	CREDIT

Req. 1

Req. 2

FLOW OF PRODUCTION	FLOW OF PHYSICAL UNITS	EQUIVALENT UNITS	
		TRANSFERRED IN	CONVERSION COSTS

Footnotes

Req. 3

	Transferred In	Conversion Costs	Total

Req. 3

	Transferred In	Conversion Costs	Total

S22-2

Req. 1

Req. 2

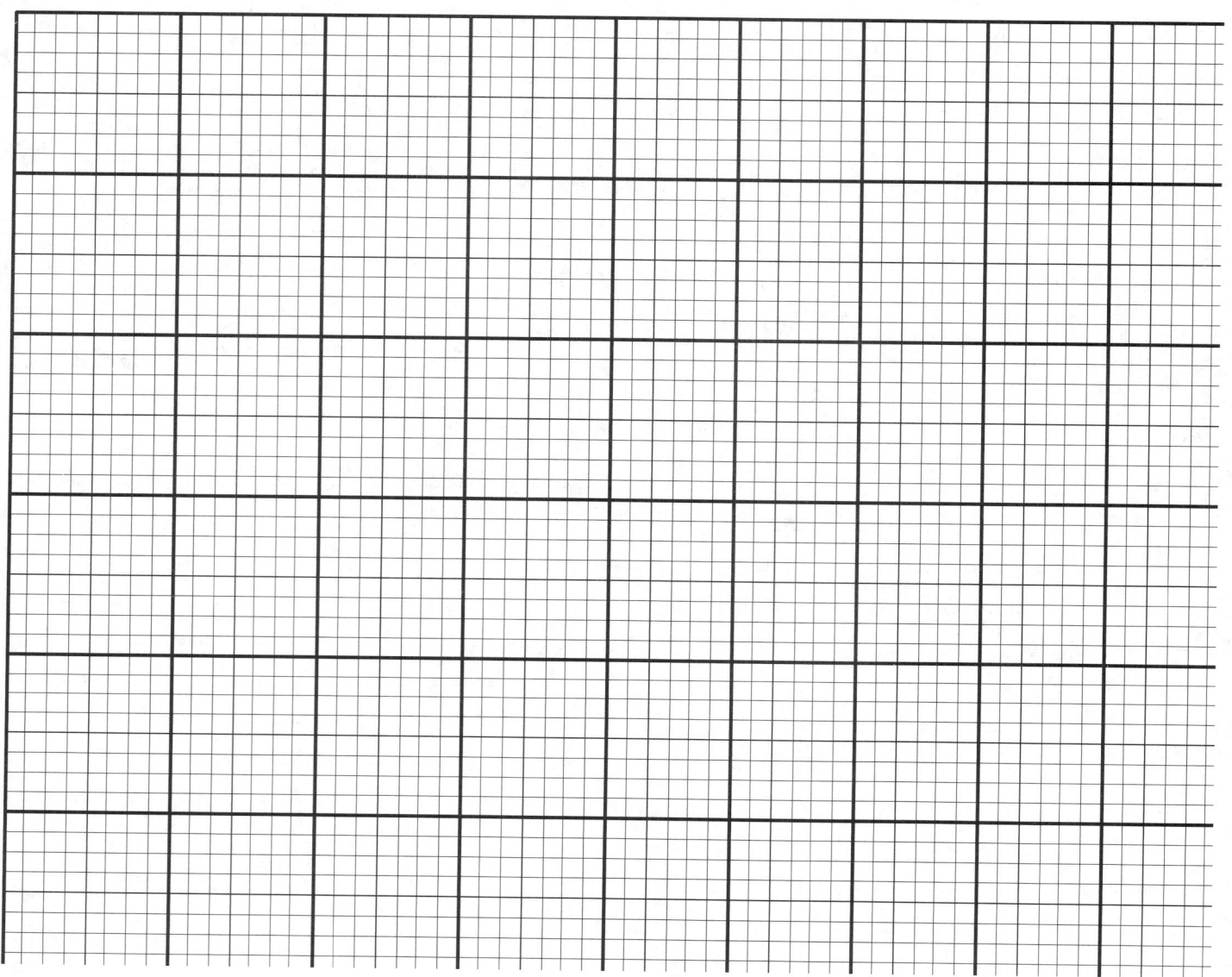

Reqs. 1–2

NAME
SECTION
DATE

a.

b.

c.

d.

e.

f.

g.

h.

i.

j.

Req. 1

Req. 2

Req. 1

Req. 2

Reqs. a.–c.

Reqs. a.–c.

Req. 1

Req. 2

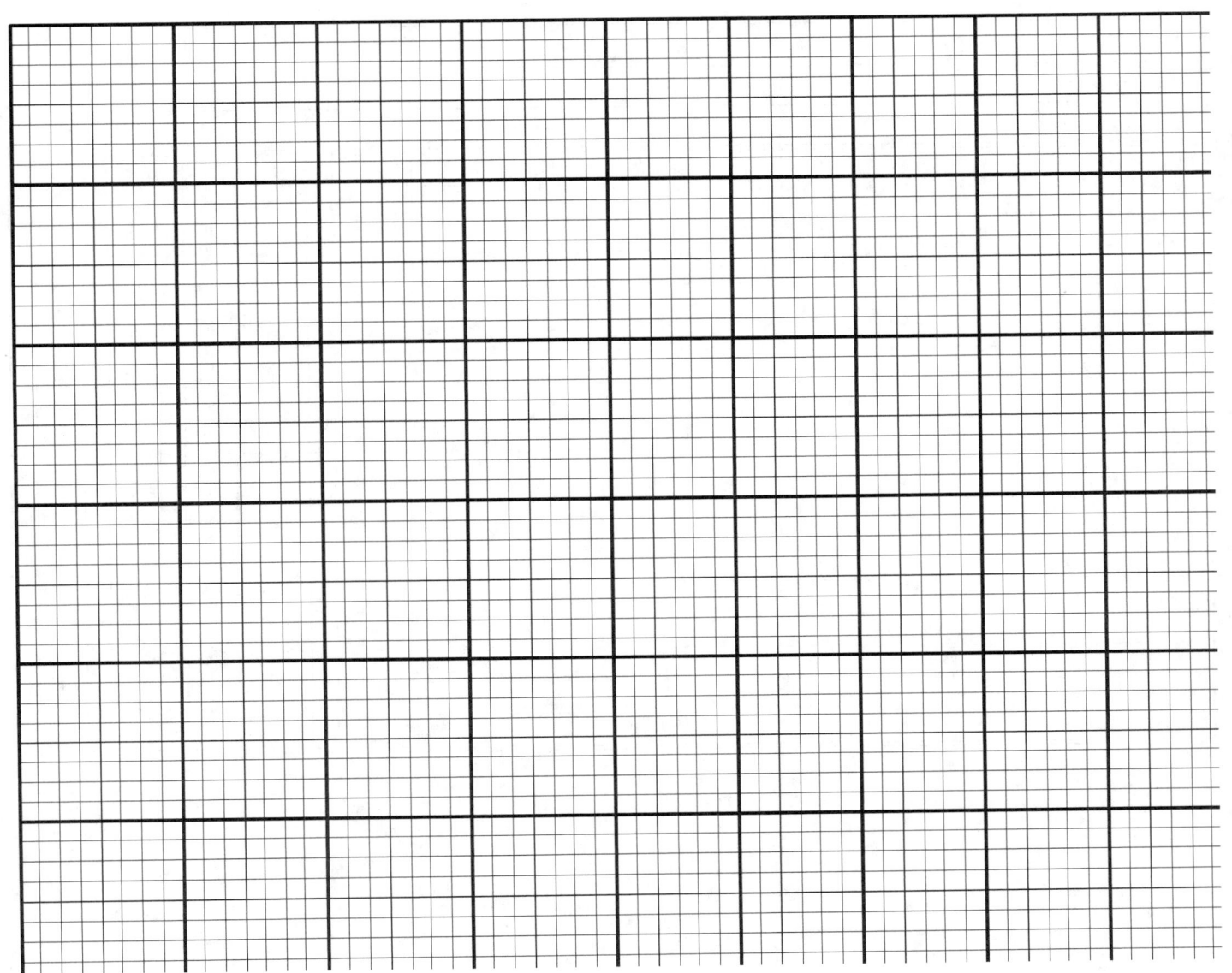

Req. 1

Req. 2

Reqs. 1 and 2

Req. 1

Req. 2

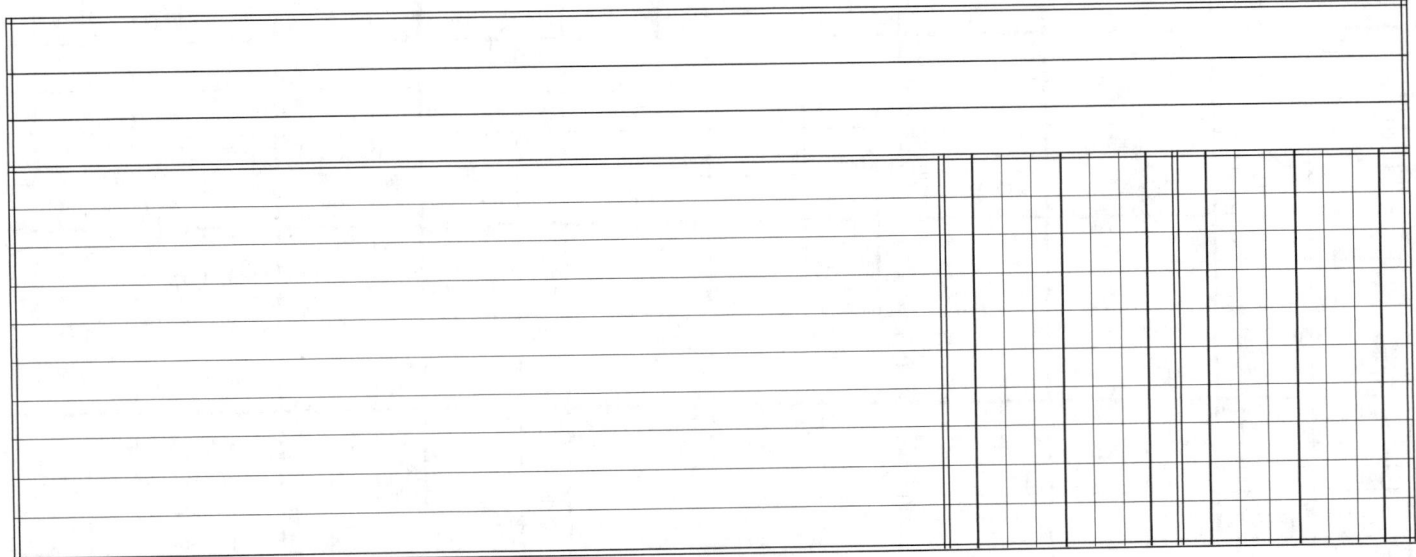

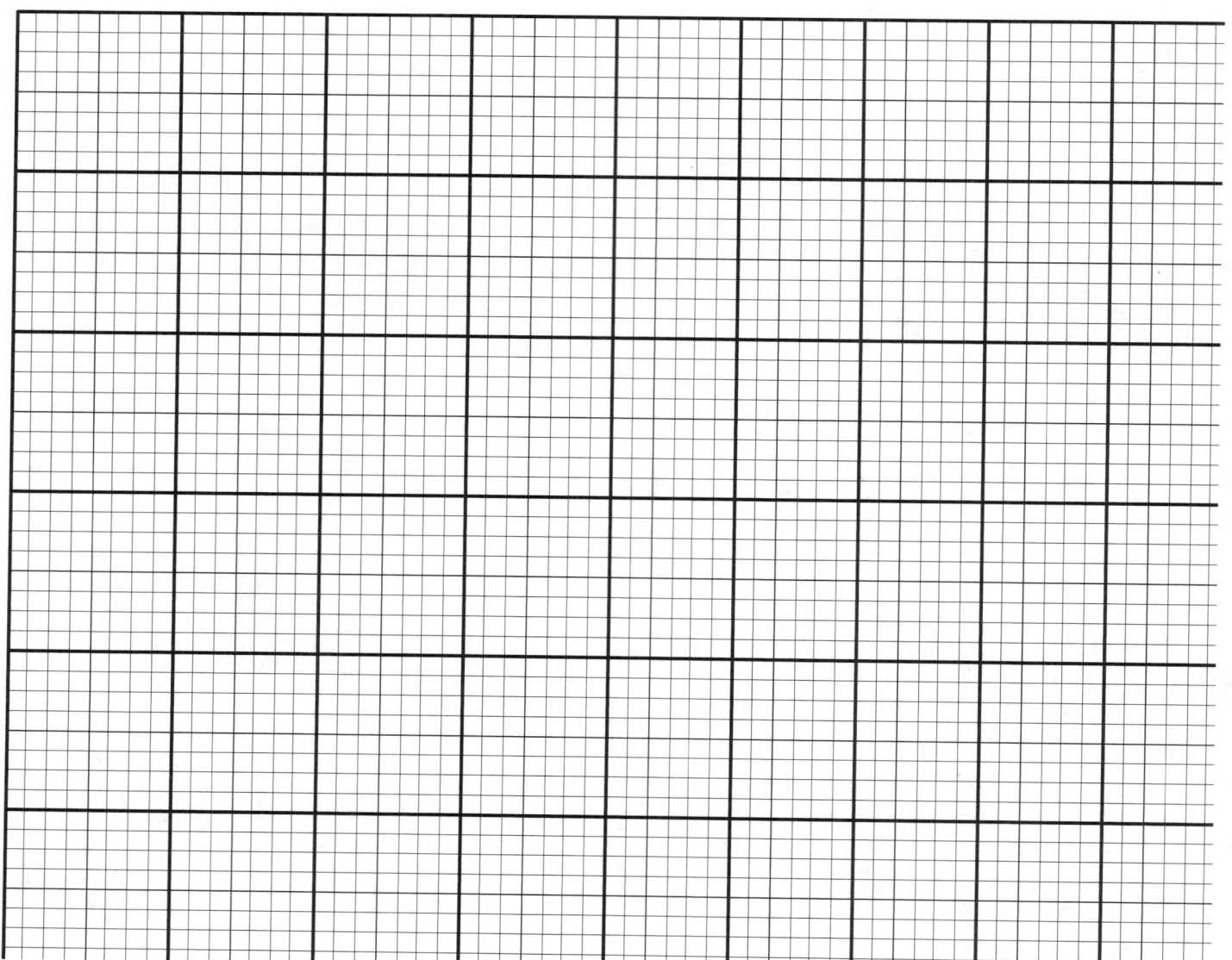

Reqs. 1 and 2

Req. 3

NAME
SECTION
DATE

Req. 1

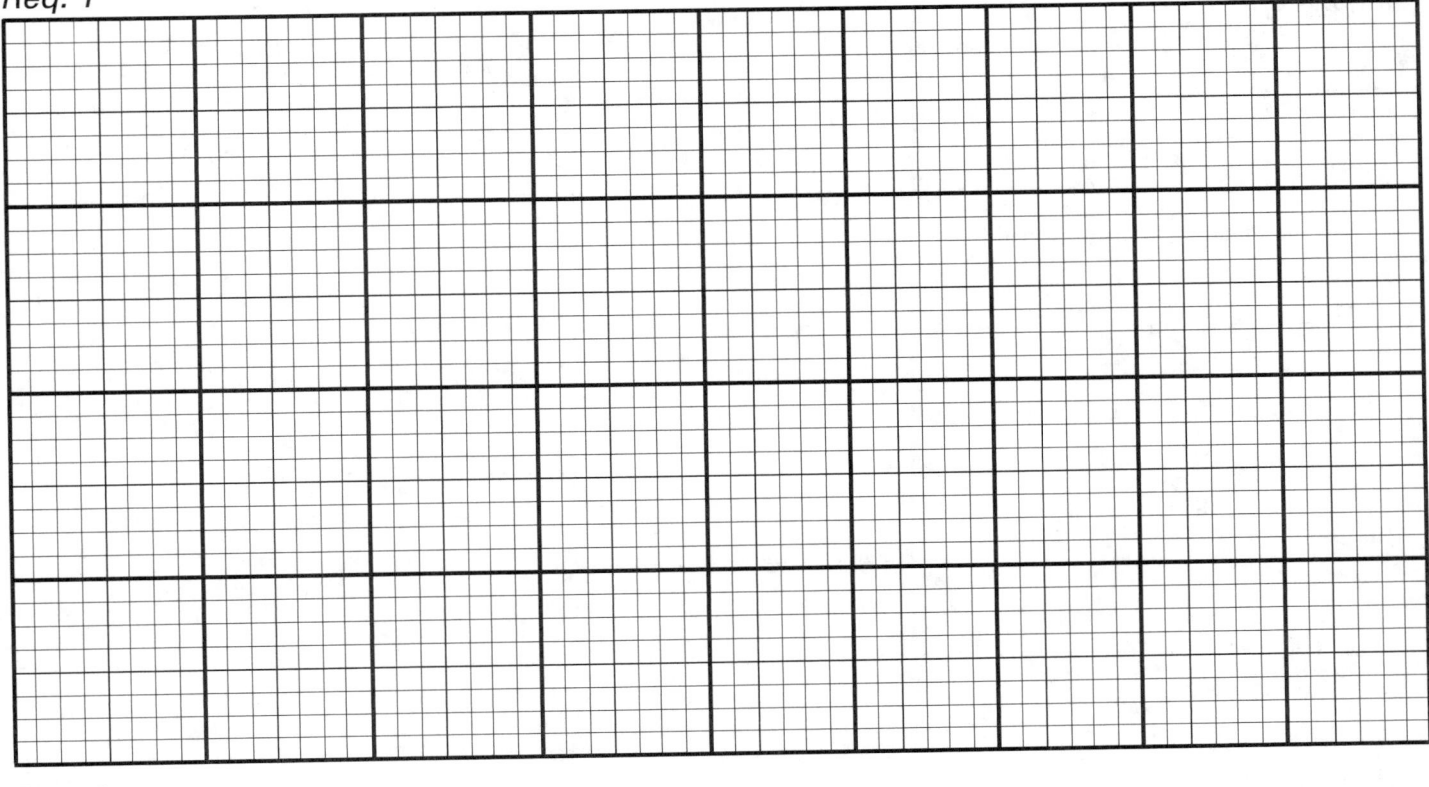

Req. 2

Reqs. 1 and 2

Req. 1

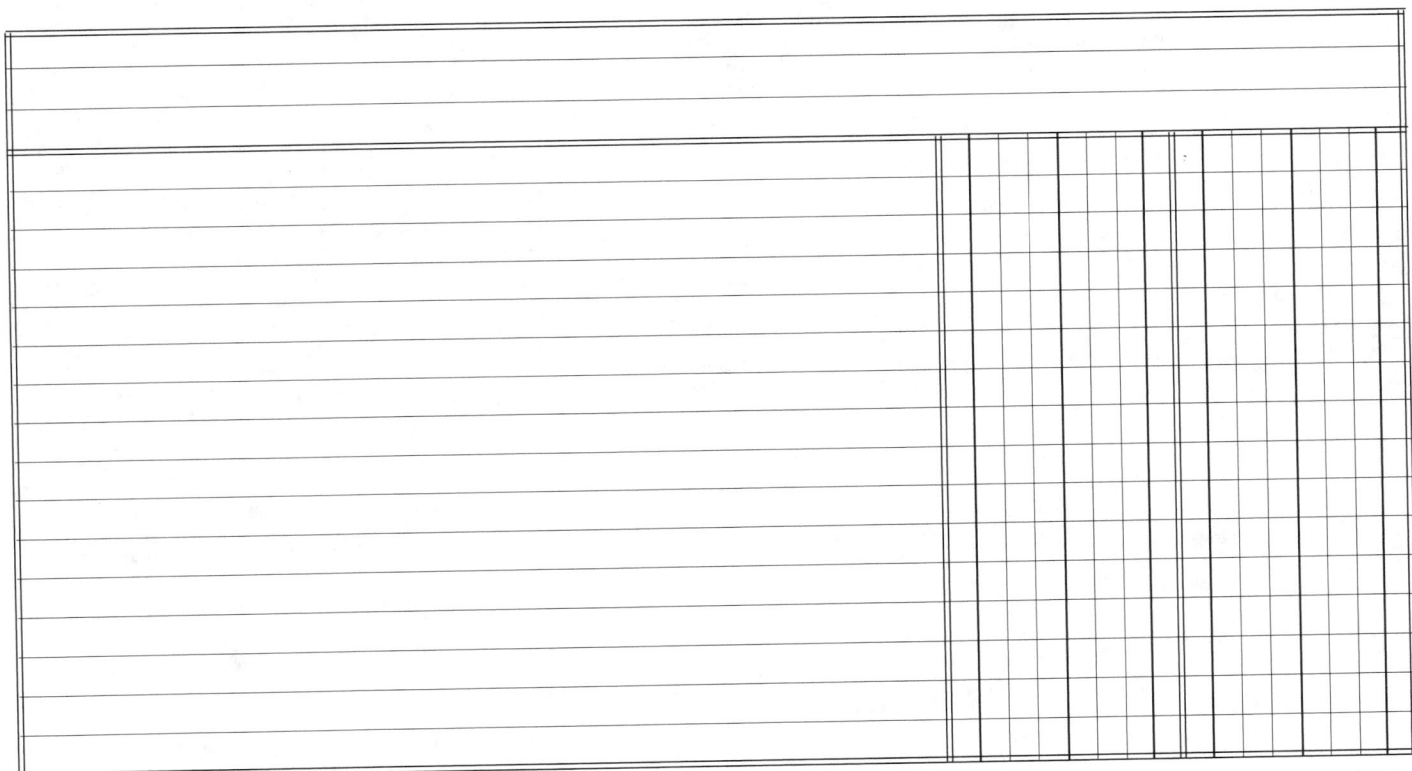

Reqs. 2 and 3

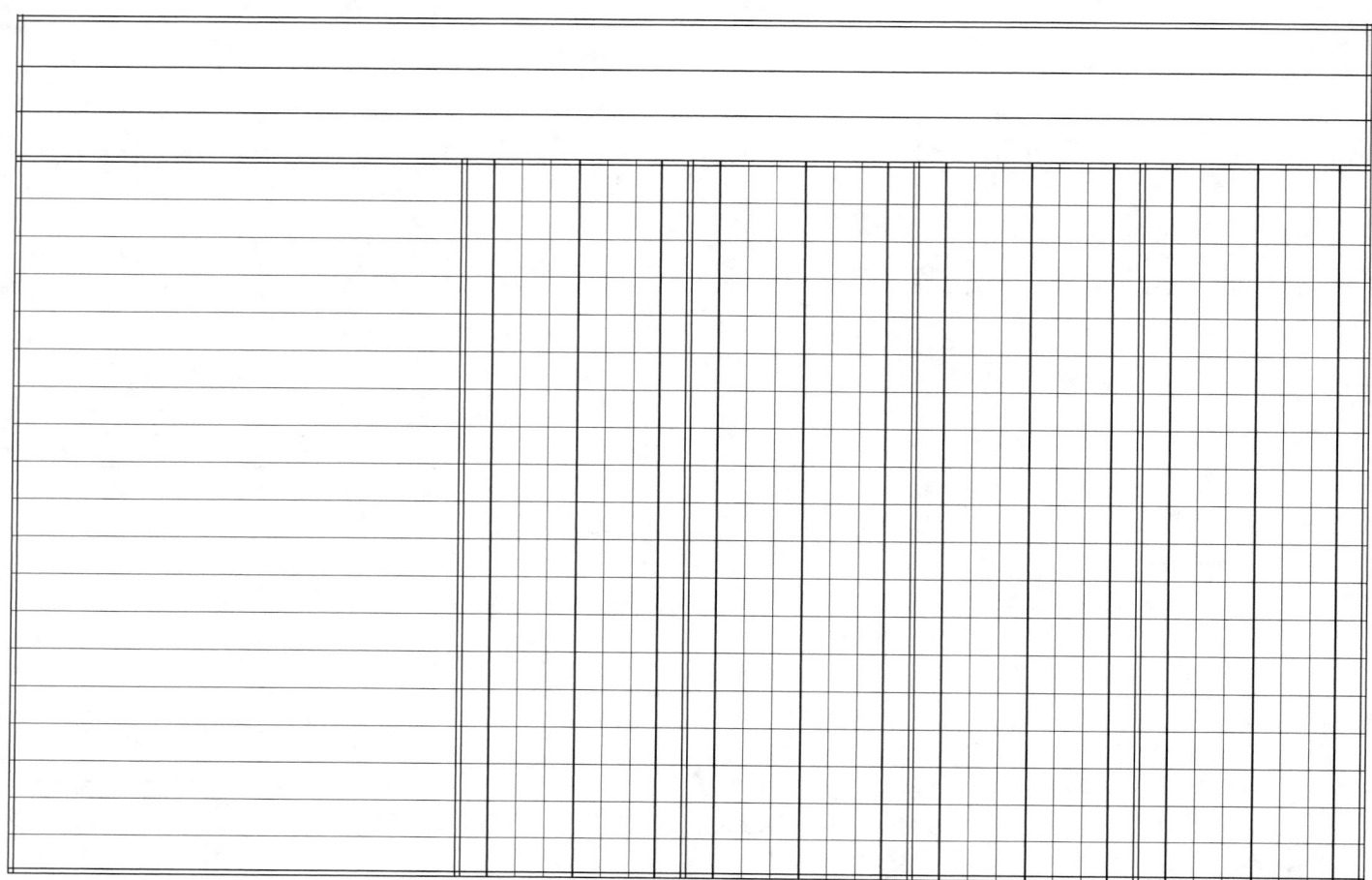

COMPUTATIONS:

Req. 1

Req. 2

Req. 3

Req. 4

Req. 1

Req. 2

Req. 3

Req. 4

Req. 4 (Continued)

Req. 5

Reqs. 1 & 2

Req. 3

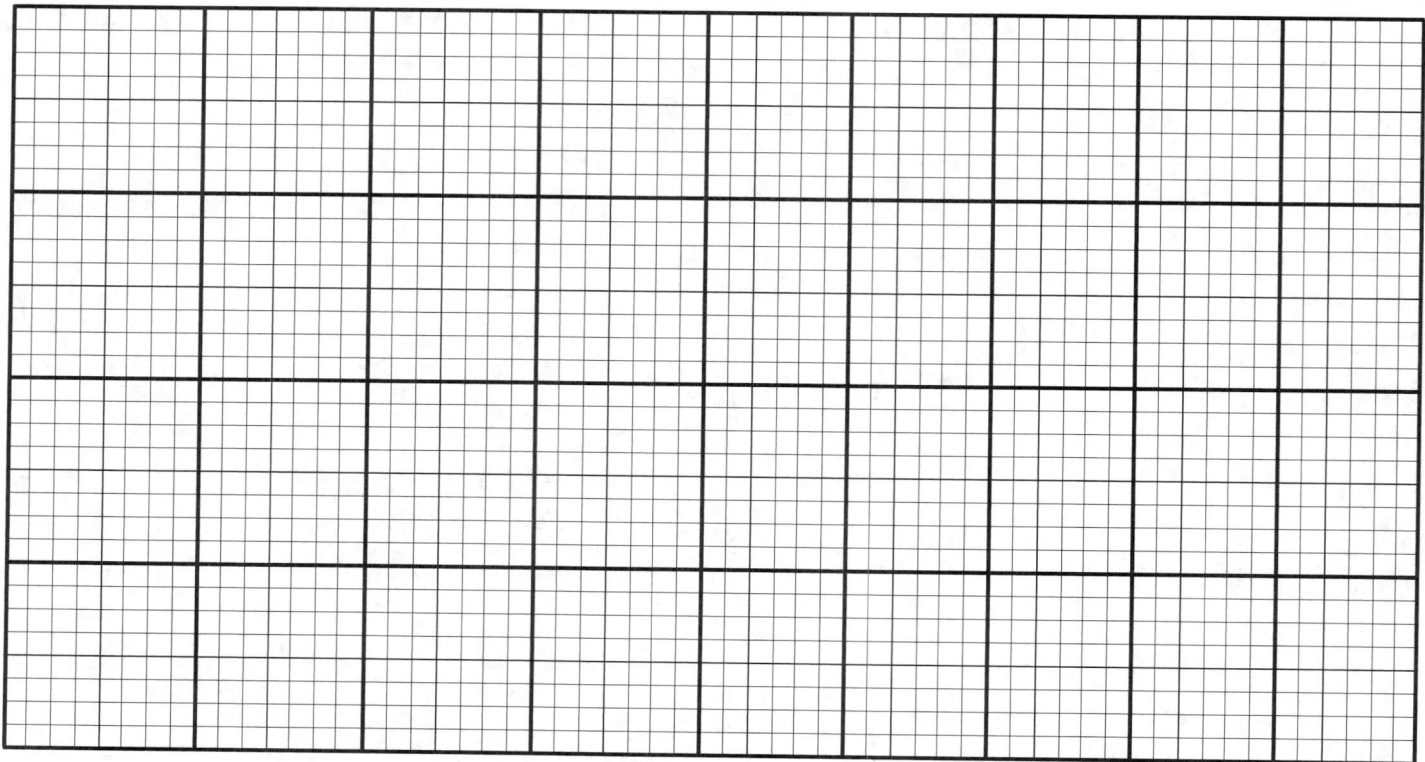

Req. 4

Req. 1

Req. 2a

Req. 2a (Continued)

Req. 2b

Req. 2b (Continued)

Req. 3

Req. 3 (Continued)

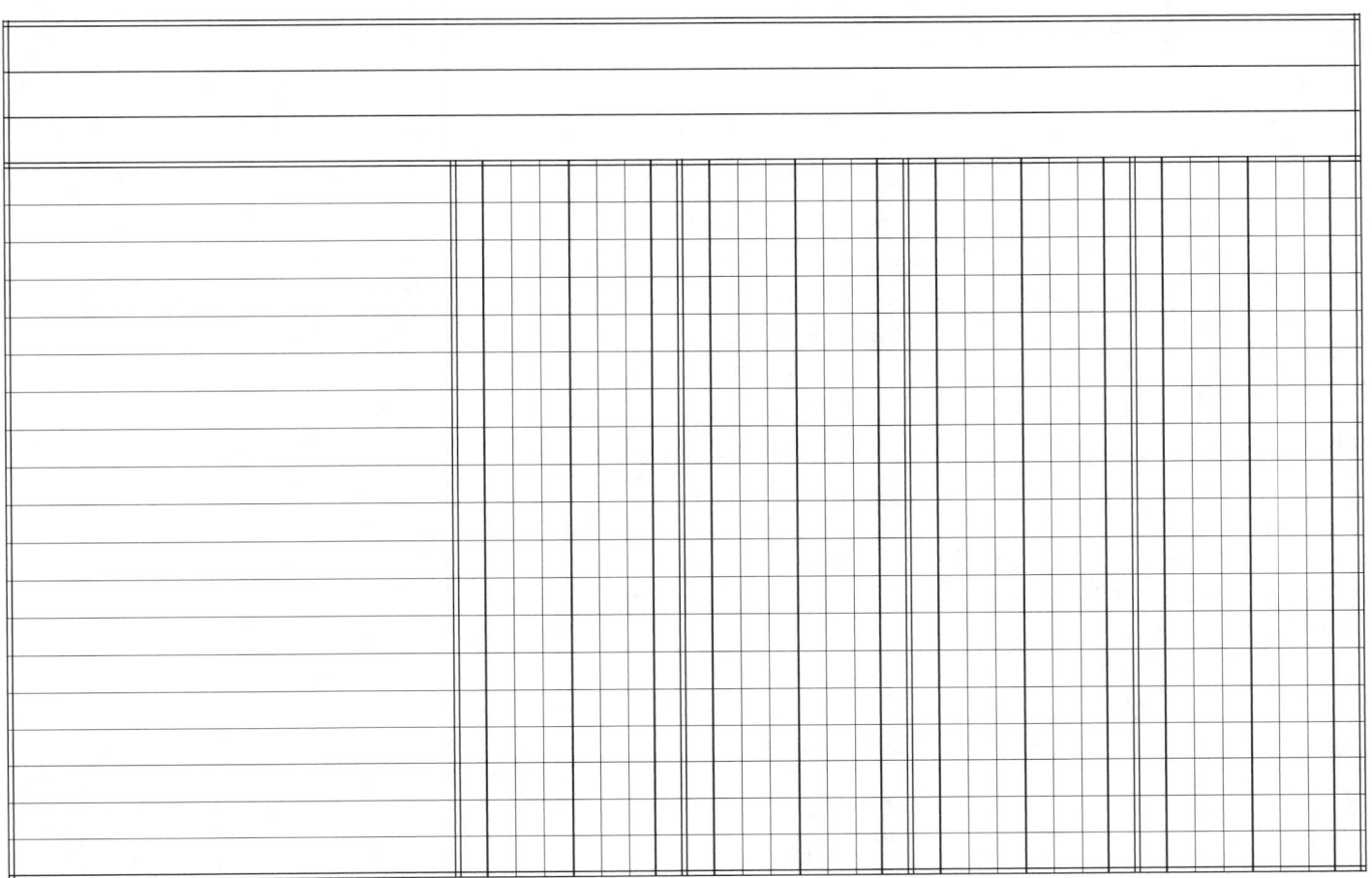

COMPUTATIONS:

Req. 1

Req. 2

Req. 3

Req. 4

Reqs. 1 and 2

Req. 3

Req. 4

Req. 4 (Continued)

Req. 5

Reqs. 1 & 2

Req. 3

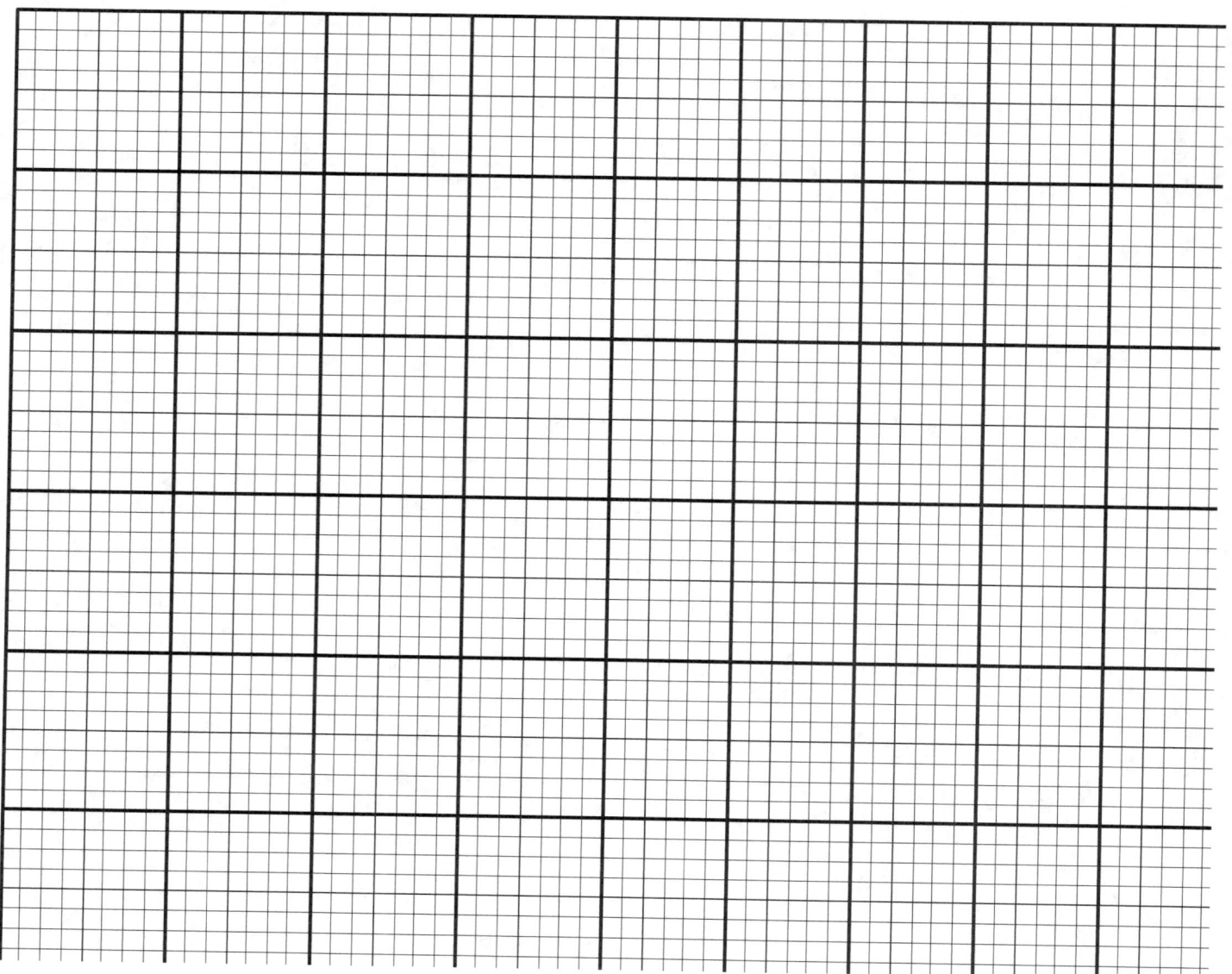

Req. 4

Req. 1

Req. 2a

Req. 2a (Continued)

Req. 2b

Req. 2b (Continued)

Req. 3

Req. 3 (Continued)

Decision Case 1

NAME
SECTION
DATE

Chapter 22

Decision Case 1
(Continued)

NAME
SECTION
DATE

Chapter 22

Decision Case 2

NAME
SECTION
DATE

Chapter 22

Decision Case 2
(Continued)

Reqs. 1–4

NAME
SECTION
DATE

Chapter 22

Ethical Issue
(Continued)

Reqs. 1–4 (Continued)

Financial Statement Case

Reqs. 1–6

NAME
SECTION
DATE

Chapter 22

**Financial
Statement Case**
(Continued)

Reqs. 1–6 (Continued)

NAME
SECTION
DATE

Chapter 22

**Financial
Statement Case**
(Continued)

Reqs. 1–6 (Continued)

Team Project

Team Project
(Continued)

Reqs. 2–3

Team Project

(Continued)

Req. 4

Team Project

(Continued)

Req. 5

Team Project

(Continued)

Board of Directors:
Reqs. 1–4

NAME
SECTION
DATE

Chapter 22

Team Project
(Continued)

Reqs. 1–4 (Continued)

NAME
SECTION
DATE

Chapter 22

Team Project

(Continued)

Team Project

(Continued)

Req. 5

Team Project

(Continued)

Req. 5 (Continued)

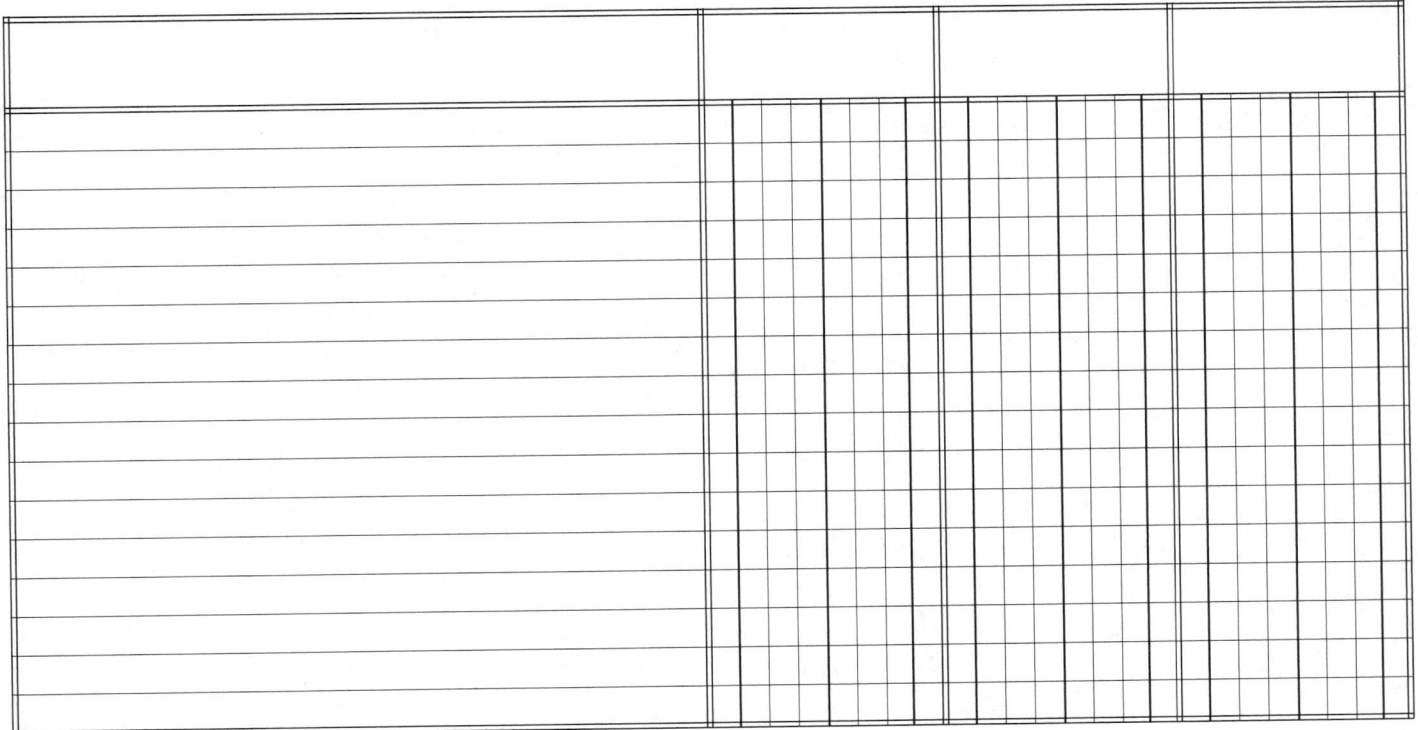

S22A-2

Req. 1

Req. 2

Req. 3

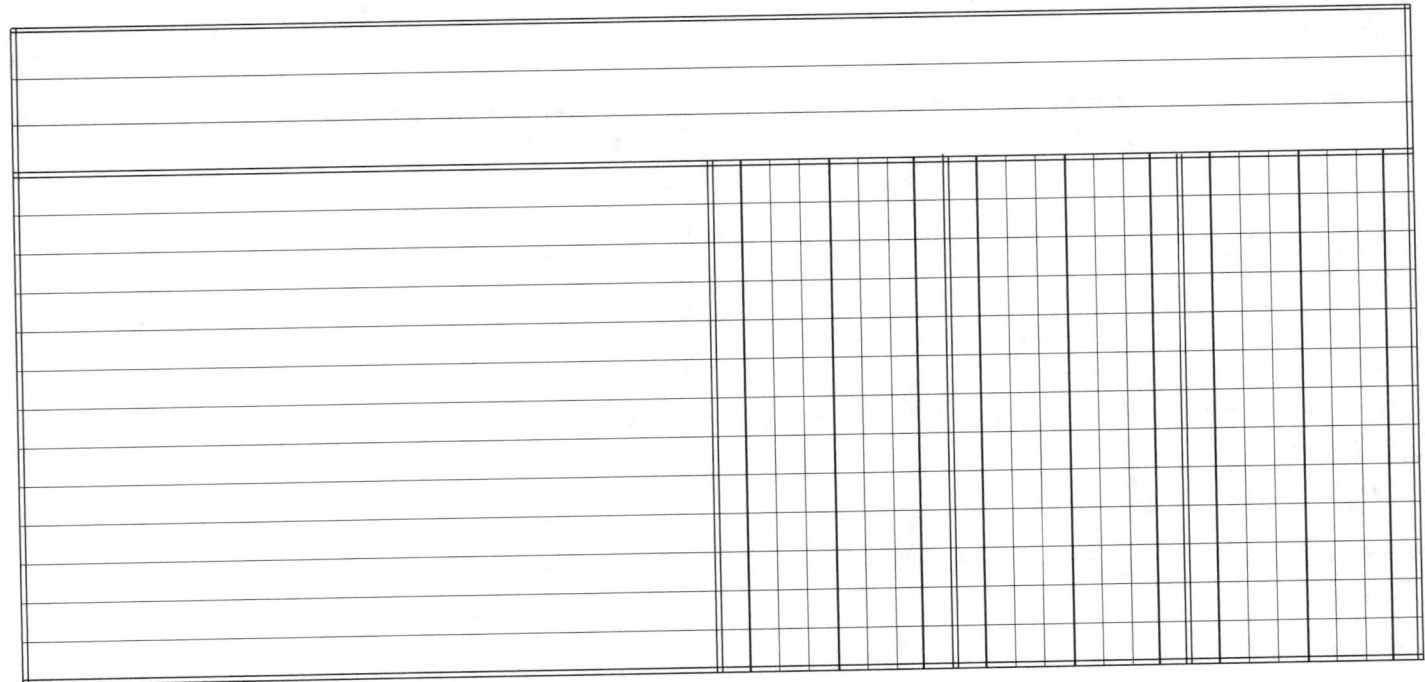

S23-4

S23-12

	QUARTER ENDED			NINE MONTH TOTAL
	MARCH 31	JUNE 30	SEPT. 30	

NAME
SECTION
DATE

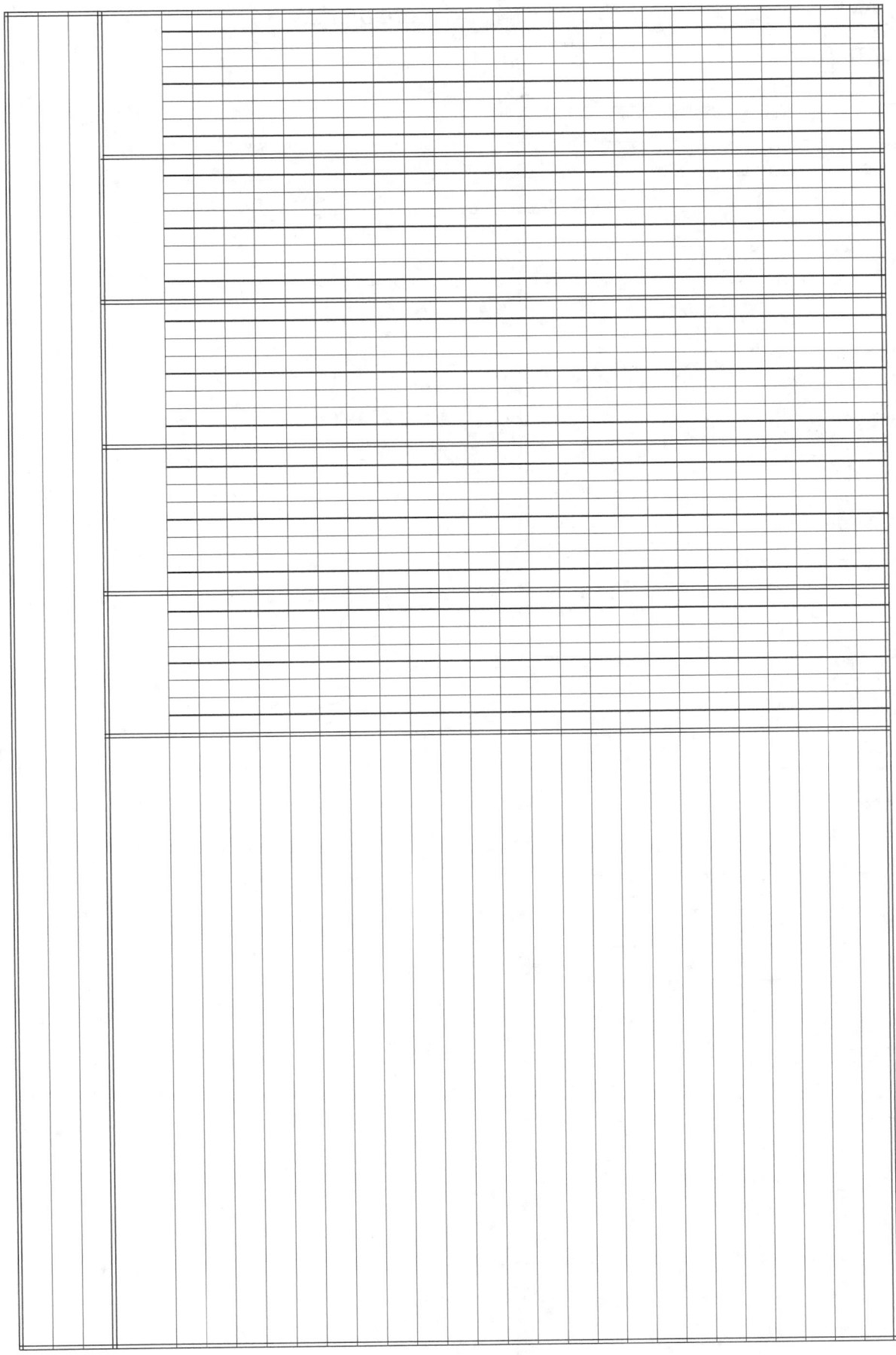

Req. 1

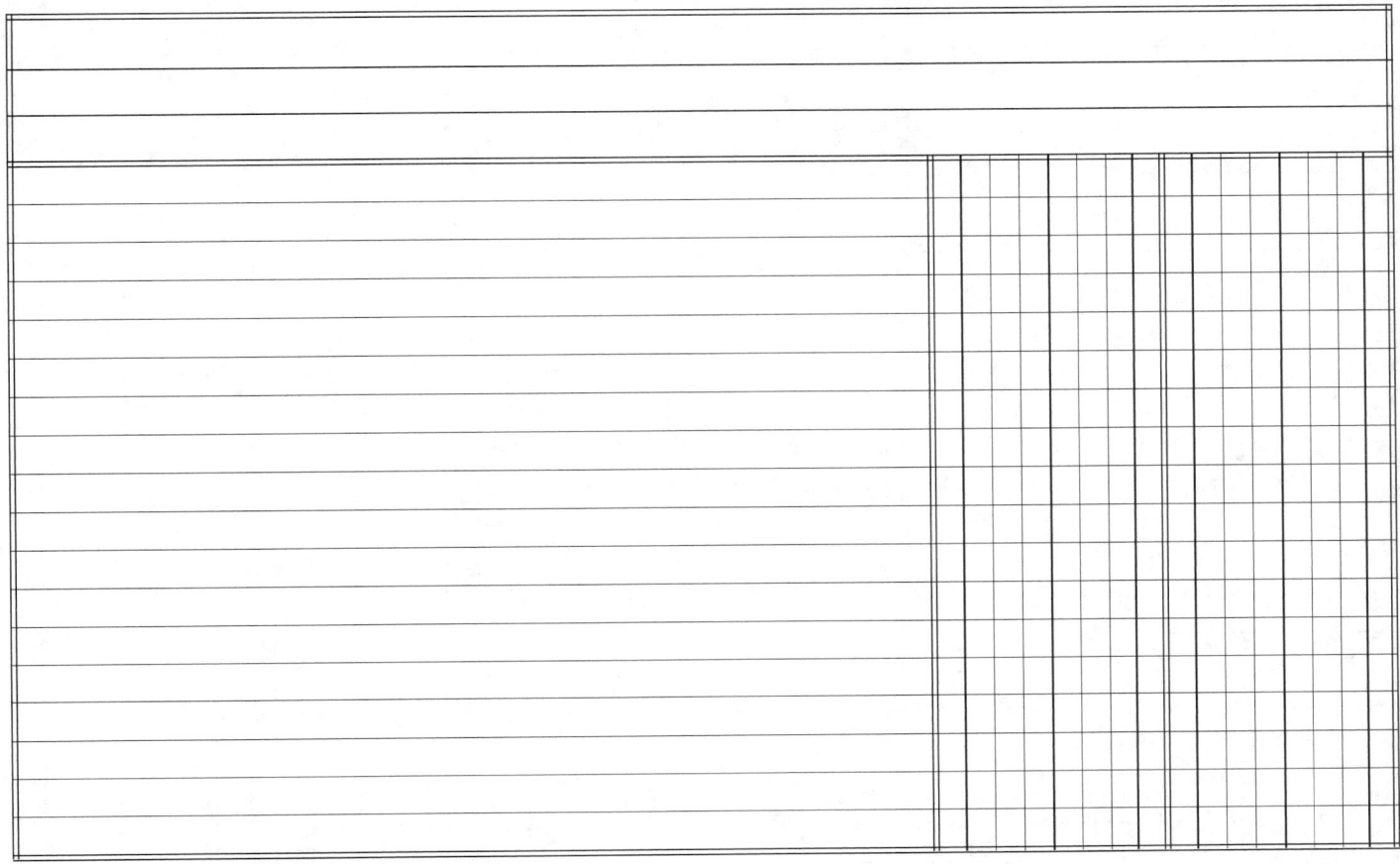

Req. 2

COMPUTATIONS:

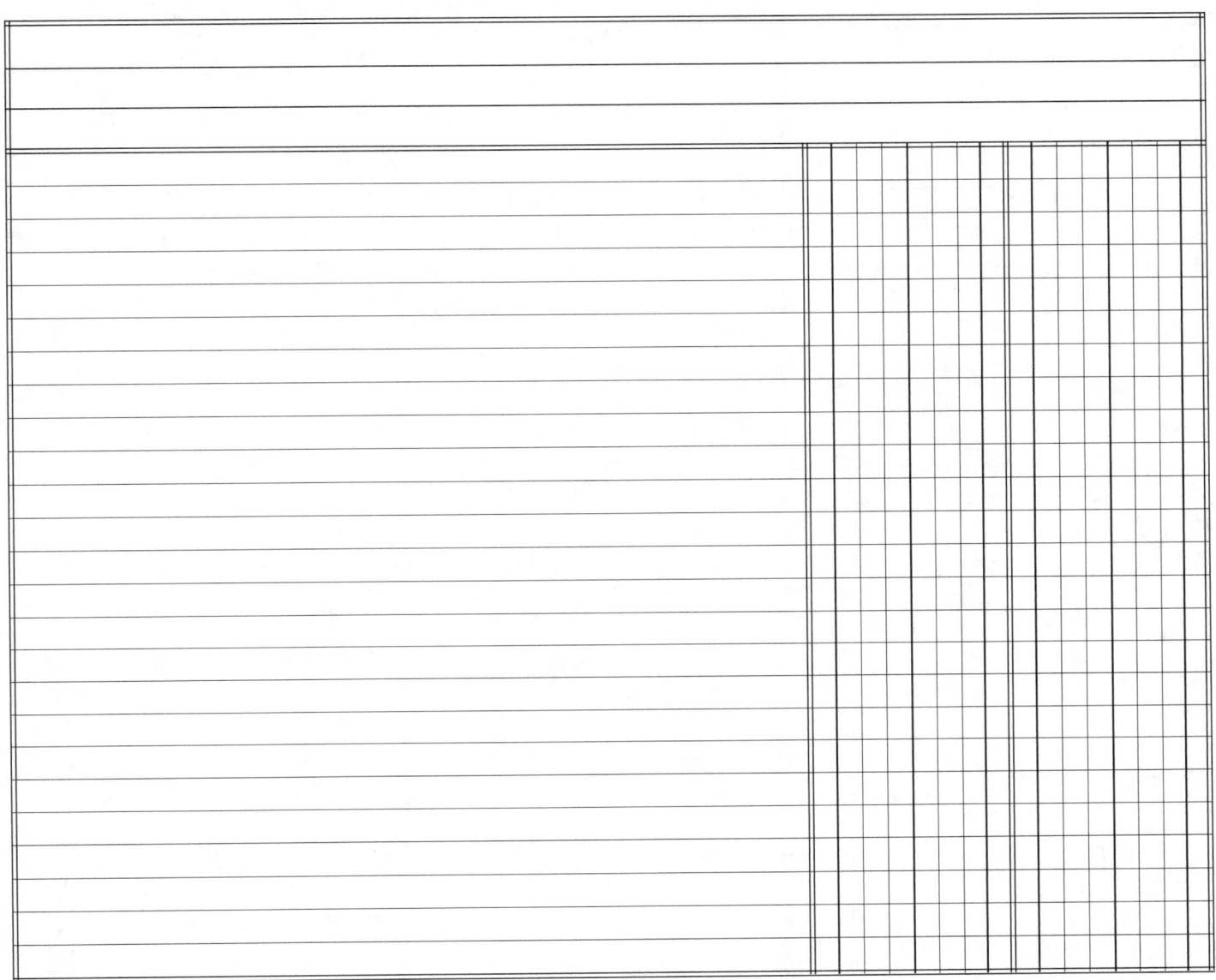

COMPUTATIONS:

a. _____

b. _____

c. _____

d. _____

e. _____

f. _____

g. _____

h. _____

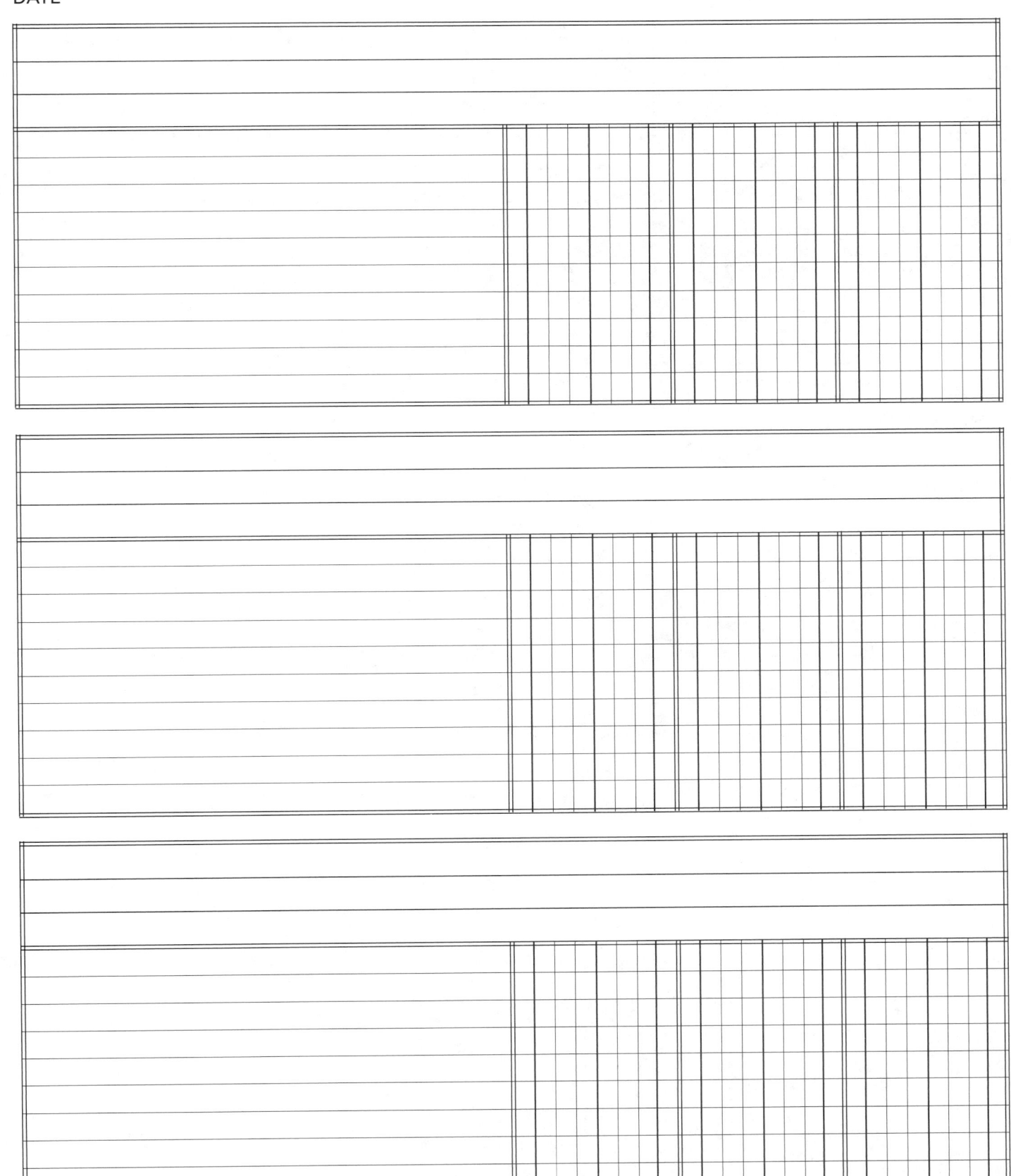

Chapter 23

NAME
SECTION
DATE

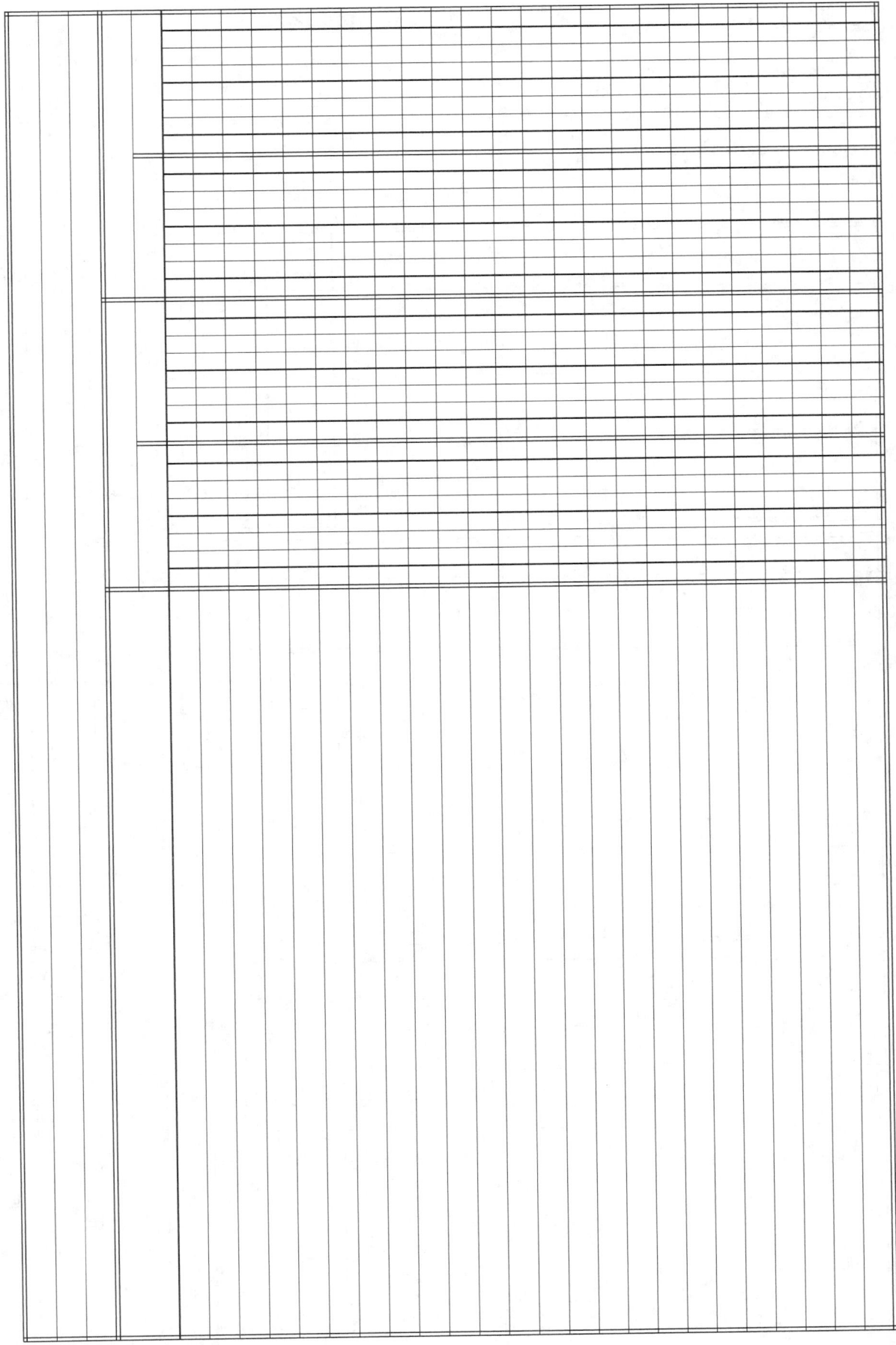

Req. 1

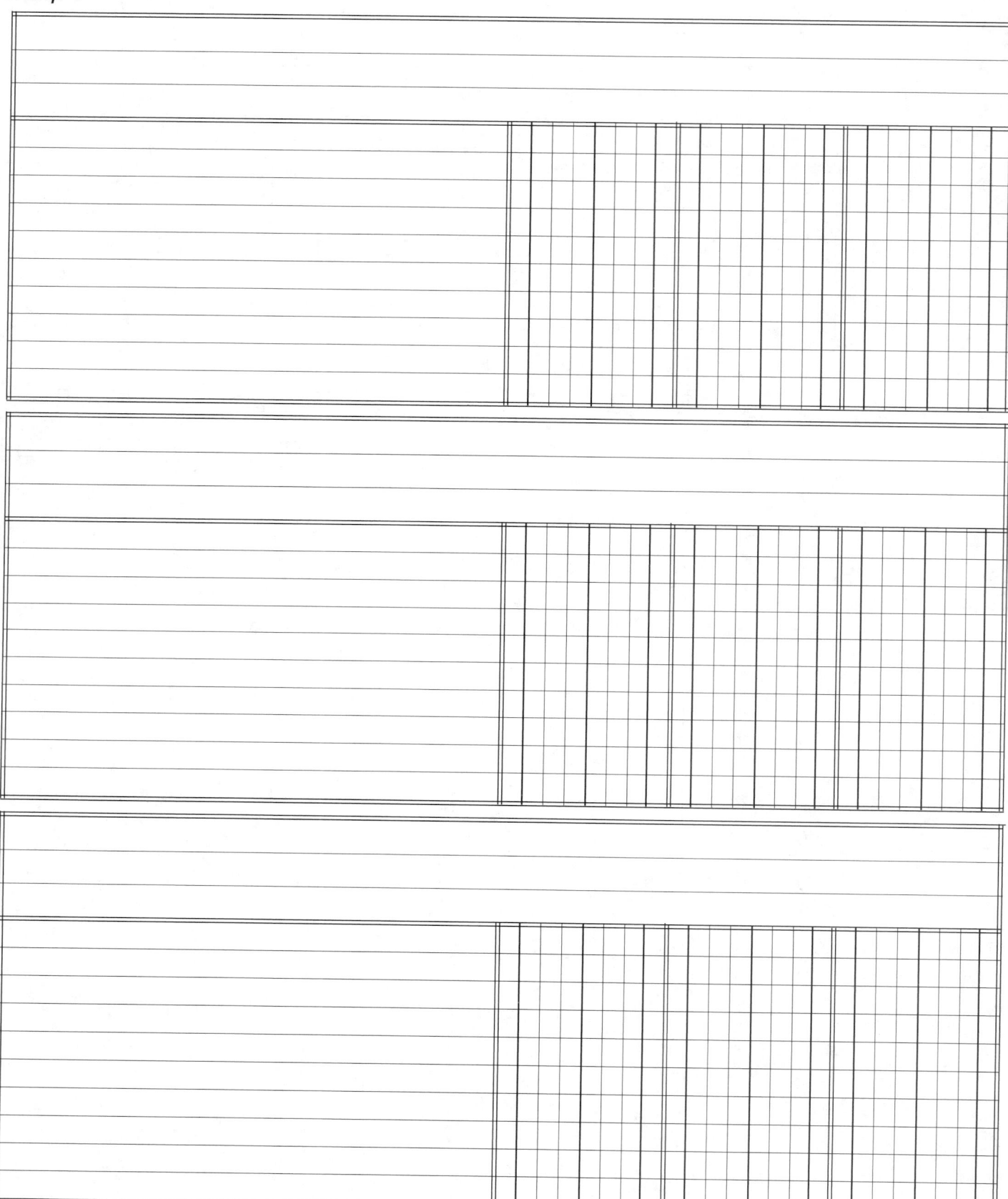

Req. 2

Req. 1

COMPUTATIONS:

Req. 1 (Continued)

Req. 2

Req. 3

Req. 1

Req. 1 (Continued)

Reqs. 2–3

Req. 1

COMPUTATIONS:

Req. 1 (Continued)

COMPUTATIONS:

Req. 1 (Continued)

COMPUTATIONS:

Reqs. 2 & 3

Chapter 23

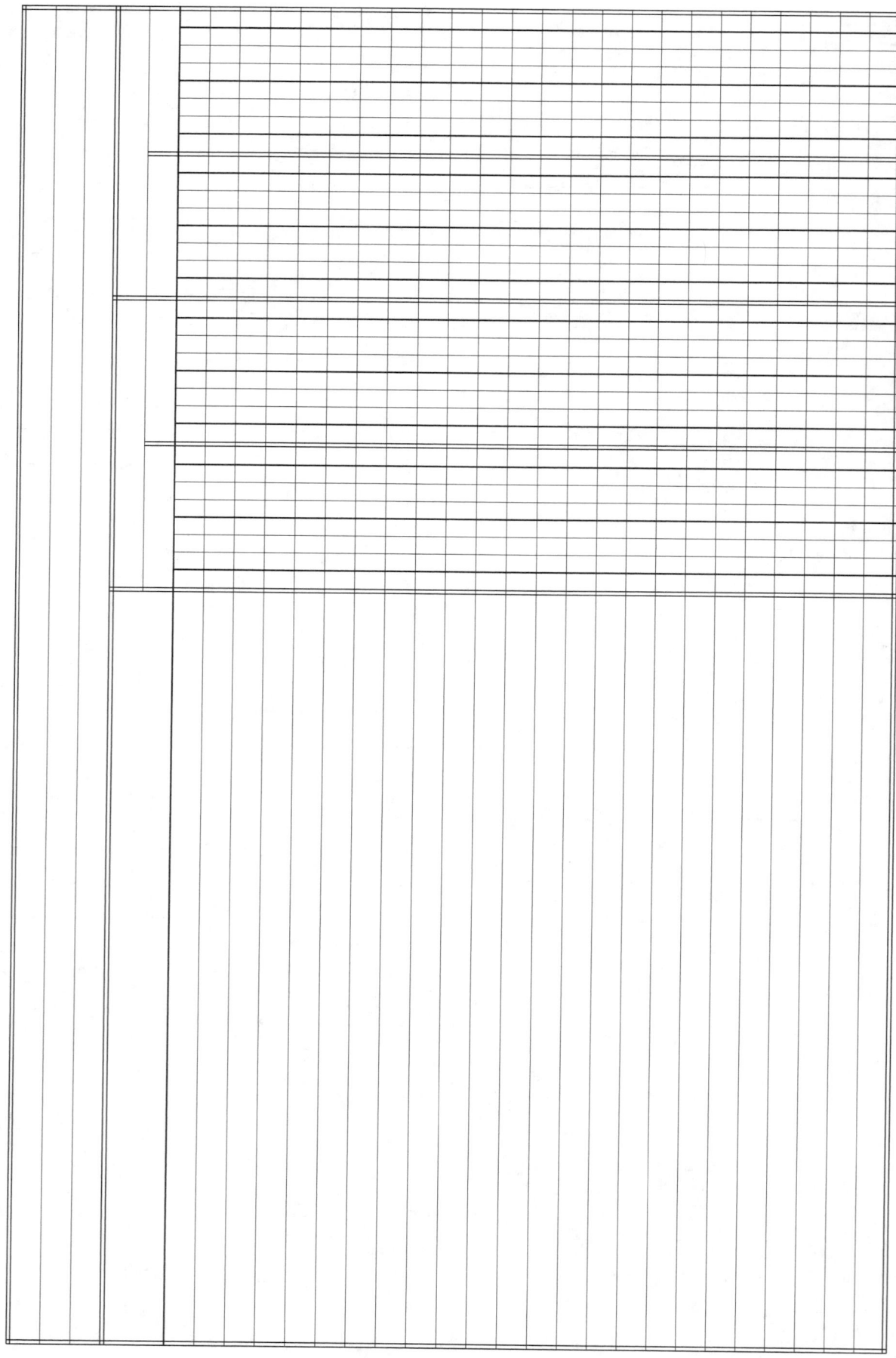

Req. 1

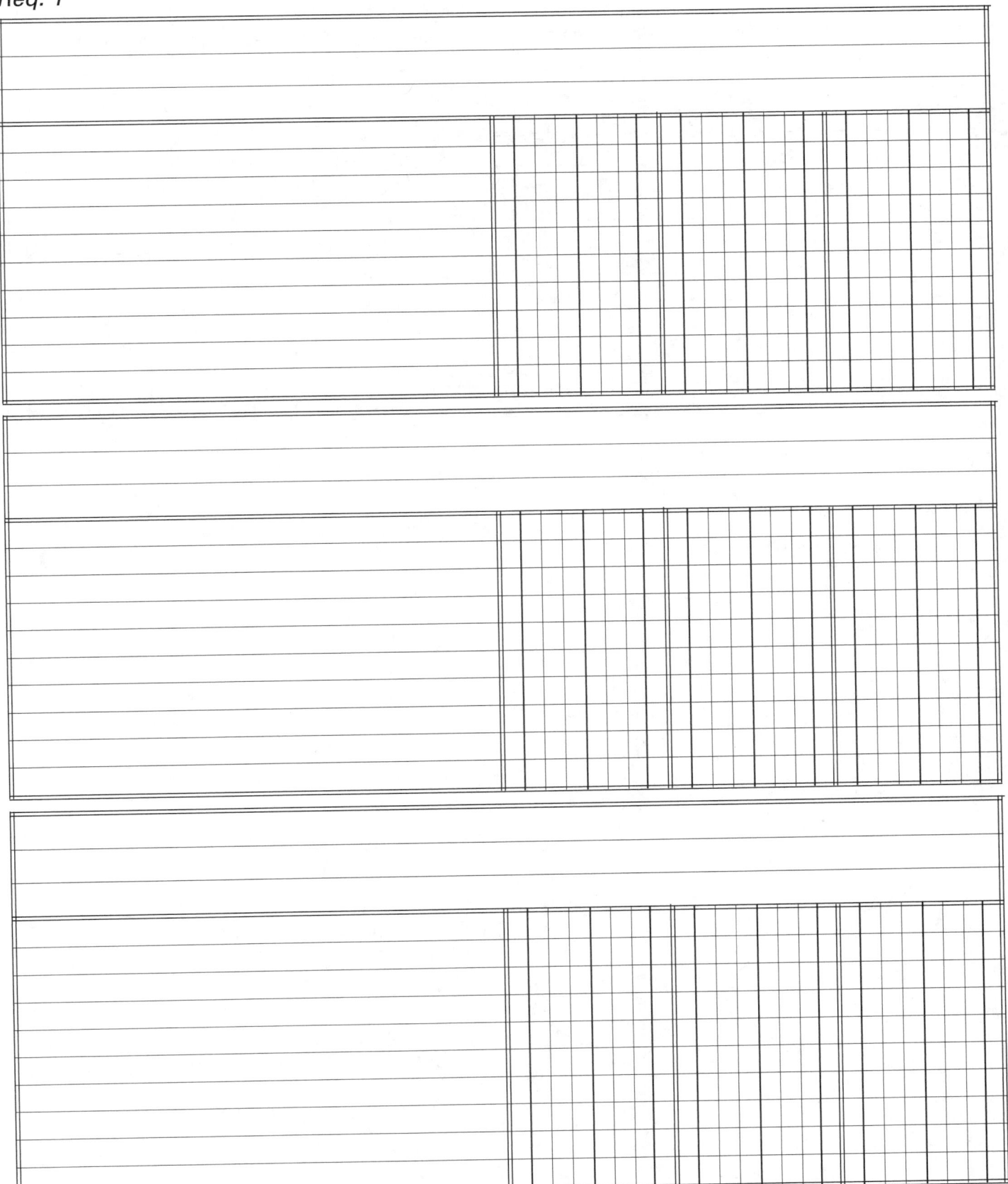

Req. 2

Req. 1

COMPUTATIONS:

Req. 1 (Continued)

Req. 2

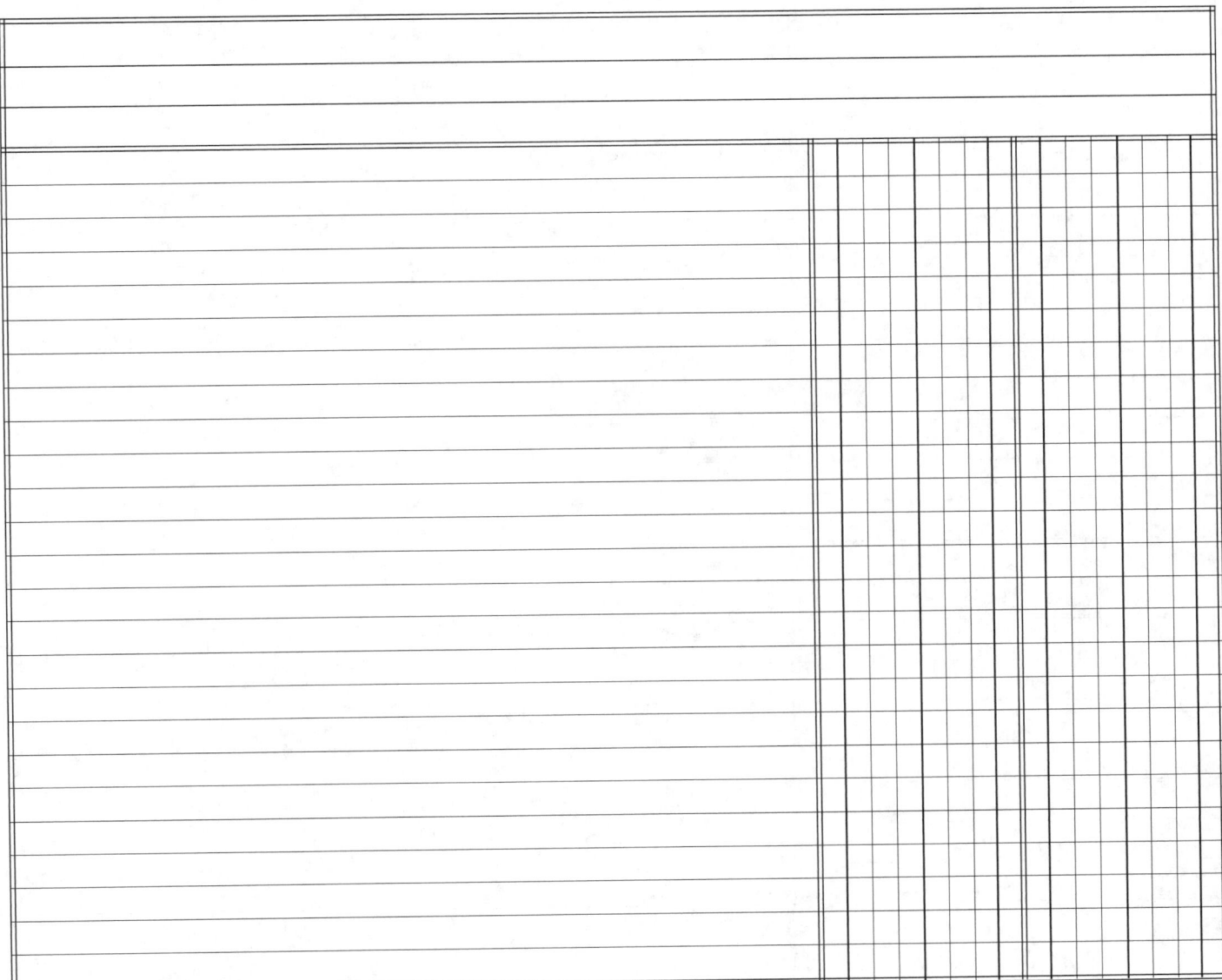

Req. 3

Req. 1

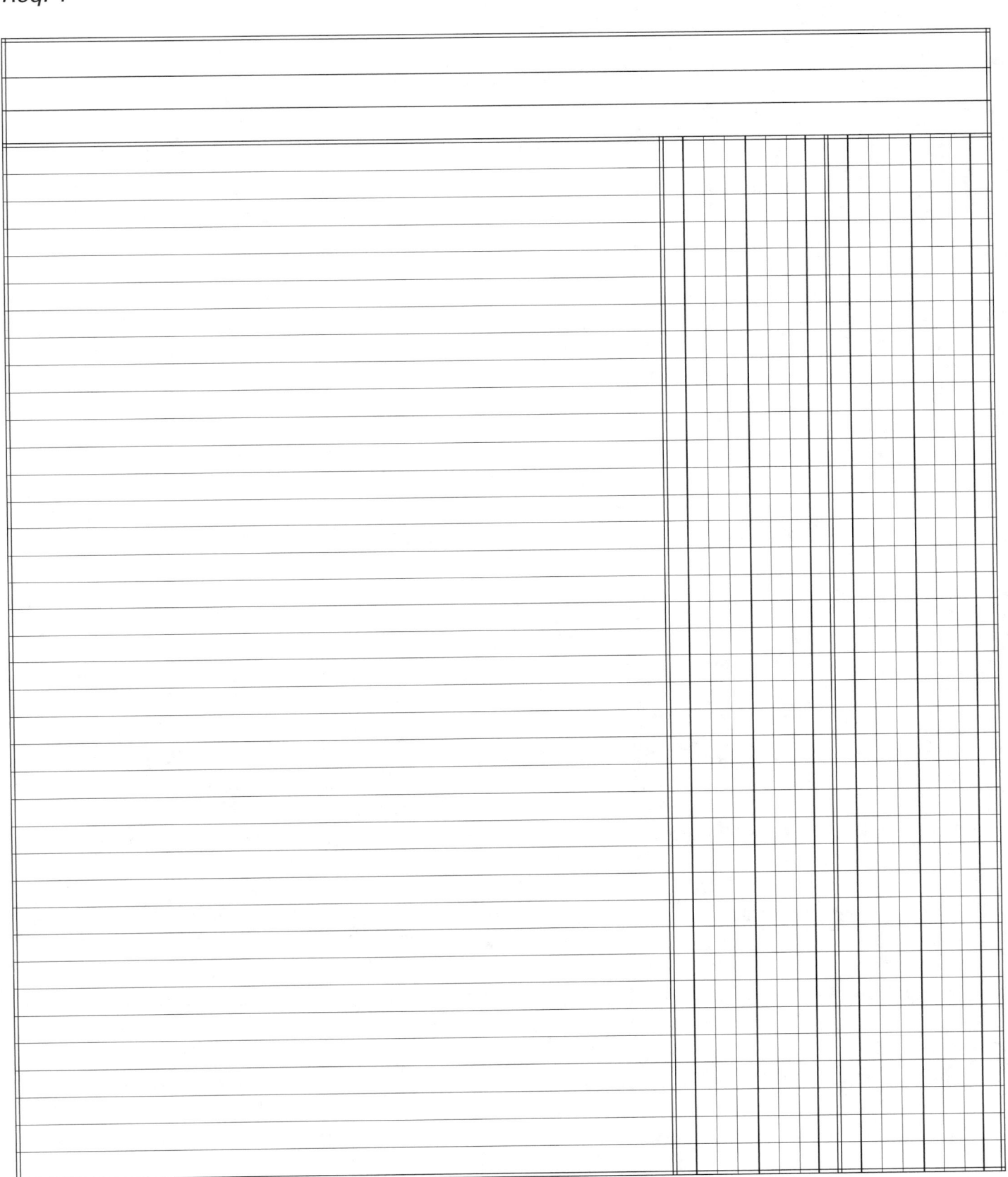

Req. 1 (Continued)

Reqs. 2–3

Req. 1

COMPUTATIONS:

Req. 1 (Continued)

COMPUTATIONS:

Req. 1 (Continued)

COMPUTATIONS:

Reqs. 2 & 3

Chapter 23

Decision Case 1

Decision Case 2

Req. 1

NAME
SECTION
DATE

Chapter 23

Decision Case 2
(Continued)

Req. 1 (Continued)

NAME
SECTION
DATE

Chapter 23

Decision Case 2
(Continued)

Req. 1 (Continued)

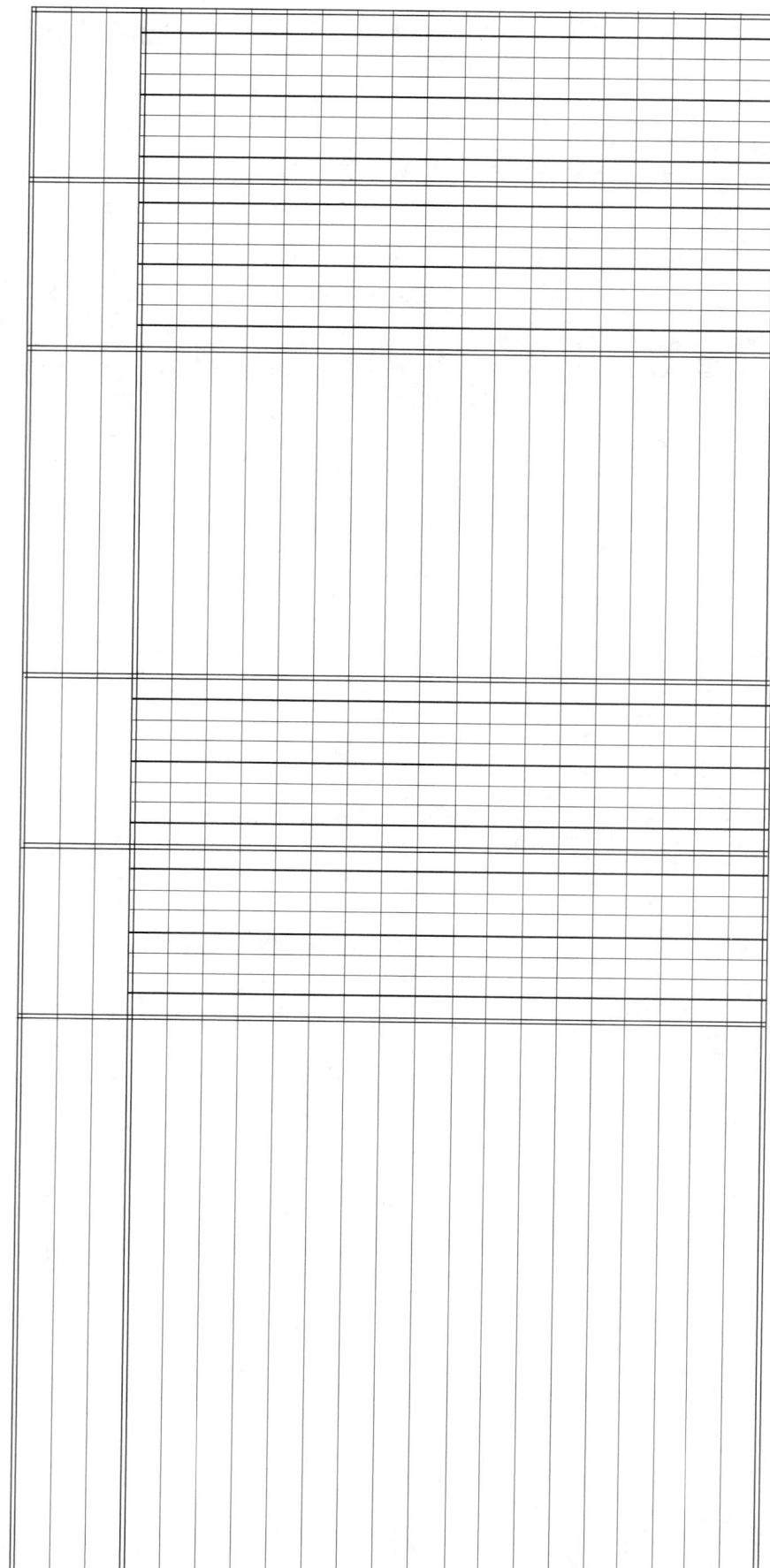

NAME
SECTION
DATE

Chapter 23

Decision Case 2
(Continued)

Req. 2

COMPUTATIONS:

NAME
SECTION
DATE

Chapter 23

Decision Case 2
(Continued)

Reqs. 2 (Continued) & 3

Ethical Issue

NAME
SECTION
DATE

Chapter 23

Ethical Issue
(Continued)

NAME
SECTION
DATE

Chapter 23

Ethical Issue
(Continued)

NAME
SECTION
DATE

Chapter 23

**Financial
Statement Case**

Reqs. 1 & 2

NAME
SECTION
DATE

Chapter 23

**Financial
Statement Case**
(Continued)

Req. 3

NAME
SECTION
DATE

Chapter 23

Financial
Statement Case
(Continued)

Req. 4

NAME
SECTION
DATE

Chapter 23

Team Project

(Continued)

Team Project
(Continued)

NAME
SECTION
DATE

Chapter 23

Team Project
(Continued)

Req. 1

Req. 1 (Continued)

Req. 2

Req. 1

COMPUTATIONS

Req. 2

Req. 1

Req. 1 (Continued)

Req. 2

Req. 3

Req. 1

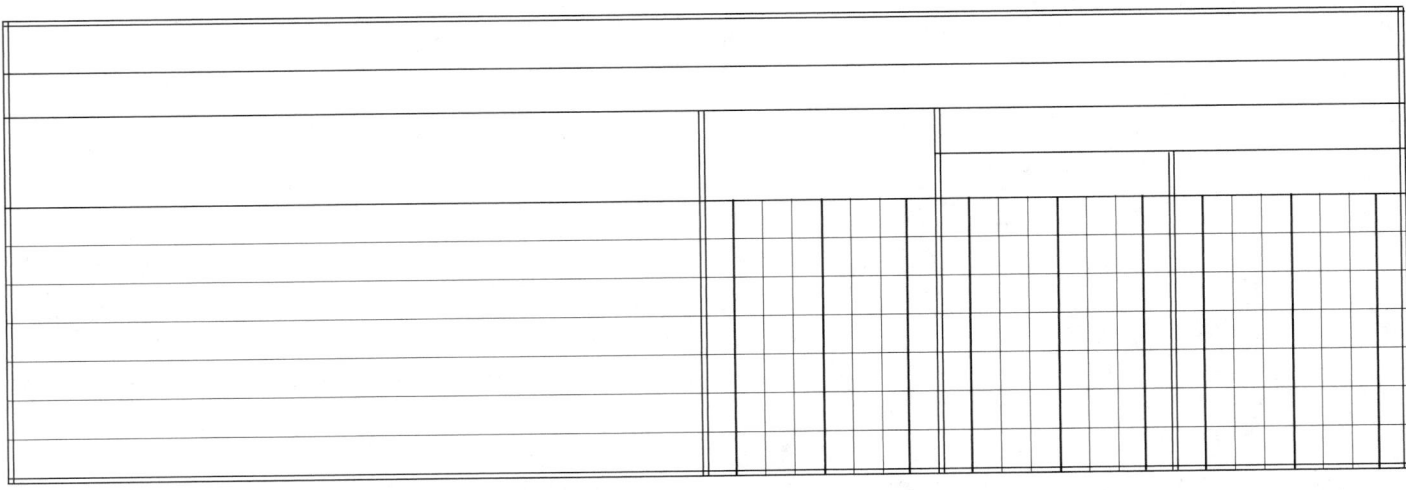

Req. 2

Reqs. 1 and 2

General Journal

DATE	ACCOUNTS AND EXPLANATIONS	DEBIT	CREDIT

General Journal

DATE		ACCOUNTS AND EXPLANATIONS	POST. REF.	DEBIT	CREDIT

General Journal

DATE	ACCOUNTS AND EXPLANATIONS	POST. REF.	DEBIT	CREDIT

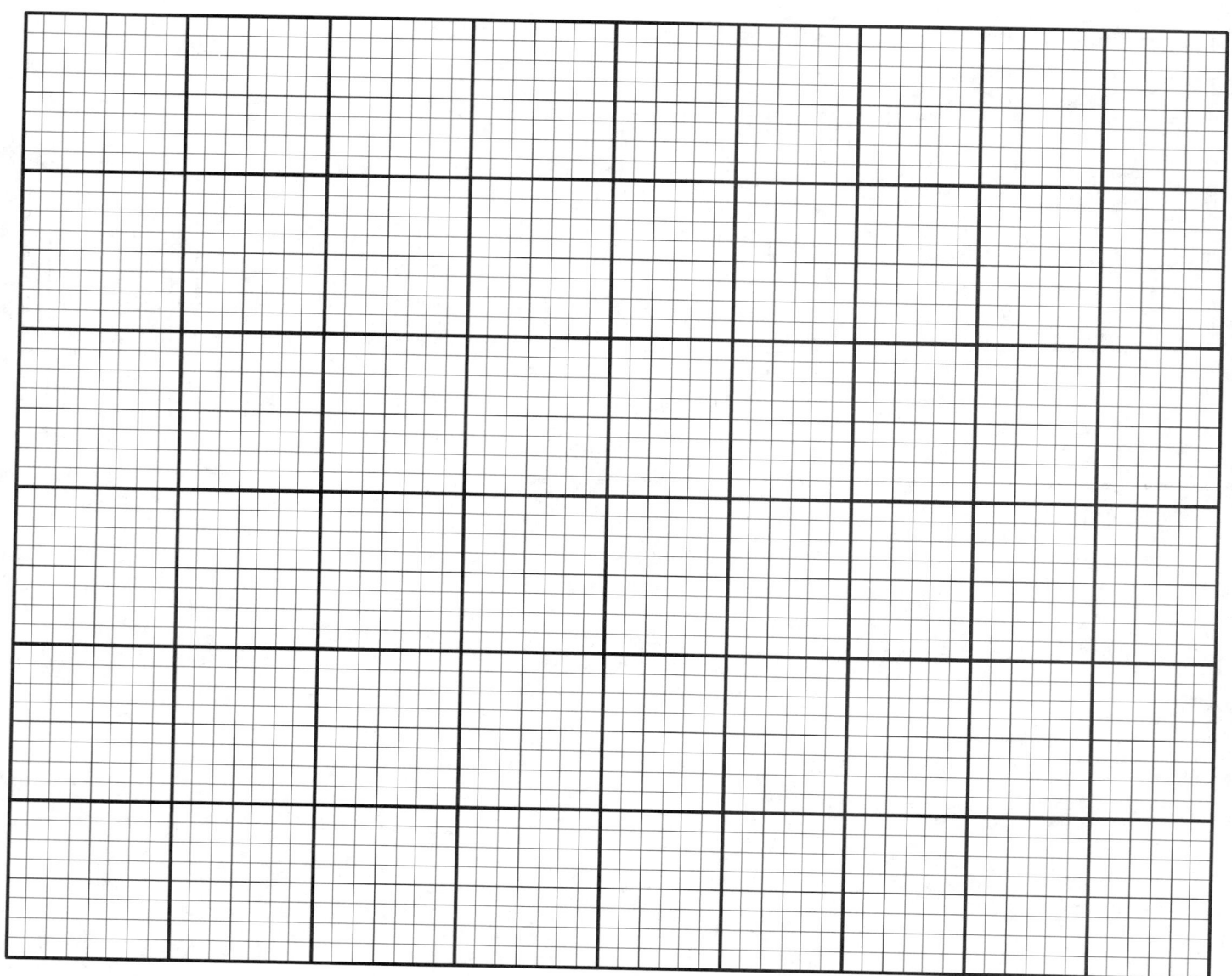

NAME
SECTION
DATE

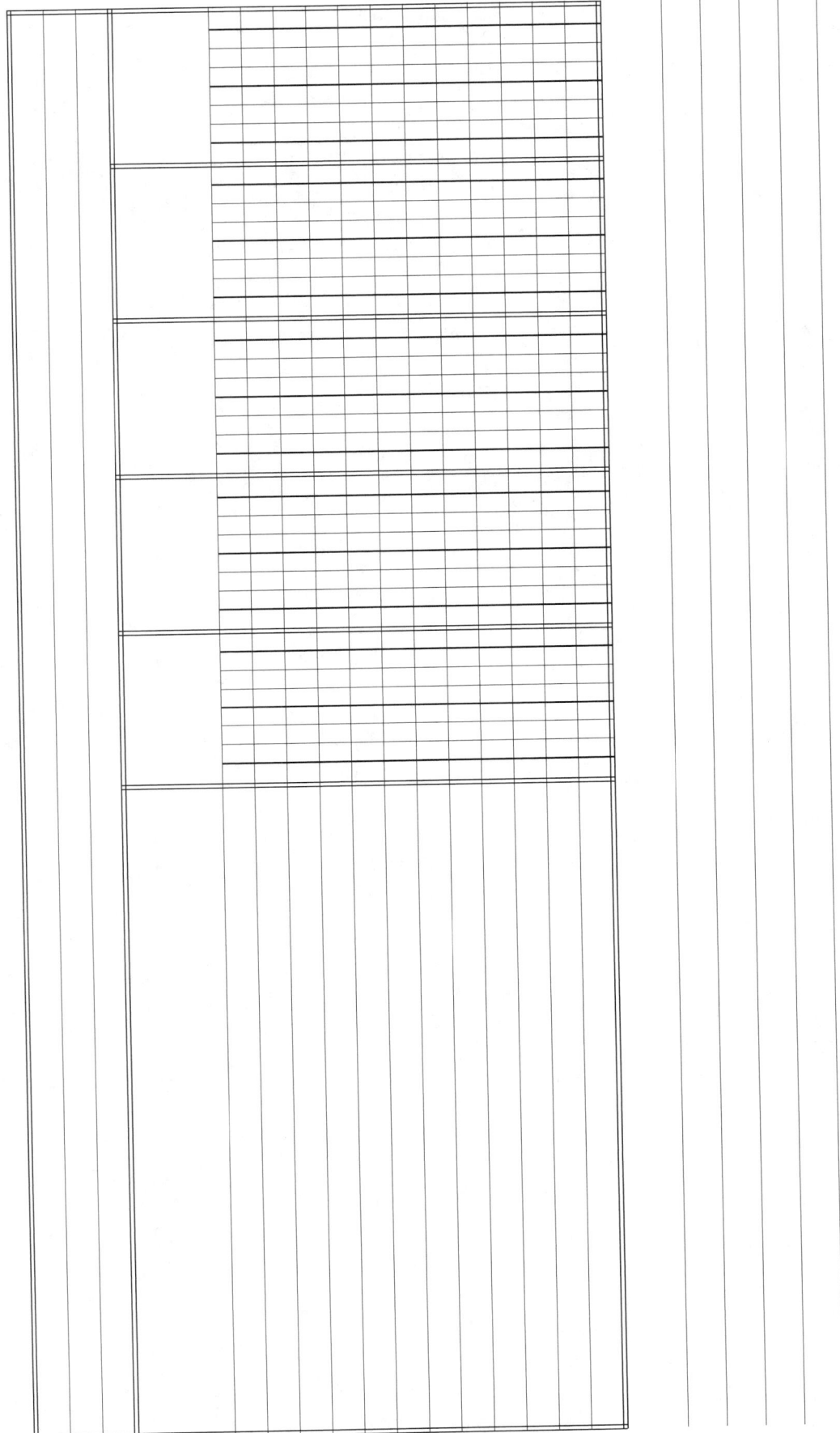

General Journal

DATE	ACCOUNTS AND EXPLANATIONS	POST. REF.	DEBIT	CREDIT

COMPUTATIONS:

Req. 1

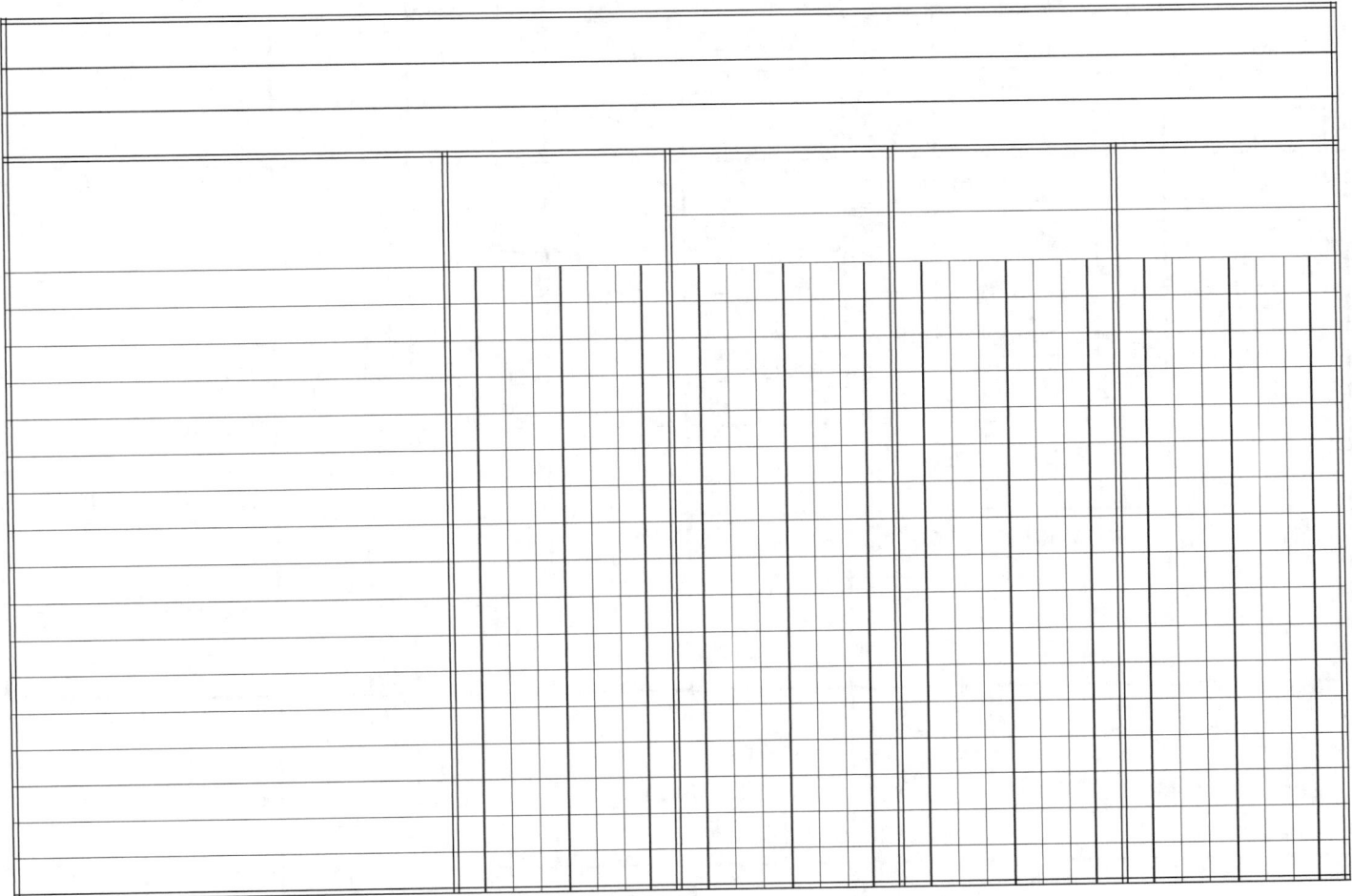

Req. 2

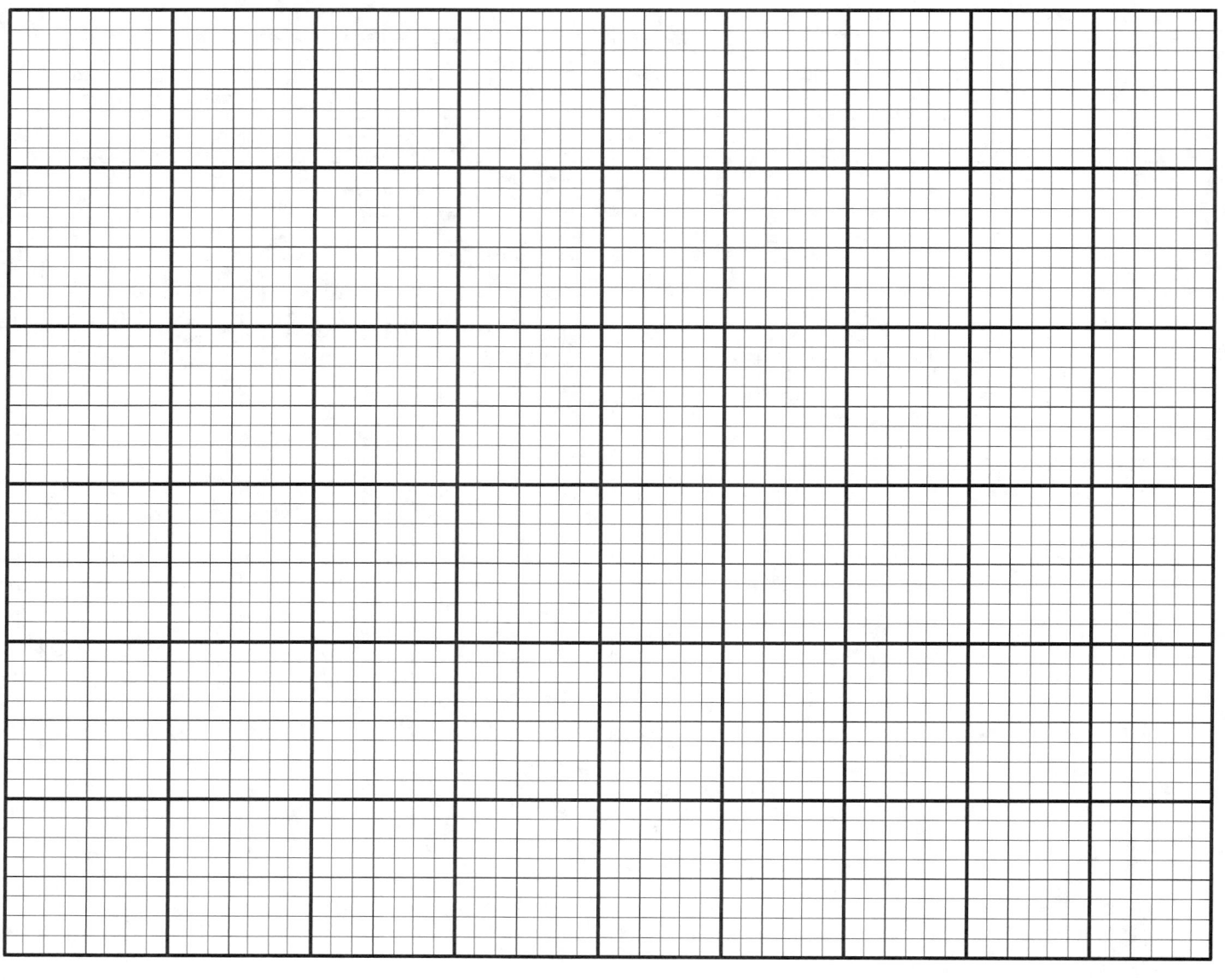

Req. 3

Chapter 24

NAME
SECTION
DATE

Req. 1

Reqs. 2 and 3

Req. 1

Req. 2

Req. 2 (Continued)

Req. 2 (Continued)

Req. 3

Req. 4

Req. 5

Req. 1

Req. 2

Req. 1

Req. 1 (Continued)

Req. 2

		General Journal															
DATE		ACCOUNTS AND EXPLANATIONS		POST. REF.		DEBIT						CREDIT					

Req. 3

Req. 4

Req. 1

Req. 1 (Continued)

Req. 2

Req. 3

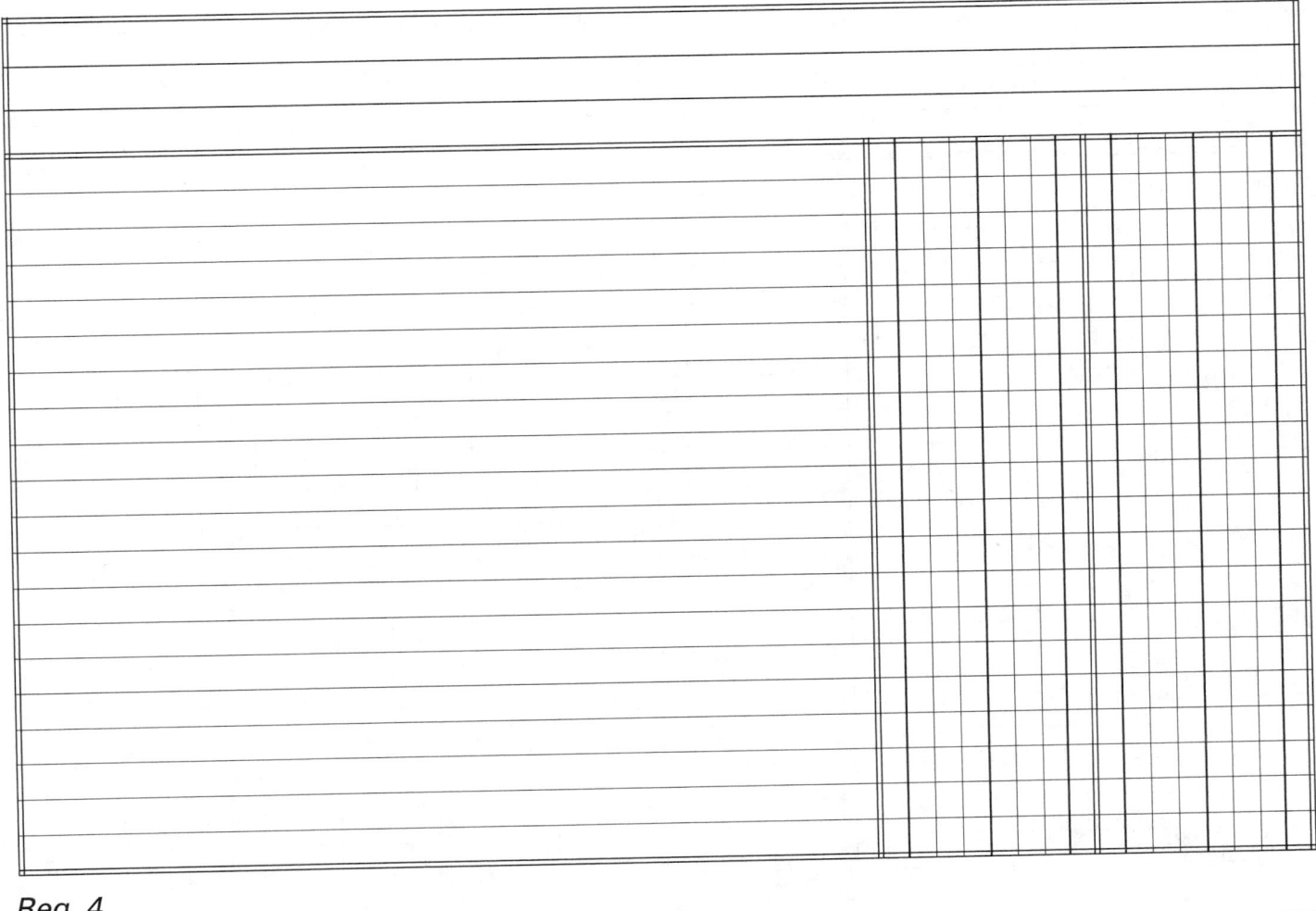

Req. 4

Req. 1

Req. 2

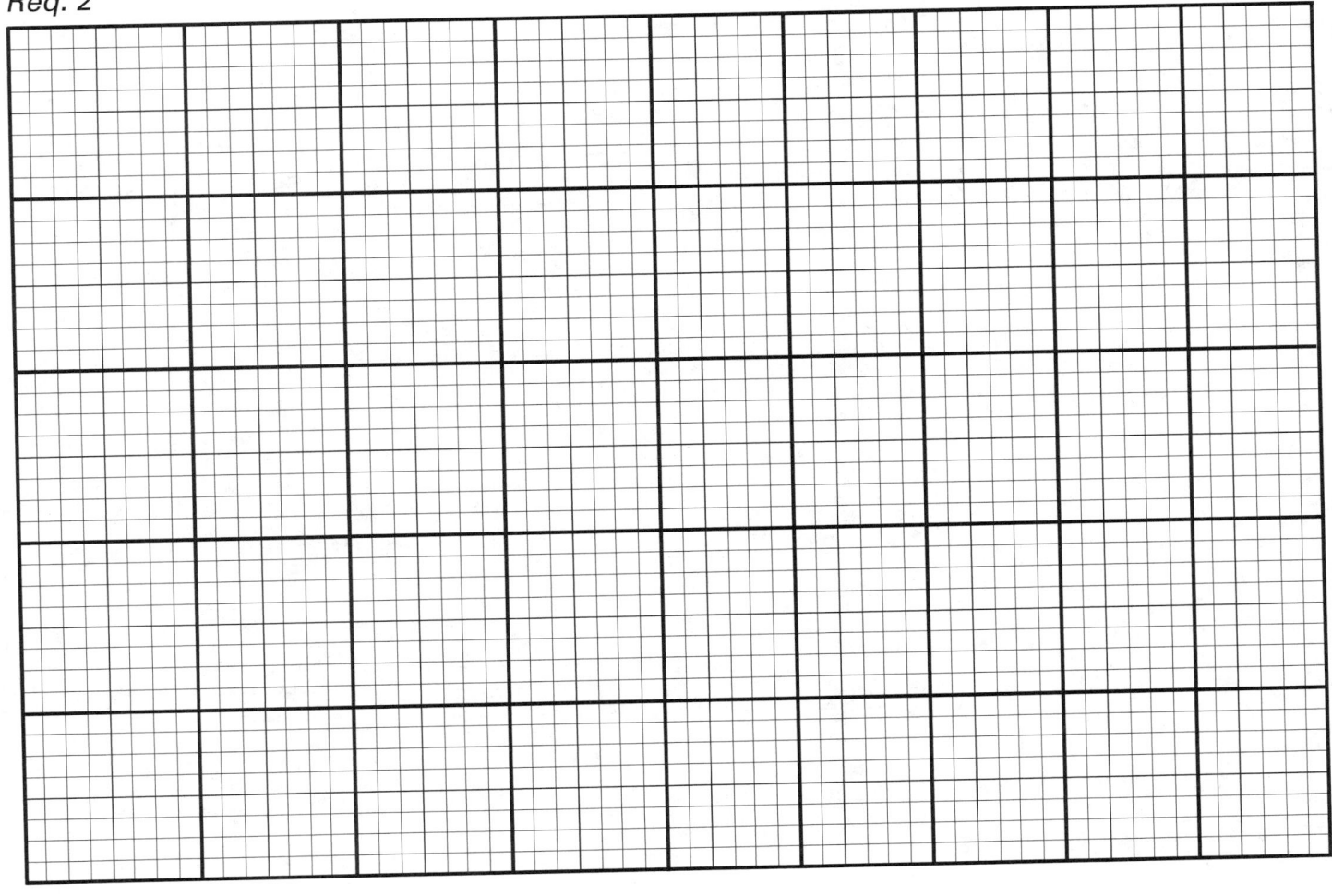

Req. 3

Req. 1

Reqs. 2 and 3

Req. 1

Req. 2

Req. 2

Req. 3

Req. 3 (Continued)

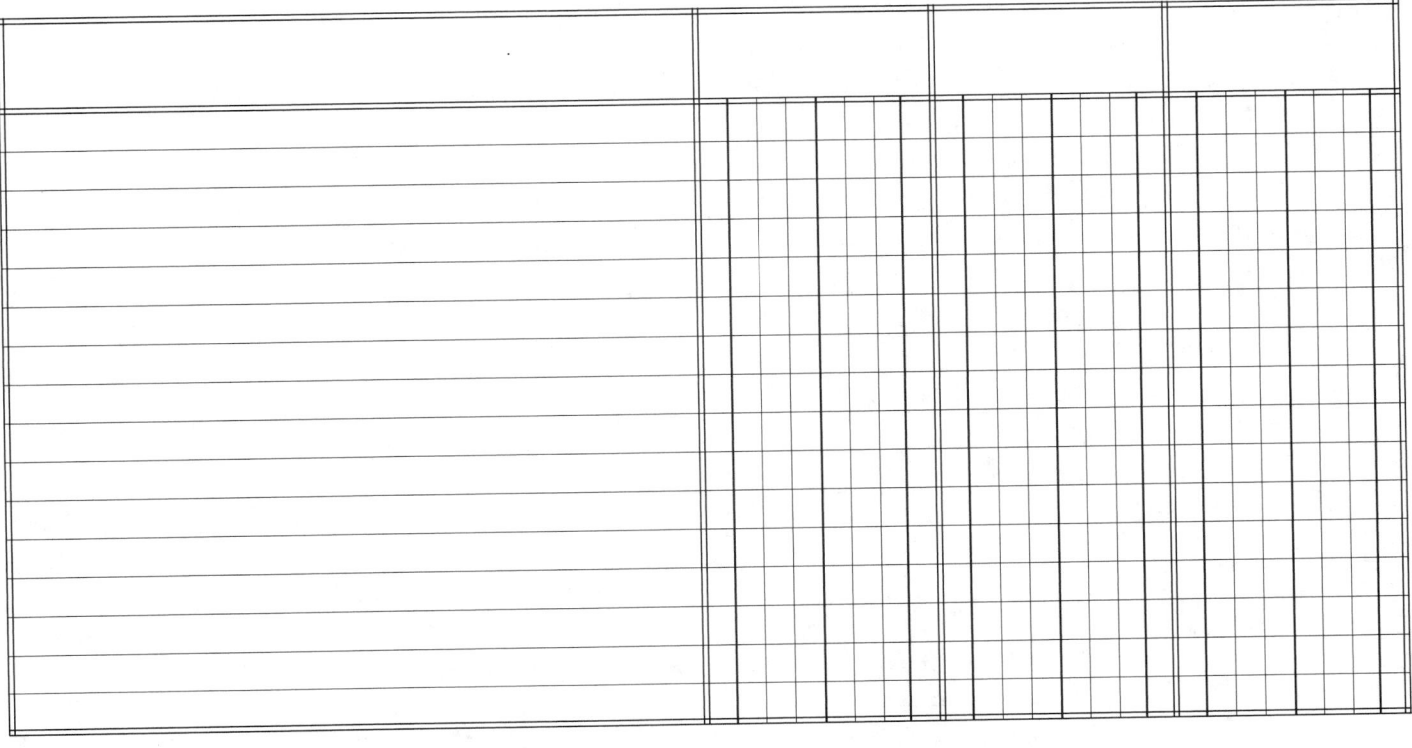

Req. 4

Req. 5

Req. 5 (Continued)

Req. 5 (Continued)

Req. 1

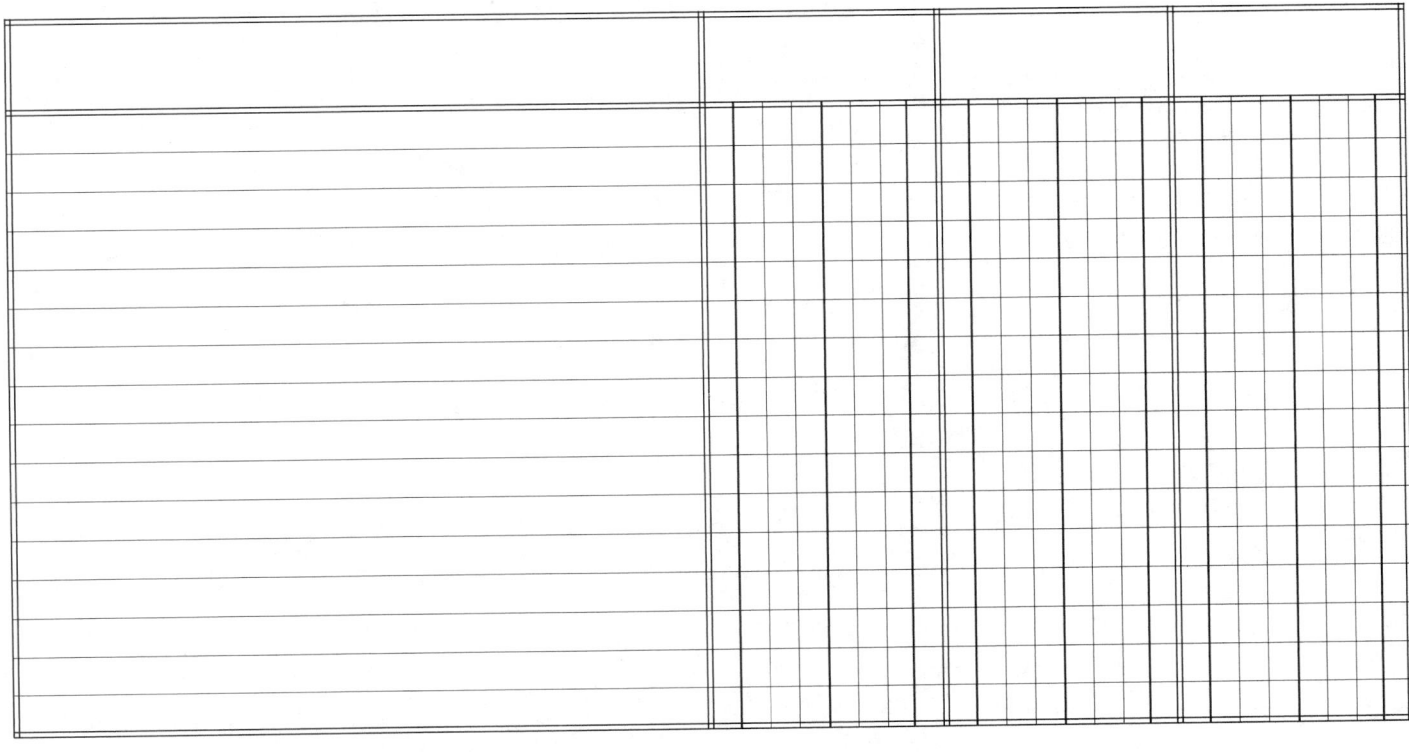

Req. 2

Req. 2 (Continued)

Req. 1

Req. 1 (Continued)

Req. 2

		General Journal			
DATE		ACCOUNTS AND EXPLANATIONS	POST. REF.	DEBIT	CREDIT

Req. 3

Req. 4

Req. 1

Req. 1 (Continued)

Req. 2

Req. 3

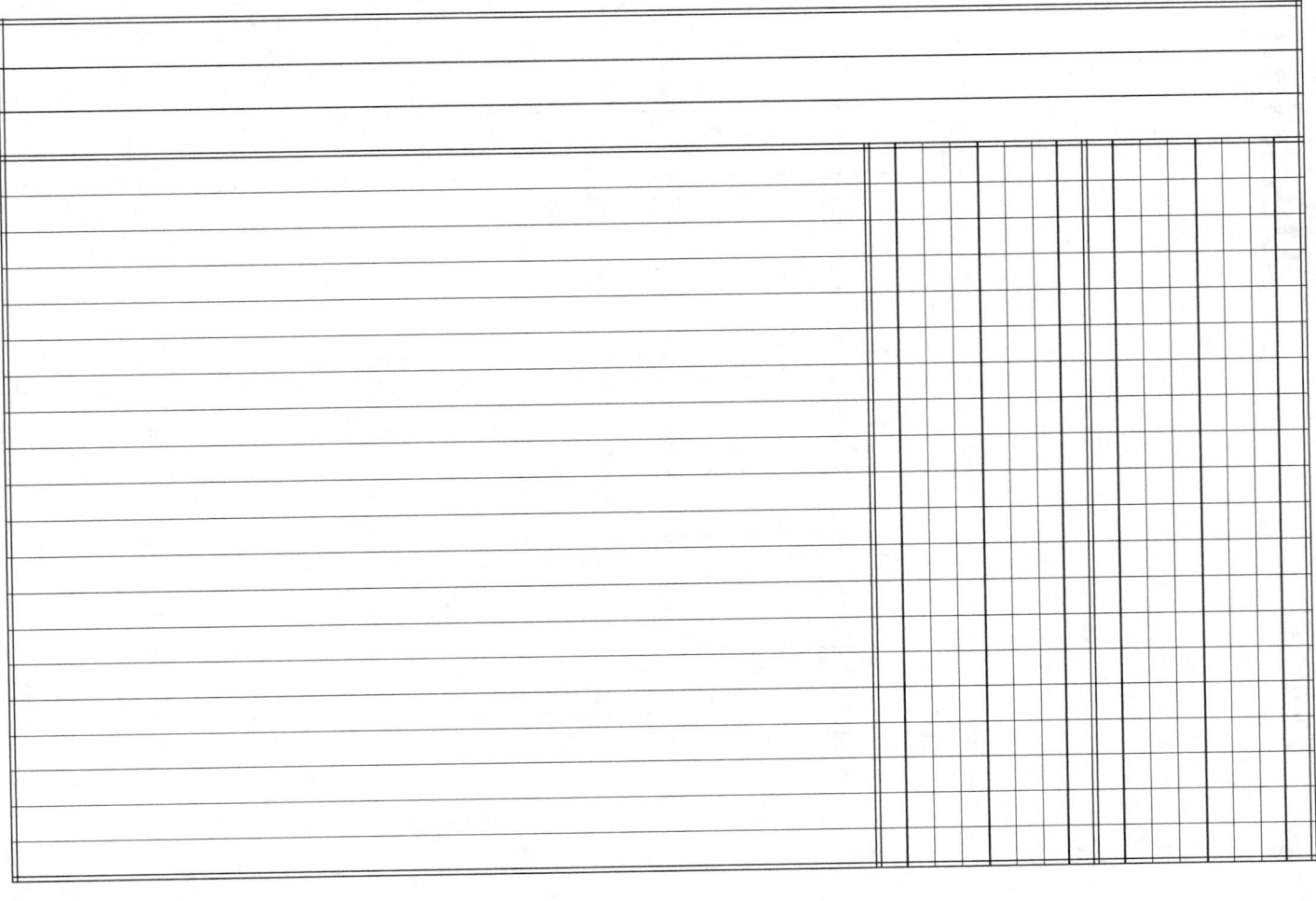

Req. 4

Chapter 24

Decision Case 1

Req. 1

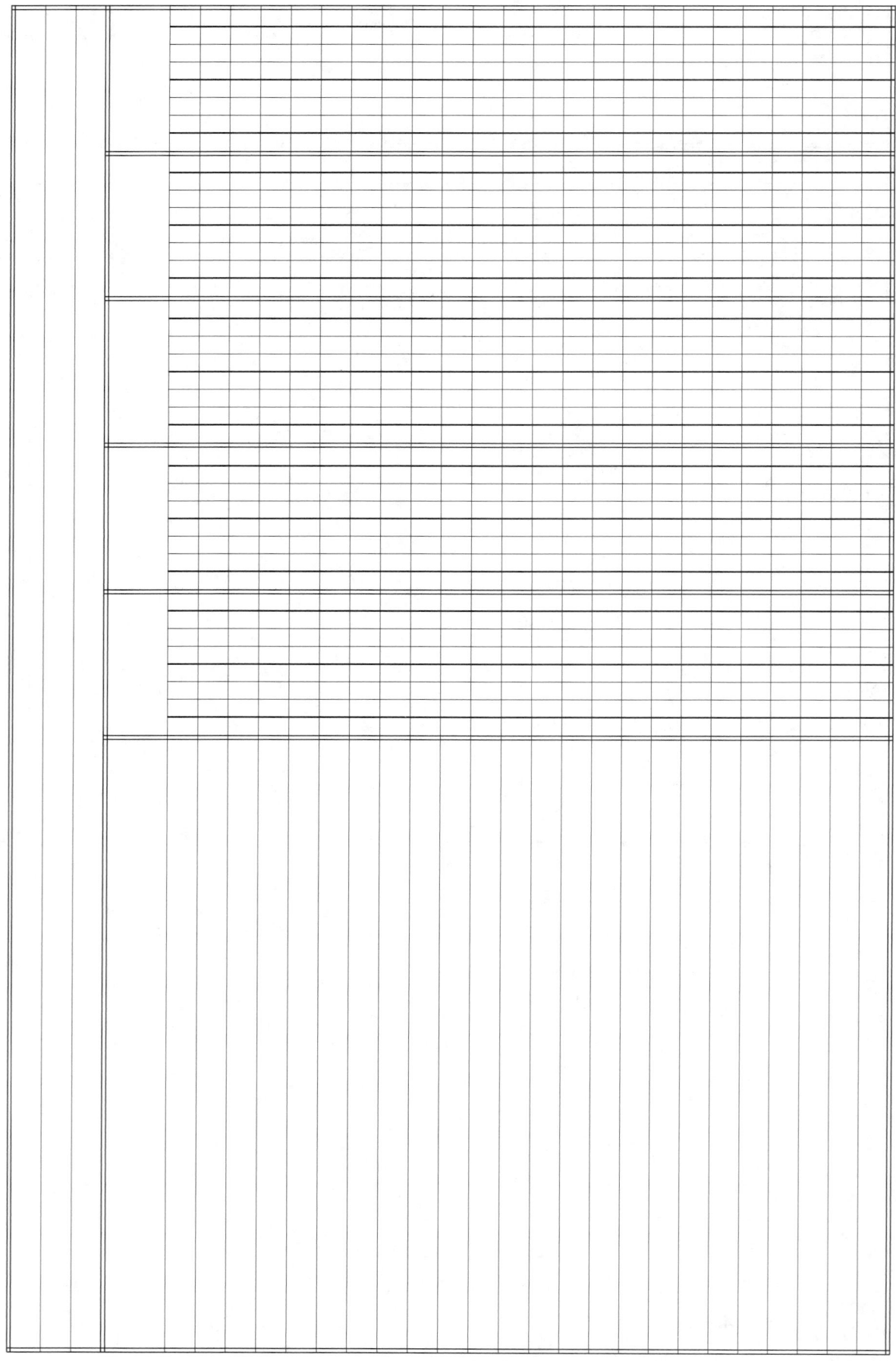

NAME
SECTION
DATE

Chapter 24

Decision Case 1
(Continued)

Req. 2

Decision Case 1
(Continued)

Req. 3

Decision Case 2

NAME
SECTION
DATE

Chapter 24

Decision Case 2
(Continued)

Req. 2

NAME

SECTION

DATE

Chapter 24

Decision Case 2

(Continued)

Req. 3

Req. 1

NAME
SECTION
DATE

Chapter 24

Ethical Issue
(Continued)

Reqs. 1 (Continued) and 2

NAME
SECTION
DATE

Chapter 24

Ethical Issue
(Continued)

Req. 2 (Continued)

NAME
SECTION
DATE

Chapter 24

Ethical Issue
(Continued)

Req. 2 (Continued)

Chapter 24

Team Project

NAME
SECTION
DATE

Chapter 24

Team Project
(Continued)

NAME

SECTION

DATE

Chapter 24

Team Project
(Continued)

NAME
SECTION
DATE

Chapter 24

Team Project
(Continued)

NAME
SECTION
DATE

Chapter 24

Team Project
(Continued)

NAME
SECTION
DATE

Chapter 24

Team Project
(Continued)

Team Project
(Continued)

Reqs. 1–3

Reqs. 1 & 2

Req. 1

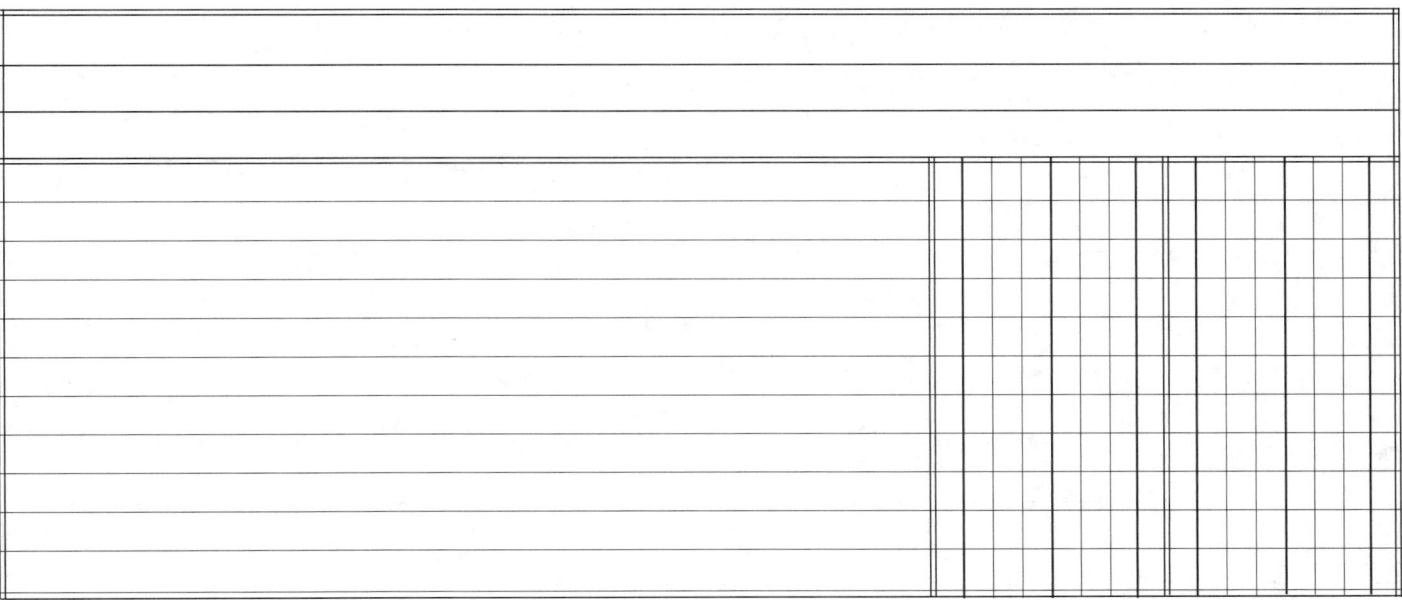

Req. 2

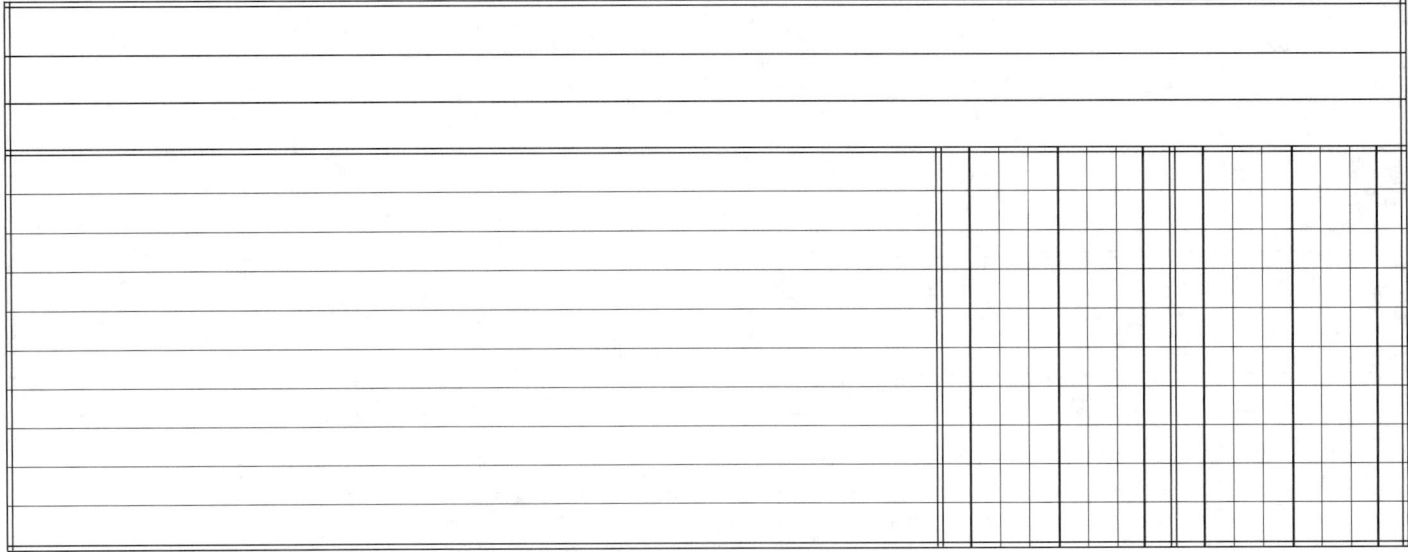

Req. 1

Req. 2

Req. 3

Req. 1

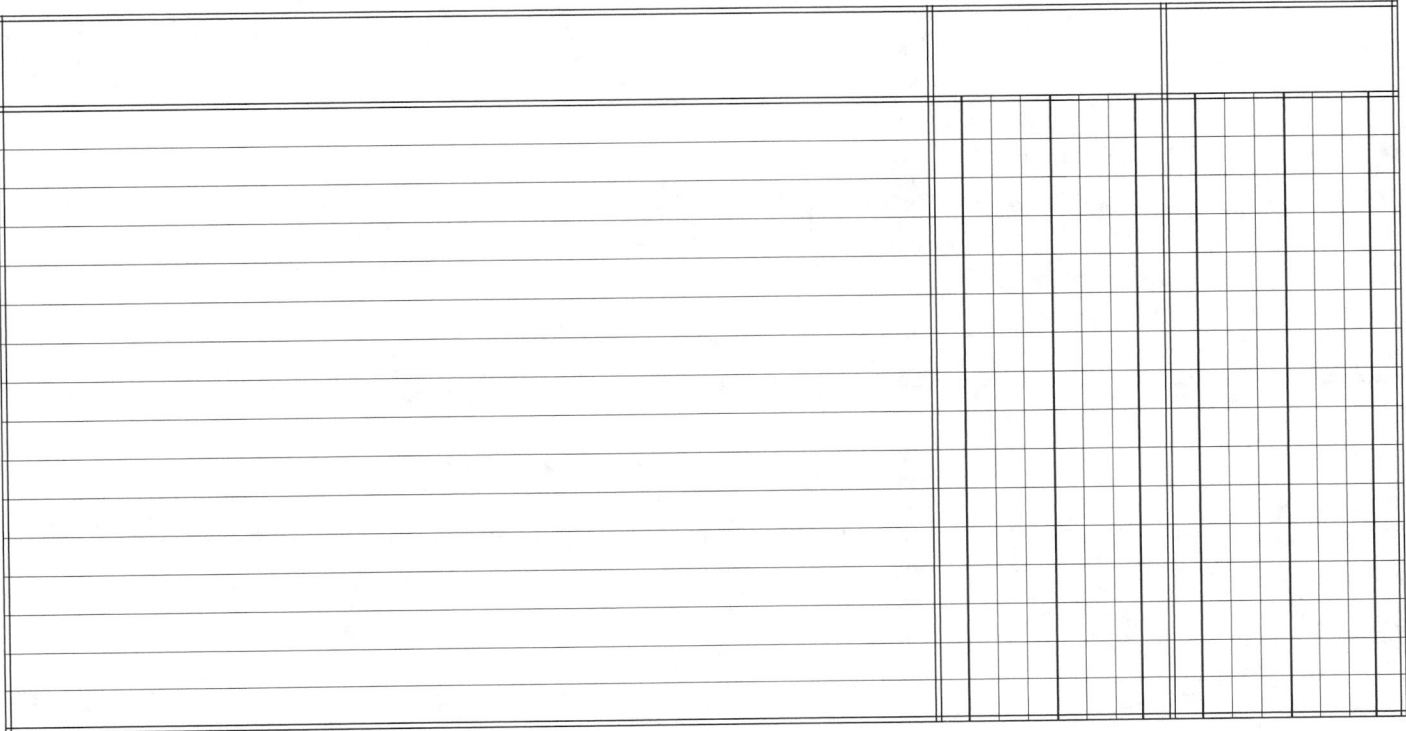

Req. 2

a.

b.

c.

d.

e.

f.

g.

h.

i.

j.

k.

Journal

DATE	ACCOUNTS AND EXPLANATIONS	POST. REF.	DEBIT	CREDIT

Req. 1

Req. 2

Req. 1

Req. 2

Req. 1

Req. 2

Req. 3

Req. 1

Req. 2

Req. 3

Req. 1

General Journal

DATE	ACCOUNTS AND EXPLANATIONS	POST. REF.	DEBIT	CREDIT

Req. 2

Req. 3

General Journal

DATE		ACCOUNTS AND EXPLANATIONS	POST. REF.	DEBIT	CREDIT

Req. 1

General Journal

DATE	DESCRIPTION	POST. REF.	DEBIT	CREDIT

Req. 2

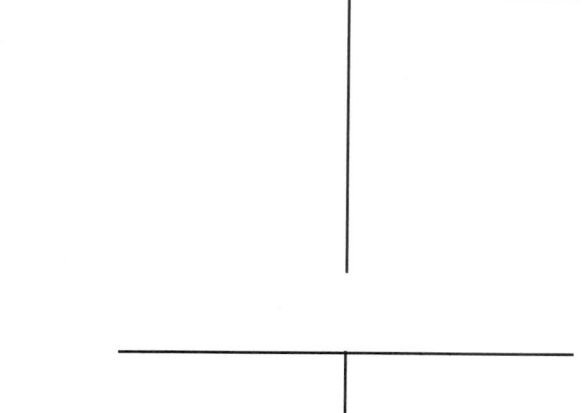

a. _____

b. _____

c. _____

d. _____

e. _____

f. _____

Req. 1

Req. 2

Req. 1

Req. 2

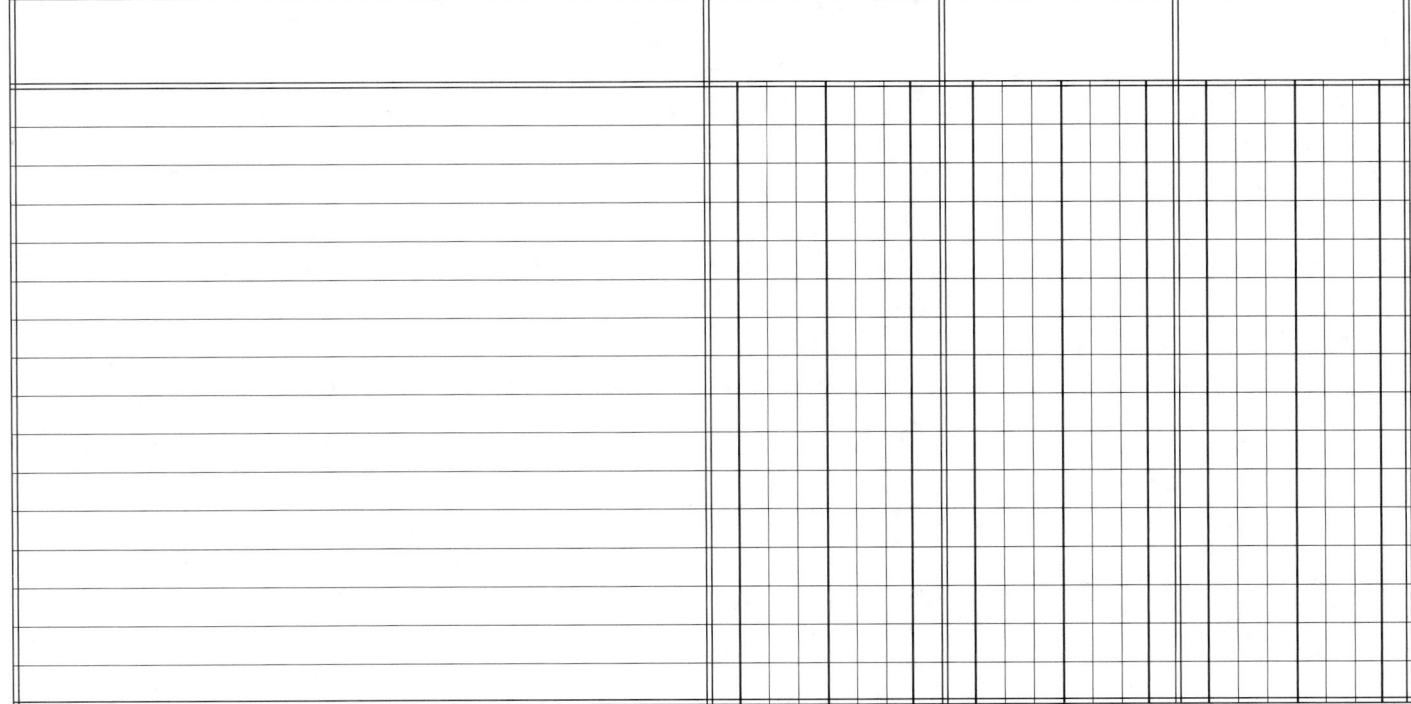

Req. 2 (Continued)

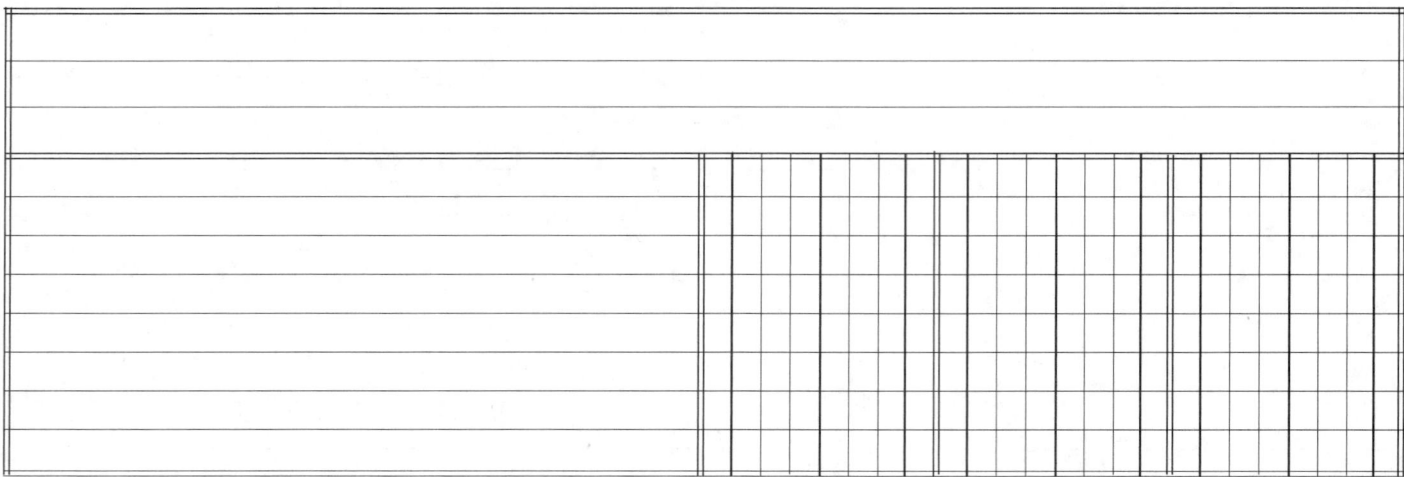

Req. 3

Req. 1

Reqs. 2 & 3

Req. 1

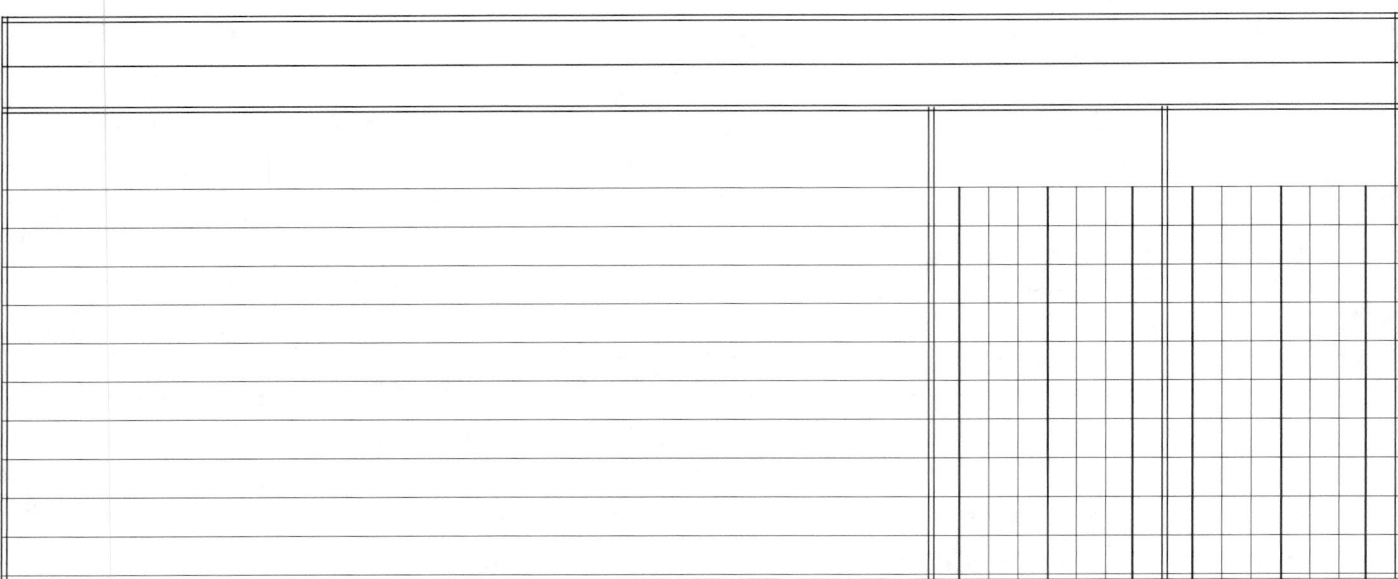

Req. 2

Reqs. 3 & 4

Req. 1

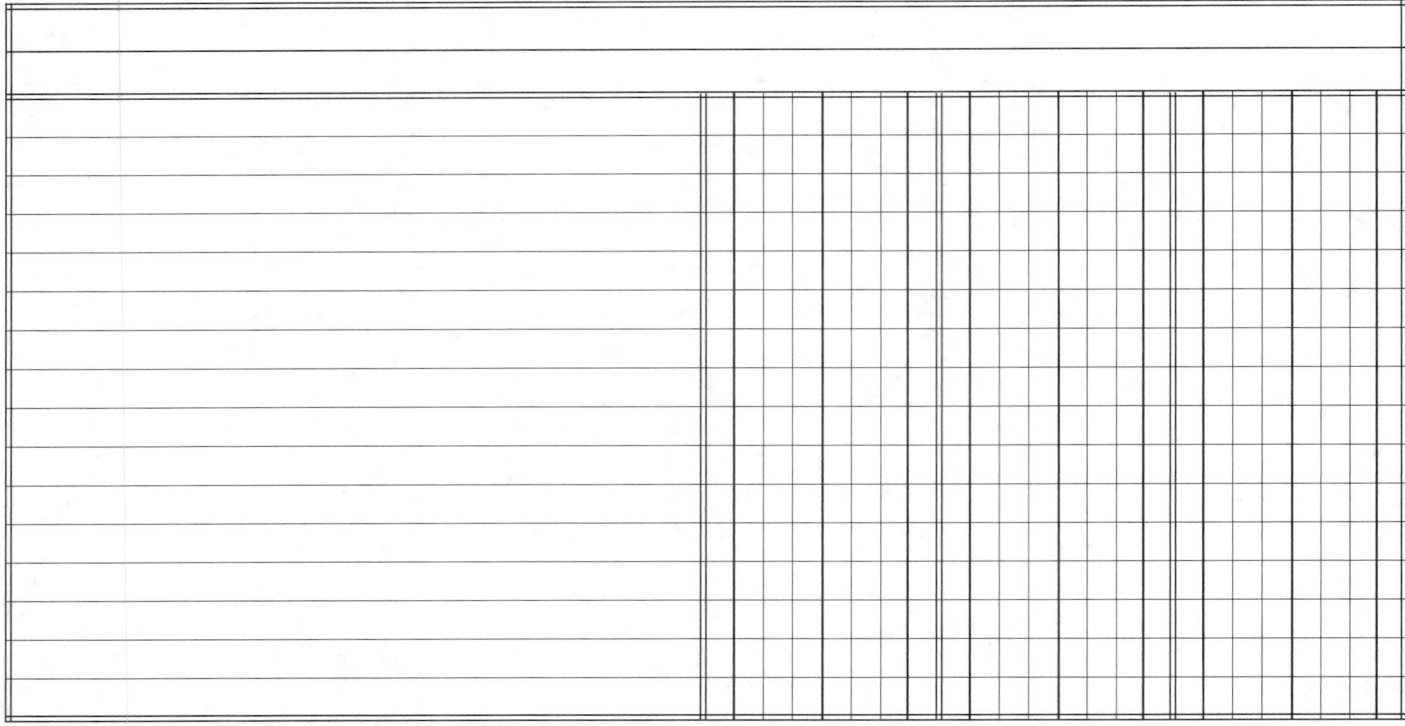

Req. 2

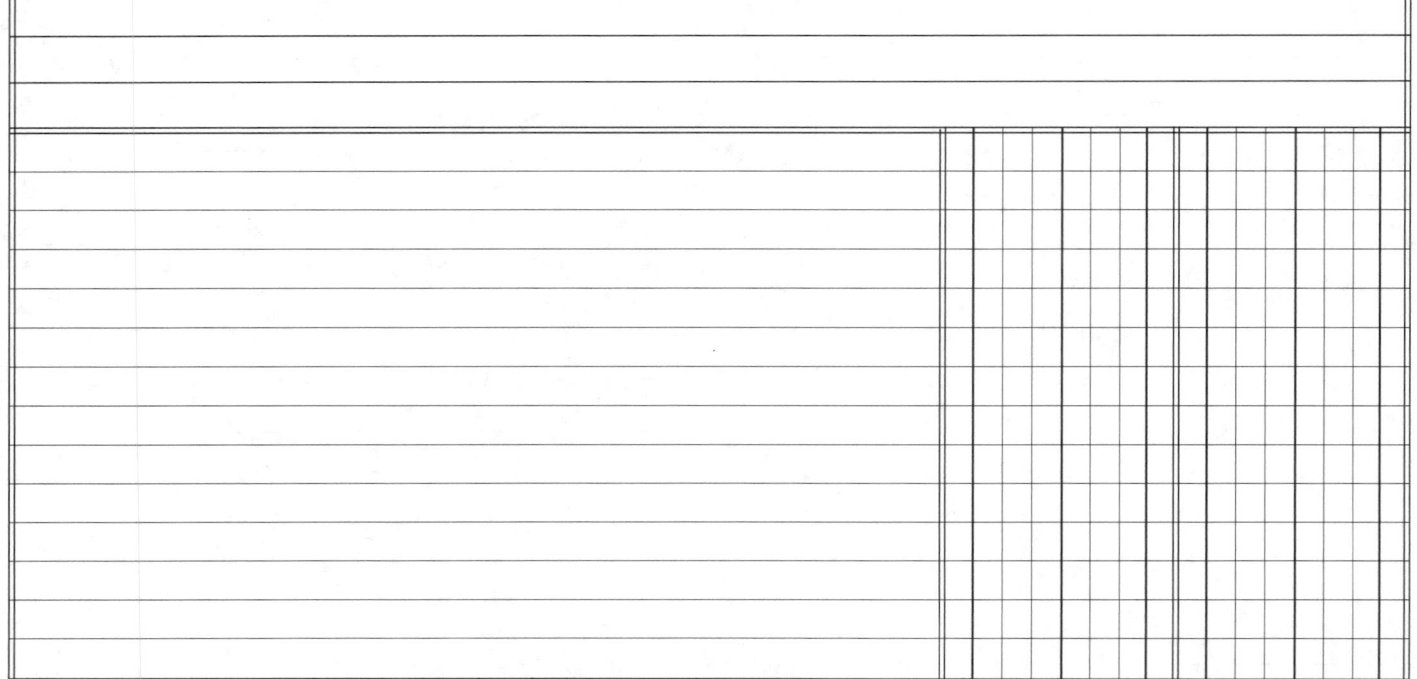

Req. 3

Req. 4

Req. 5

Req. 1

_____

_____

_____

_____

_____

_____

_____

_____

_____

_____

_____

_____

_____

_____

_____

_____

_____

_____

_____

_____

_____

Req. 2

Req. 3

Req. 4

Req. 1

_____
_____
_____
_____
_____
_____
_____
_____
_____
_____
_____

Req. 2

	General Journal			
DATE	ACCOUNTS AND EXPLANATIONS	POST. REF.	DEBIT	CREDIT

Req. 2 (Continued)

Req. 3

Req. 1

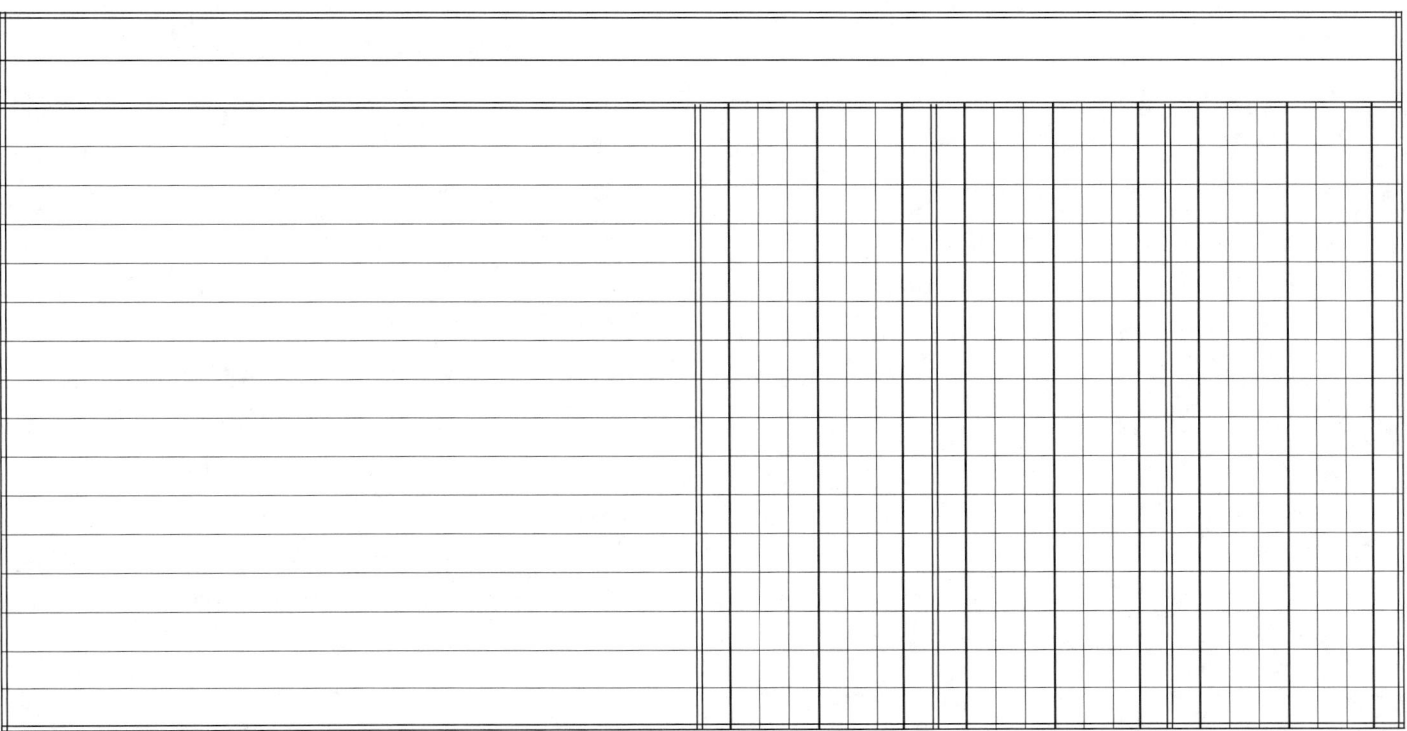

Req. 2

Req. 3

Req. 1

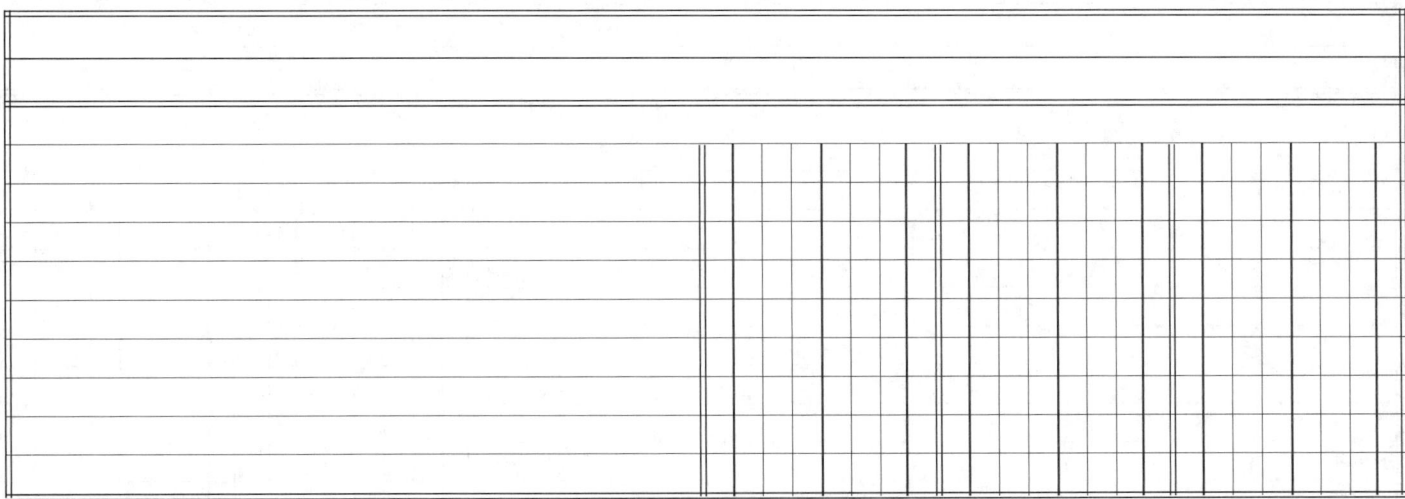

Reqs. 2 & 3

Req. 1

Req. 2

Reqs. 3 & 4

Req. 1

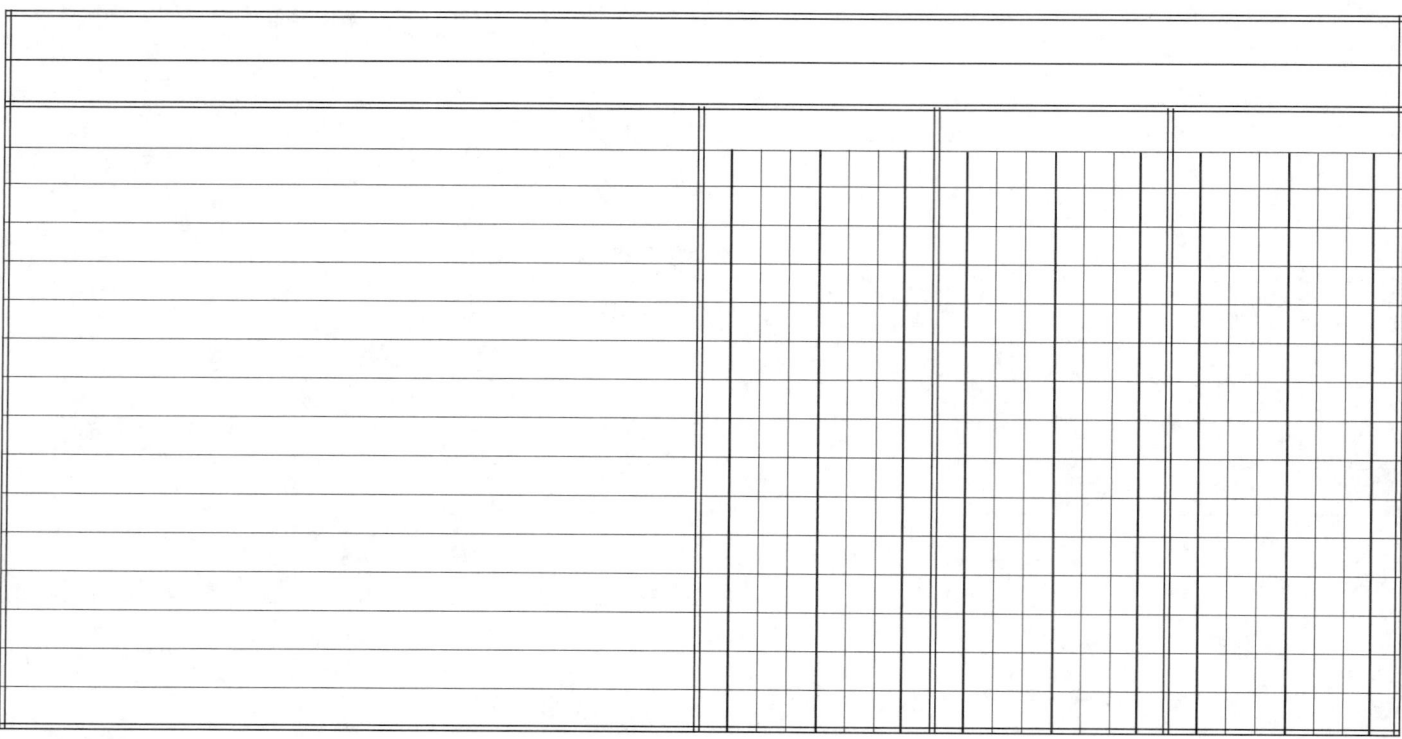

Req. 2

Req. 3

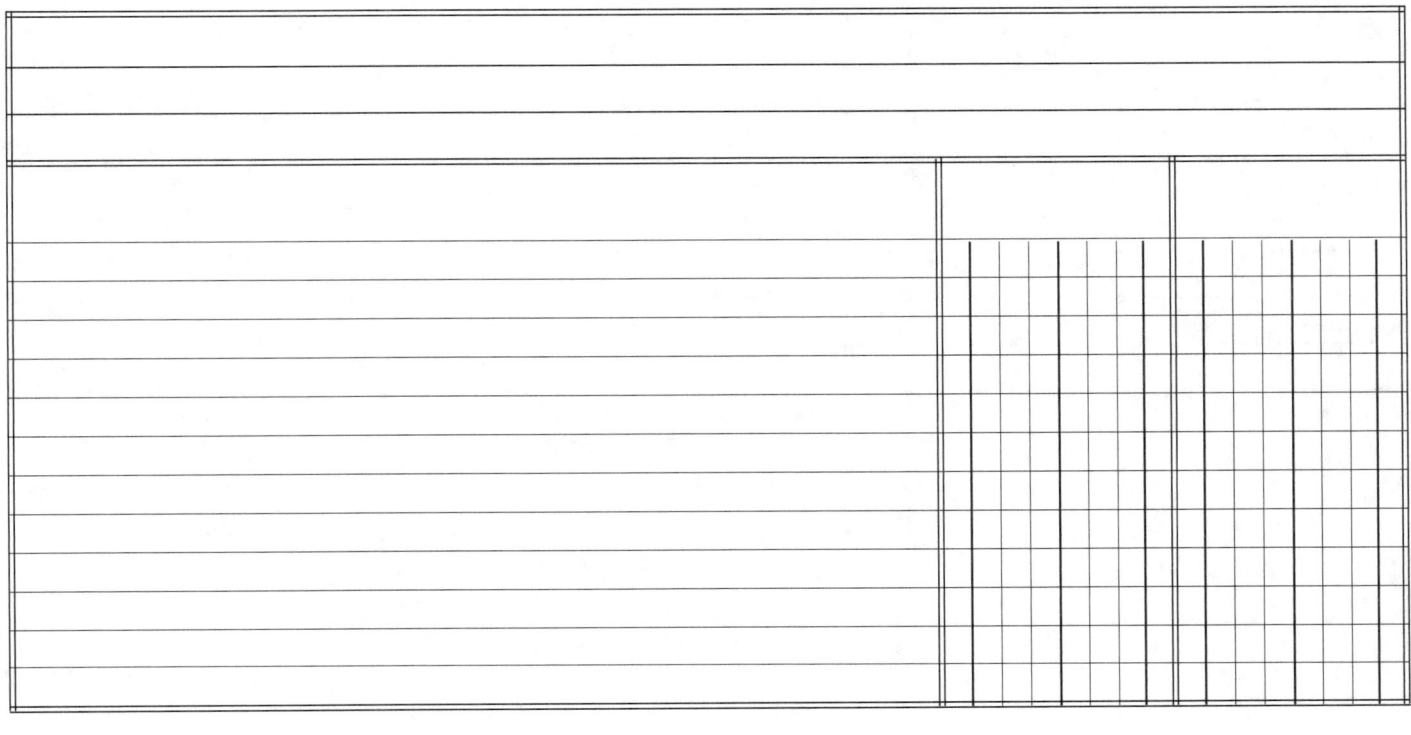

Req. 4

Req. 5

Req. 1

Req. 2

Req. 3

Req. 4

Req. 1

Req. 2

		General Journal				
DATE		ACCOUNTS AND EXPLANATIONS	POST. REF.	DEBIT		CREDIT

Req. 2 (Continued)

Req. 3

Req. 1

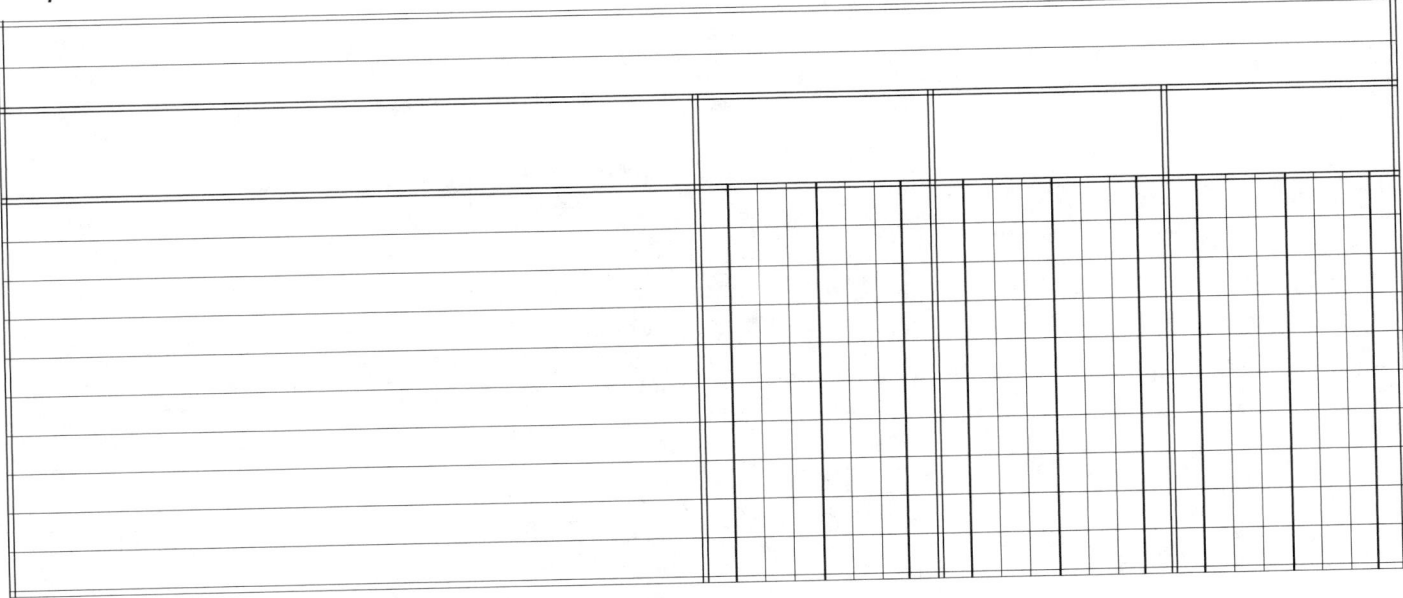

Req. 2

Req. 3

Req. 1

Req. 2

NAME
SECTION
DATE

Chapter 25

Decision Case 1
(Continued)

Reqs. 2–4

NAME
SECTION
DATE

Chapter 25

Decision Case 1
(Continued)

Reqs. 3 & 4 (Continued)

Decision Case 2

Ethical Issue

NAME
SECTION
DATE

Chapter 25

Ethical Issue
(Continued)

Financial Statement Case

NAME
SECTION
DATE

Chapter 25

**Financial
Statement Case**
(Continued)

Req. 2

NAME
SECTION
DATE

Chapter 25

**Financial
Statement Case**
(Continued)

Req. 3

Team Project

Req. 1

NAME

SECTION

DATE

Chapter 25

Team Project
(Continued)

Req. 2

Team Project
(Continued)

Req. 3

Team Project
(Continued)

NAME
SECTION
DATE

Chapter 25

Team Project
(Continued)

Req. 4

NAME
SECTION
DATE

Chapter 25

Team Project
(Continued)

S26-10

S26-13

Req. 1

Req. 2

Req. 1

Req. 1 (Continued)

Req. 2

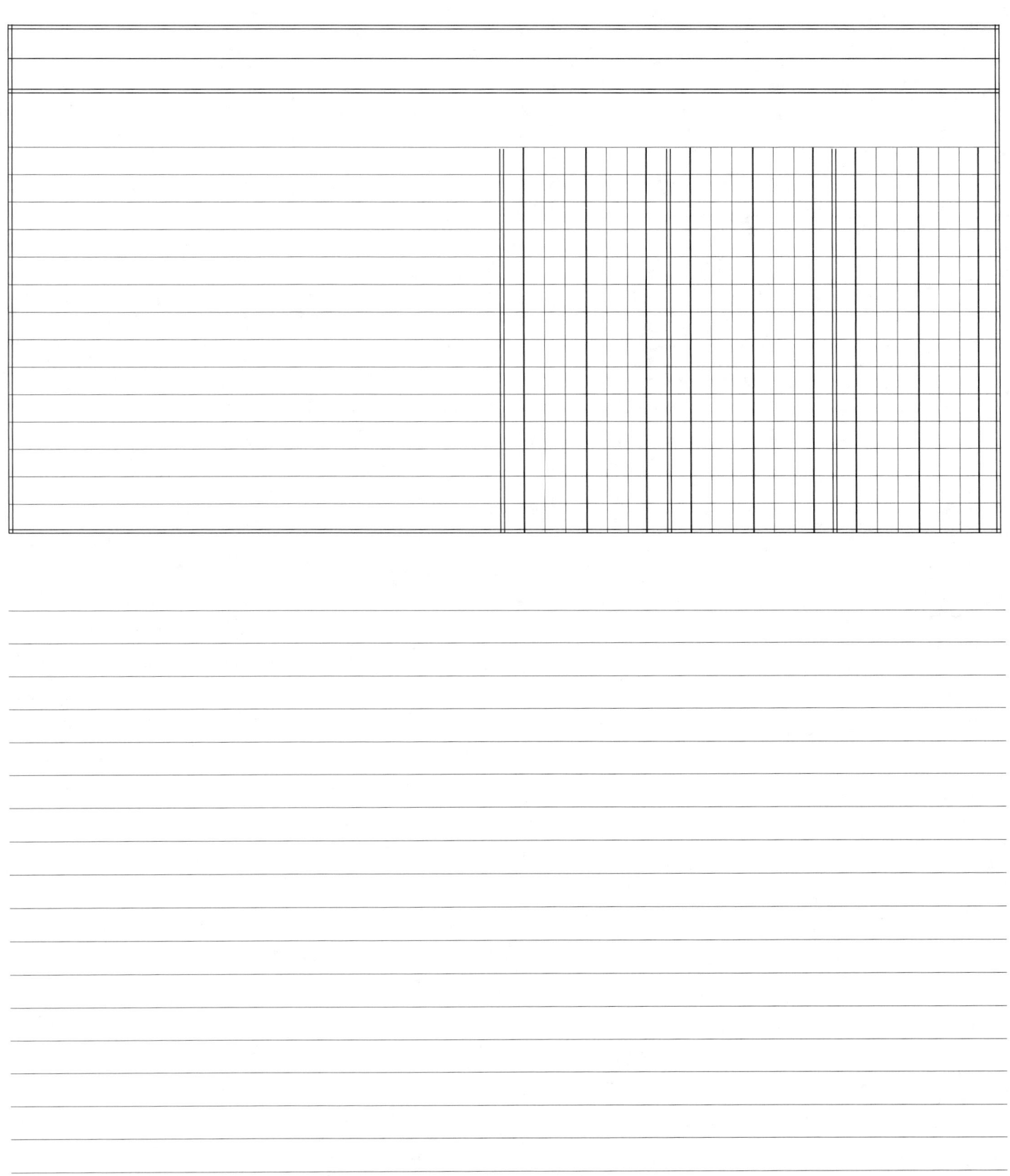

E26-9

NAME
SECTION
DATE

Req. 1

Req. 2

Req. 2 (Continued)

Req. 1

Req. 2

Req. 1

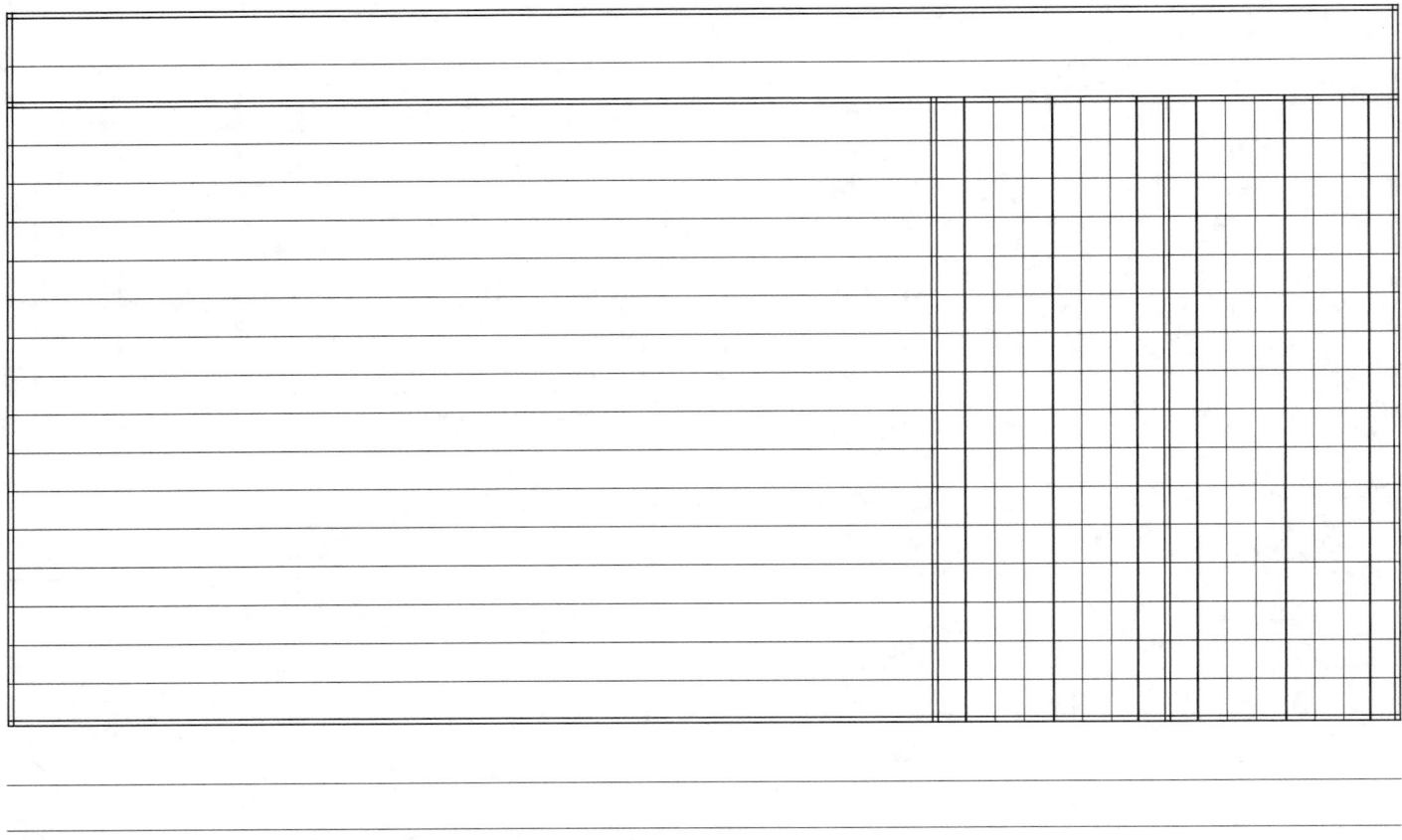

Req. 2

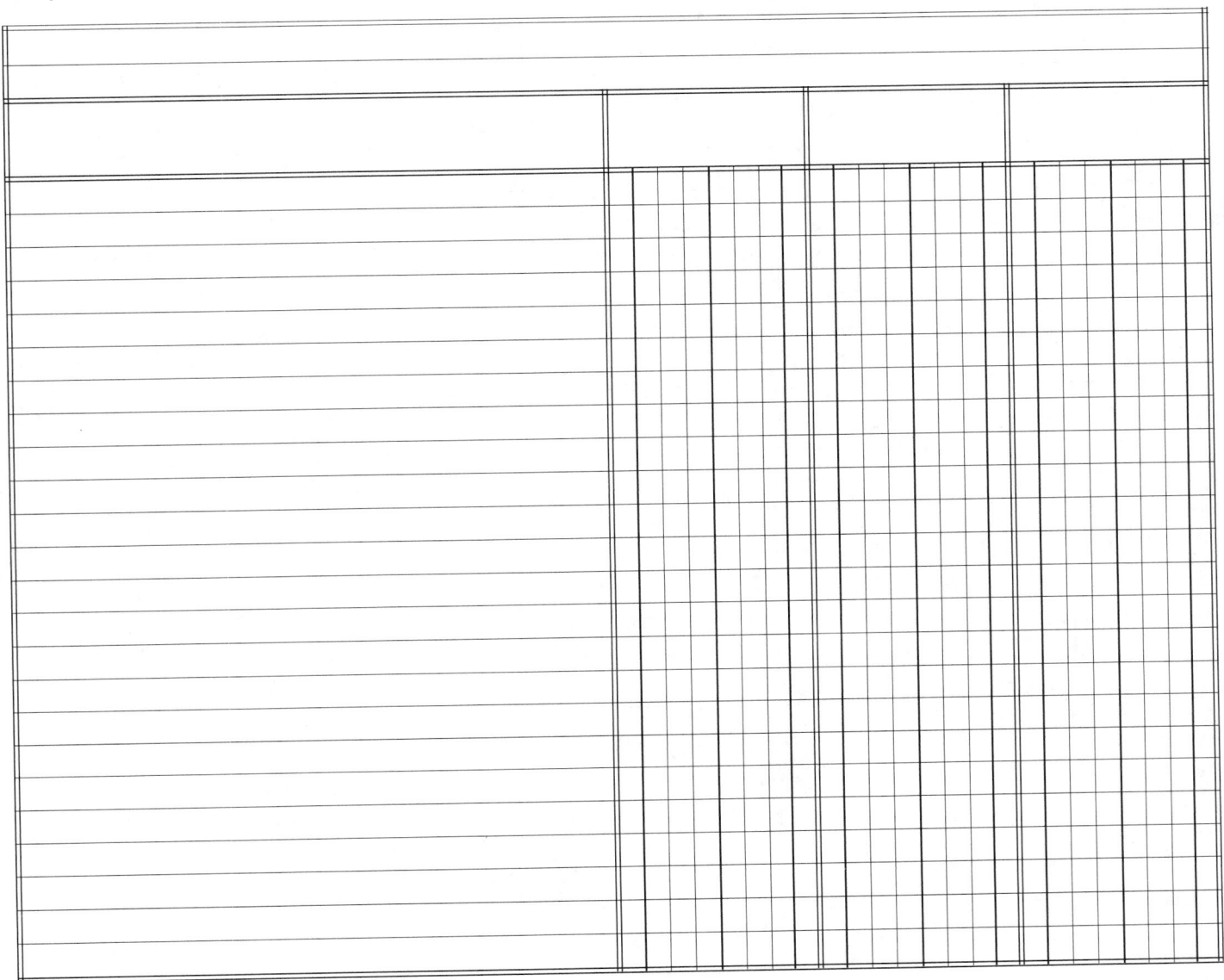

Req. 2 (Continued)

Req. 1

_____

_____

_____

_____

Req. 2

_____

_____

_____

Req. 1

Req. 2

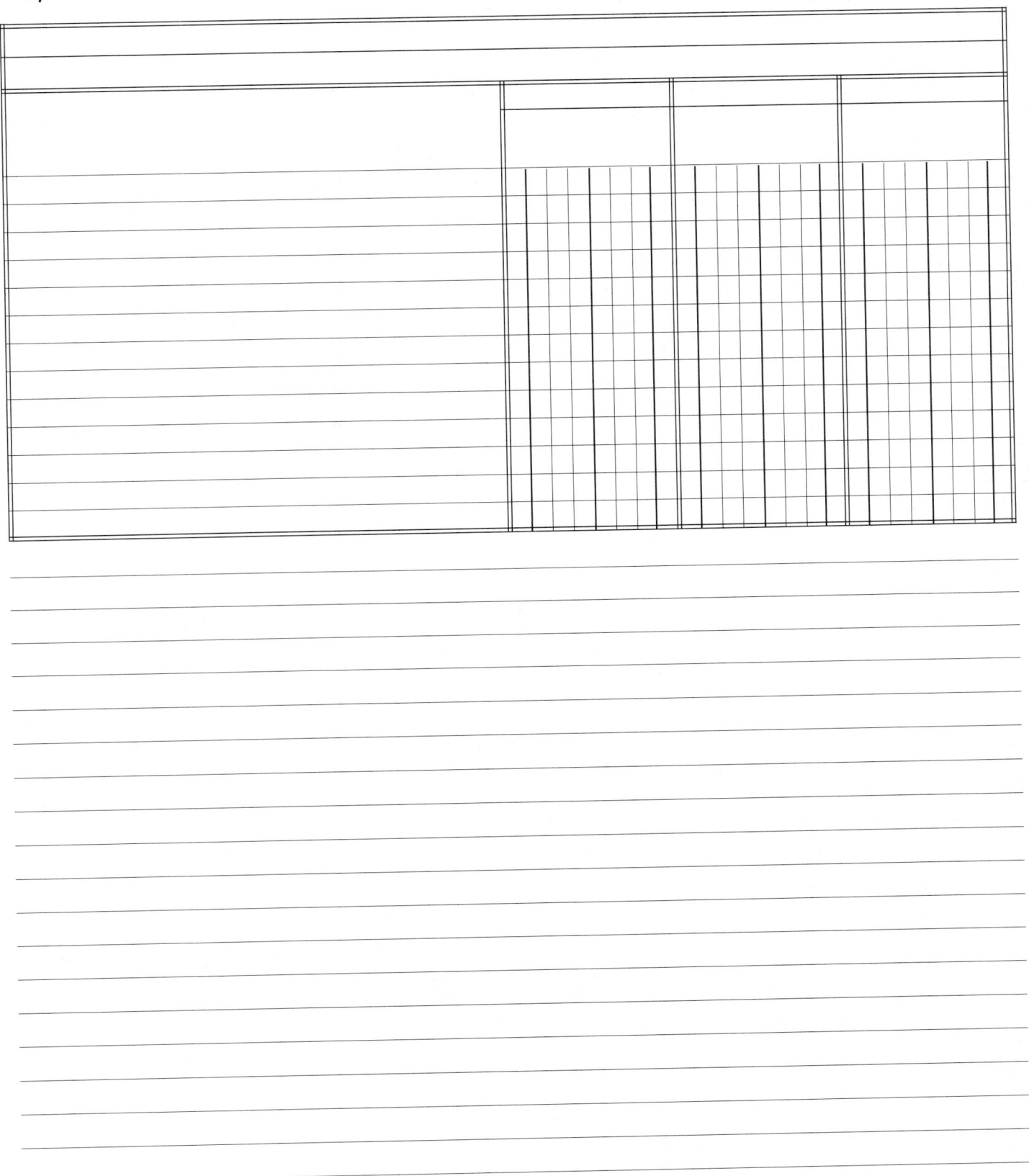

Req. 1

Req. 2

_____
_____
_____
_____
_____
_____
_____
_____
_____
_____

Req. 3

Req. 1

Req. 2

Req. 1

Req. 1 (Continued)

Req. 1 (Continued)

Reqs. 2 & 3

Req. 1

Req. 2

Req. 1

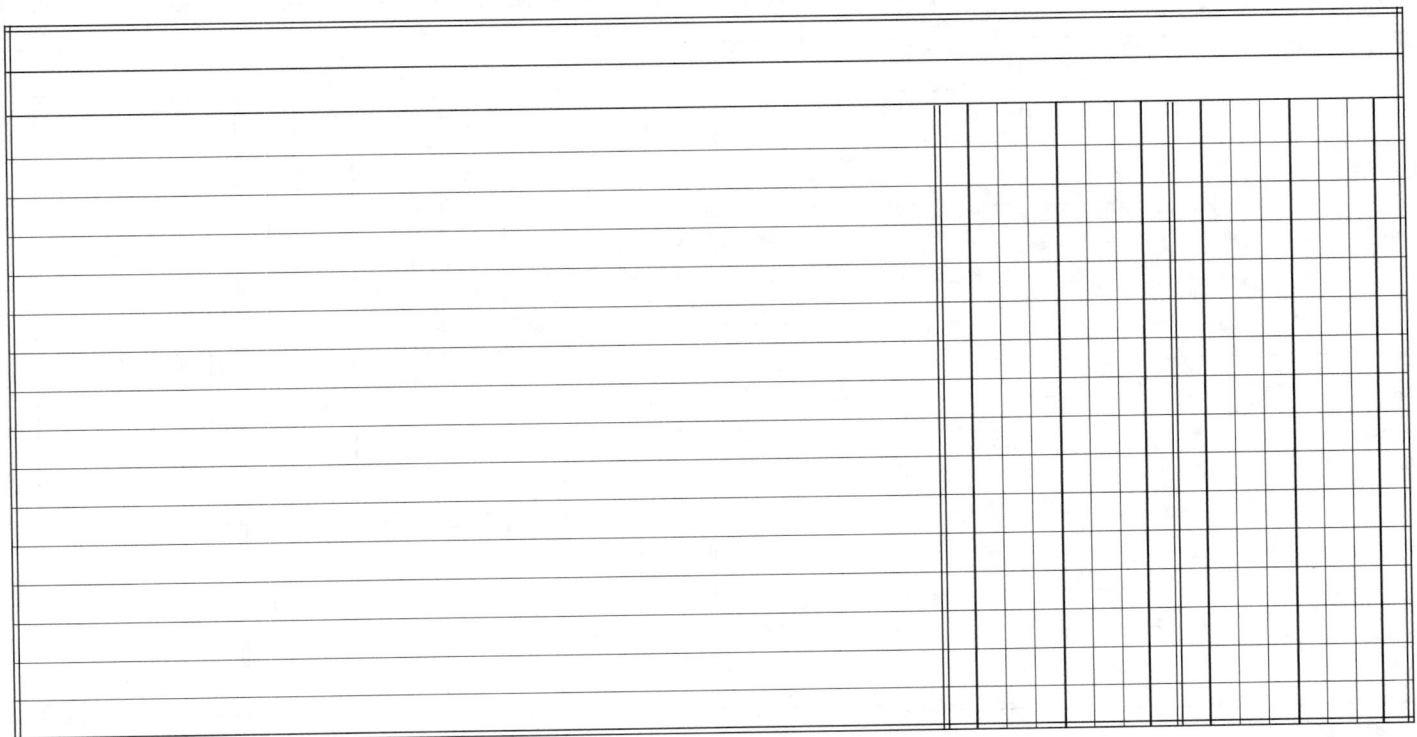

Req. 2

NAME
SECTION
DATE

Req. 1

Req. 2

Req. 1

Req. 2

Req. 1

Req. 2

_____
_____
_____
_____
_____
_____
_____
_____
_____
_____

Req. 3

Req. 1

Req. 2

Req. 1

Req. 1 (Continued)

Reqs. 2 & 3

Req. 1 (Continued)

Reqs. 2 & 3

Req. 1

NAME

SECTION

DATE

Chapter 26

Decision Case 1
(Continued)

Req. 2

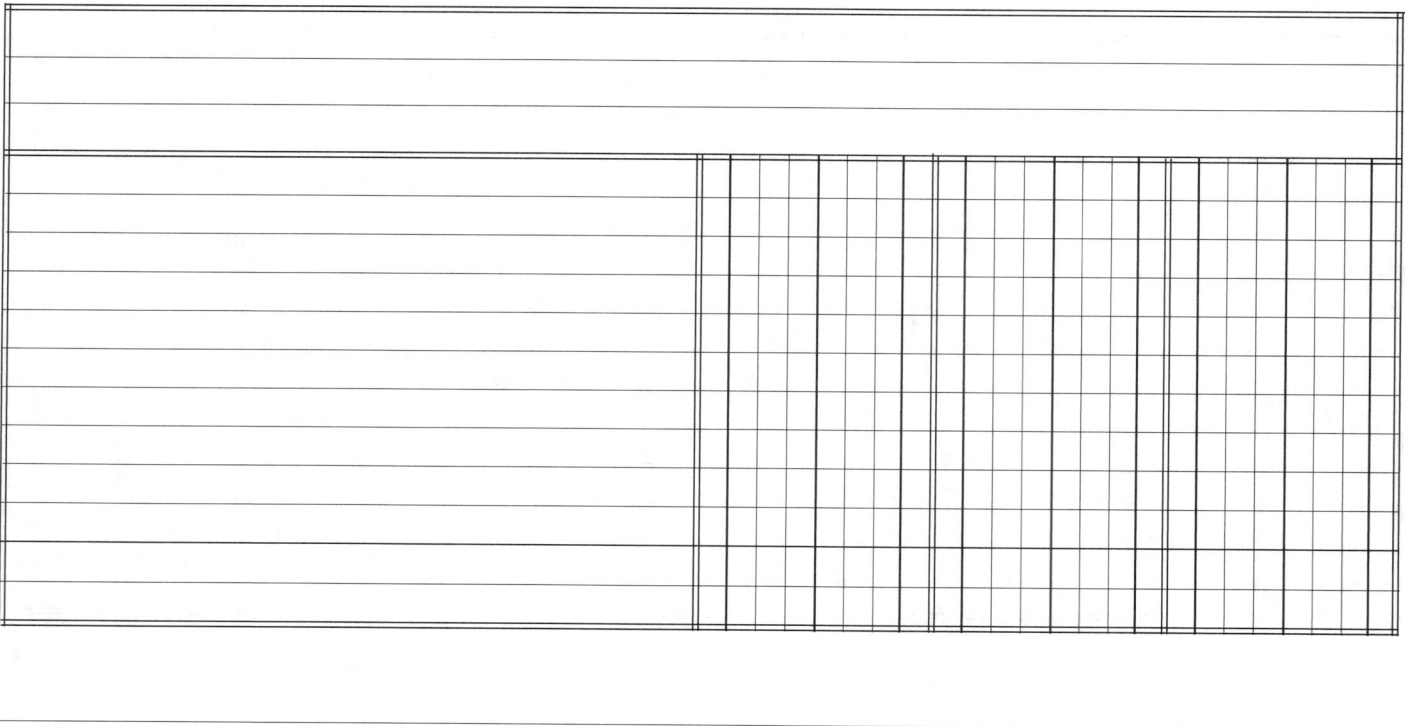

Req. 3

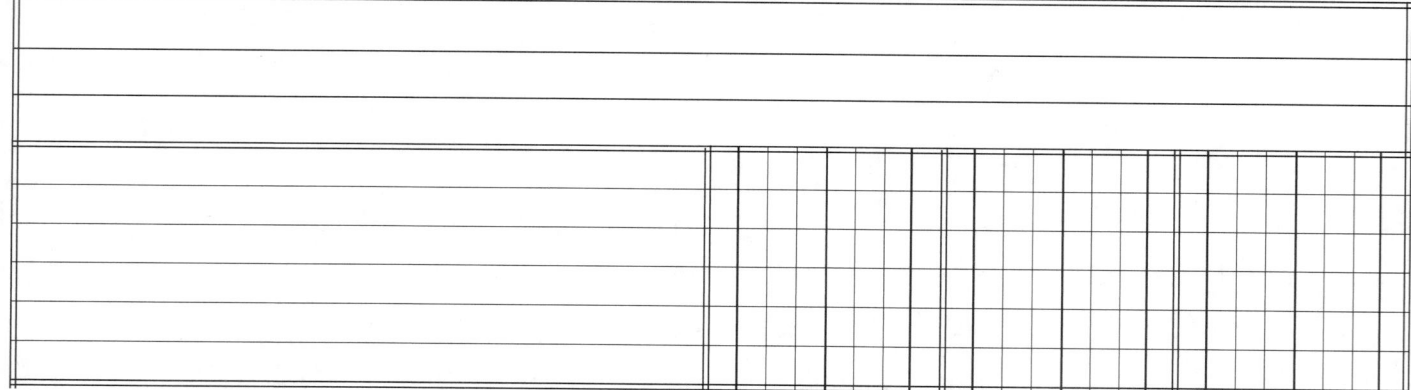

Reqs. 1–2

NAME
SECTION
DATE

Chapter 26

Decision Case 2
(Continued)

Reqs. 1–2 (Continued)

Reqs. 1–2

NAME
SECTION
DATE

Chapter 26

Decision Case 2
(Continued)

Reqs. 1–2 (Continued)

Reqs. 1–2

Ethical Issue

(Continued)

Reqs. 1–2 (Continued)

Financial
Statement Case

Reqs. 1–4

NAME
SECTION
DATE

Chapter 26

Financial
Statement Case
(Continued)

Reqs. 1–4 (Continued)

NAME
SECTION
DATE

Chapter 26

Financial
Statement Case
(Continued)

Reqs. 1–4 (Continued)

NAME
SECTION
DATE

Chapter 26

**Financial
Statement Case**
(Continued)

Reqs. 1–4 (Continued)

Team Project

Req. 1

NAME
SECTION
DATE

Req. 2

Team Project

Req. 1

Chapter 26

Team Project
(Continued)

Req. 2

Counter tops			Cabinets			Picnic Tables		
Make	Out-source	Difference	Make	Out-source	Difference	Make	Out-source	Difference

Team Project
(Continued)

Req. 3

Team Project
(Continued)

Req. 3 (Continued)

NAME
SECTION
DATE

Chapter 26

Team Project
(Continued)

Req. 4

Ms. American Pie

Ms. American Pie

BUTTERY GOOD PIE RECIPES AND BOLD TALES
FROM THE AMERICAN GOTHIC HOUSE

BETH M. HOWARD

Race Point
PUBLISHING

A division of the Quarto Publishing Group USA Inc.
276 Fifth Avenue, Suite 206
New York, NY 10001

RACE POINT PUBLISHING and the distinctive Race Point
Publishing logo are trademarks of the Quarto Publishing Group USA Inc.

ISBN: 978-1937994-68-6

Library of Congress Cataloging-in-Publication Data is available

Text: Beth M. Howard
Photography: Kathryn Gamble
Editorial Director: Jeannine Dillon
Designer: Jacqui Caulton
Illustrations: Melissa Wood
Copyeditor: Lindsay Herman

p198, American Gothic, 1930 by Grant Wood reproduced by permission of the Art Institute of Chicago.

Patterns pages 4, 48, 53, 56, 69, 84, 106, 126, 128, 146, 163, 170, 177, 194, 200, 204, and graph paper © iStockphoto
Patterns pages 24, 43, 60, 62, 67, 72, 73, 79, 83, 87, 92, 99, 100, 105, 115, 120, 135, 142, 144, 149, 154, 169, 173, 185,
188, 193, 196, endpapers, and notepaper © Shutterstock

Printed in China

3 5 7 9 10 8 6 4 2

Contents

Veggie Pot Pie
Pulled-Pork Hand Pies

Peach
Strawberry Rhubarb
Strawberry Crumble
Blueberry
Apple Crumble
Shaker Lemon
Chess
Shoofly

Rhubarb Custard
Double-Crust Rhubarb
Gooseberry
Apple Sour Cream Walnut
Lemon Meringue
Sweet Potato
Avocado
Goat Cheese & Spinach
BLT
Venison

Key Lime
Shaker Orange
Strawberry Margarita
Macadamia Nut
Atlantic Beach
Fresh Strawberry
Coconut Custard
S'more
Grasshopper
Tomato Basil

Frank Barnett's Pecan
Amish Funeral
Sour Cream Raisin

INTRODUCTION:

MAKE YOUR OWN D*MN PIE!

My name is Beth Howard, though many people call me "The Pie Lady." I just shrug when they call me that, as there are many, many other pie ladies out there. The more, the better, I say. Anyway, I am not just a pie lady. I have a long and varied past of careers and labels, including journalist, public relations executive, web producer, coffee importer, forest ranger, world traveler, adventure sports athlete, middle child, cheerleader, free spirit, dog mom, and, my least favorite, widow. I am also the proud and privileged resident of the American Gothic House.

Ms. American Pie is my second book, which I like to think of as a follow-up or companion to my first one, *Making Piece: A Memoir of Love, Loss, and Pie*, published in 2012. *Making Piece* is also about pie, mostly about how making—and sharing—pie helped me heal from the grief over my husband Marcus's untimely death. Marcus was 43 and died suddenly and unexpectedly of a ruptured aorta. I still miss him every day.

I'm a longtime writer. Before writing books, I wrote for magazines like *Real Simple*, *Natural Health*, *Shape*, *Fitness*, *Elle*, and *Sports Illustrated for Women* for many years. Since 2007, I have been blogging at *The World Needs More Pie*. Though writing makes up the core of my career, pie has gradually become my mainstay, my sustenance. Especially since Marcus's death, I have found solace in pie, particularly in teaching pie-making to others. I teach classes all over the world to people from all walks of life: from Japanese businessmen to kids in a South African township to at-risk high-school students in Iowa to middle-aged women and men longing to overcome their fear of making pie dough. The reward of seeing others' sense of accomplishment, buoyed by their newfound confidence, gives me a sense of purpose and provides a meaningful way to connect with people. (See "Pies for Teaching.")

For the past several summers, I've run the Pitchfork Pie Stand inside the house in which I live, the American Gothic House in Eldon, Iowa. (More on that in "Pies of the Pitchfork Pie Stand.")

The American Gothic House is the little white farm house that appears in the background of Grant Wood's iconic painting *American Gothic*, the famous and oft-parodied masterpiece where the old couple stands in front holding a pitchfork. I don't own the house—it's owned by the State of Iowa Historical Society—but I have been renting, living, and baking pies in the tourist attraction for nearly four years. (For more on how I came to live here, see "Pies to Compete in the Iowa State Fair.")

I was born in Iowa, only 15 miles from the American Gothic House, in the town of Ottumwa (also the hometown of Radar O'Reilly of "*MASH*" and actor/comedian Tom Arnold). I did not, however, learn to make pie from my Midwestern grandmothers or my mother. I learned how to make pie when I was 17, when during a bicycle trip down the West coast I was caught stealing apples from an orchard. The orchard owner happened to be a retired pastry chef, and when he realized we were just innocent kids on bikes, he invited us in for a pie lesson. Pie has been my thing ever since.

I baked many pies over the ensuing years, trying to impress boyfriends with my homemade creations. And though my pies worked their charm with the smiley faces I carved as vent holes on top (see page 149, "Pies to Seduce"), my crusts were tooth-breakingly hard. I had not yet learned how to handle the dough lightly. I had not yet learned about handling life lightly either.

In 2001, after spending too many hours in front of the computer, I quit a stressful job as a web producer to take a one-year pie-making sabbatical at a gourmet take-out café in Malibu, California. When asked what my pie-baking qualifications were, I replied, "I'm from Iowa." I was hired on the spot and, thanks to the patience and love of my pie mentor, Mary Spellman, my pie-making skills improved immensely. Because of the local clientele, I became a de facto "pie maker to the stars," with pie-loving customers including Dick Van Dyke, Robert Downey Jr., Barbra Streisand, Steven Spielberg, Whoopi Goldberg, Mel Gibson, and surely many others whom I didn't recognize behind their dark glasses.

After Marcus died in 2009, I turned to pie to heal my grief. The exercise of making pie—the feel of my bare hands rubbing flour and butter together, the meditative nature of peeling apples, the satisfaction of crimping a ruffled-edge crust to create edible art— was therapeutic. But what was even more helpful in restoring my spirit was sharing my pie with others, giving pie to those who were suffering more and were in greater need than me.

Exactly one year after my husband died I volunteered to be a pie judge at the Iowa State Fair, the granddaddy of all pie competitions. That was fun—and fattening, since I judged all 17 categories— but most important, it was a welcome distraction on the anniversary of my husband's death.

After the fair, I drove to southeast Iowa to visit my birthplace and stumbled upon the American Gothic House. I fell in love with the tiny, humble farmhouse, discovered that it happened to be for rent, and I moved in two weeks later.

No sooner did my furniture arrive, I opened the Pitchfork Pie Stand. Someone had to provide pie

to all those hungry tourists! I had always talked of opening a pie shop, but that seemed too committal, too permanent for someone of my mercurial nature. So a pie stand, a seasonal business, was the ideal solution. Within the first year, and subsequently propelled by the publication of *Making Piece*, my little summer pie business turned into a national media sensation. I am still amazed that some people have driven over 700 miles for my handmade, buttery, fruit-filled pies—and to get their picture taken in front of the famous house. (The visitor center and museum next door offers free costumes and pitchforks.) My pie stand has grown to the point that we are bursting the seams of the tiny American Gothic House kitchen where we bake. We make over 100 pies every summer weekend, using just one kitchen table and one domestic-size oven. I've become so tired (some would say "cranky") that I am reevaluating my direction. Mass production is hard on my body (you should see the scars from my oven burns) and doesn't leave enough time for teaching pie classes or for writing.

While I have made thousands of pies—and taught hundreds of pie classes—I am not a big fan of recipes. I don't study them or create them, and when I do seek out a recipe, it's only because I want to understand the basic ingredients and ratios. And even then I don't usually follow them too closely. I use recipes as a rough guide, not as gospel. I guess I am a little fearless—or reckless—in that way. But me? Write a pie cookbook? What the…?

The reason I wanted to—er, agreed to—write this cookbook is so I could share my philosophy (and sometimes my rants), to help instill courage and confidence in novice bakers and to demonstrate flexibility to experienced bakers (go ahead, just try not refrigerating your dough, dare to use salted butter, and throw away those measuring spoons; I promise you'll be surprised). Mainly, my hope is to spread love and goodwill in the world through the many positive influences this iconic dish offers.

I'd like to think that when you finish reading my essays, you too will be convinced that homemade pie is the answer to world peace and, really, acts as a cure for just about everything.

Also, I felt this book would be appreciated because it's filled with not just pictures of pie but also photos of real life and real people. It offers a glimpse inside the famous, historic house (which is and always has been a private residence), and a fly-on-the-wall view of the pie-filled exploits taking place behind the curtain. If you've always dreamed of moving from the city to the country, this will enable you to experience the adventure vicariously—without having to deal with the real-life terror of discovering snakes living in your basement or mice chewing their way through your toothbrush drawer!

As for the pie recipes, many are classics—the most basic kind your grandma or great-grandmother (or your grandfather) might have made. These best represent pie to me. I'm a stickler for keeping it simple. Life is complicated enough without complicating pie! I value simplicity so much that I absolutely, positively do not use food processors and I avoid the use of other mechanical aids whenever possible. Which is almost always. (For example, whisking egg whites by hand to make meringue is not only rewarding, it keeps your arms toned.) My approach to recipes is so basic, I start from the question: What would the pilgrims do? Think of this book not as "Pie-Baking for Dummies," but rather "Pie-Making for Purists."

In some cases I've culled from other recipes to create my own, simplified versions. And in other cases, I'm proud to present recipes I've collected from friends and fellow pie makers, including my own pie mentor, Mary Spellman. Like an old-fashioned church cookbook, every recipe has its own little story and, gratefully, this book allows room to include them.

Thanks for reading. And for your interest in pie. Now go make some!

MY PIE-DEOLOGY

PIE BUILDS CONFIDENCE.

There is nothing truer. See point on page 18 on "If you can get past your fear of pie dough, you can get past other, bigger fears."

PIE BUILDS COMMUNITY.

Baking 250 pies to hand out on the streets after the December 2012 shooting in Newtown, Connecticut, is a powerful example of this. People—strangers—came together to lend a hand to a grieving community, and lifelong friendships were formed between Newtown residents and those who came to help as a result of the volunteer pie-making and pie-giving efforts.

PIE SUPPORTS COMMUNITY.

Think about all those church and school bake-sale fundraisers that sell pie. A lot of people gather to make such events—and baked goods—possible. Pie doesn't just build community, it can literally support a community too. A good example is the American Gothic House Center next door to my house. The museum and visitor center was partly funded by, yes, pie!

PIE IS NOT ABOUT POLITICS.

I love going to dinner parties and guiding the conversation away from the contentious subject of politics toward the much more pleasant and palatable one of pie. I've even been in business meetings where, at the mere mention of the word "pie," attitudes shift and body language visibly softens. Pie is a subject that can unite the most divided and diverse opinions.

PIE KNOWS NO CULTURAL OR GEOGRAPHICAL BOUNDARIES.

"American as apple pie?" Well, no. Pie is not American. Its origins lie in Ancient Greece, when pie crust was used to preserve and transport meat. Every country and every culture has some form of pie, the definition being filling nestled in a crust. I love the fact that pie is a global dish. Bridging cultural divides begins with pie.

PIE CONNECTS PEOPLE.

I am amazed at the number of friendships that form through pie, be it through sharing recipes or pictures of pies, meeting for a slice of pie, or just talking about pie. Pie is like a screening device for new friendships. It's almost like a guarantee that any pie-loving person is…nice.

PIE IS NOSTALGIC.

I cannot count the times I've heard a sentence begin with, "My grandmother made pie…" You can just feel the love as the person talks about their family memories. And it warms my heart every single time.

PIE HEALS.

I not only wrote a whole chapter about this (see page 40, "Pies to Heal,"), I wrote an entire 320-page memoir called *Making Piece*, about the healing powers of pie. I turned to making—and sharing—pie to help divert my grief after my husband Marcus died. My heart will never fully heal, but my life has taken on a positive and powerful new direction, thanks to pie.

PIE IS NOT ABOUT COMPETITION.

I have been a pie judge many times over, but I prefer not to judge anymore. I've observed too often pie makers hoping for, but not taking, the blue or even red ribbon. I've witnessed their crestfallen faces, observed their slumped shoulders, and, sadly, seen them give up pie-making all together. My mission is to encourage people to make and share their pie, not to feel inadequate. Pie should be about making people feel better, not about being "voted off the island" or experiencing defeat.

ANYONE CAN MAKE PIE.

The pilgrims and pioneers made pie and they didn't have electricity or refrigeration or grocery stores or self-cleaning ovens or degrees from culinary schools. If that alone doesn't convince you that you don't have to be a Food Network star or Martha Effing Stewart to make a pie, hopefully this cookbook will convince you.

PIE IS MEANT TO BE SHARED.

I know it's tempting to keep a pie to yourself, but there is something so powerful about the act of sharing. Just observe someone's face light up when you offer them a slice of your pie.

PIE MAKES PEOPLE HAPPY AND HAPPY PEOPLE MAKE THE WORLD A BETTER PLACE.

See above. Pie is meant to be shared. Just try it. You will see the "pay it forward" effect happen before your very eyes. Bottom line: The world needs more pie. (So give a piece a chance.)

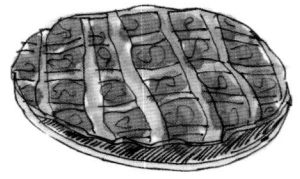

MY PIE PRINCIPLES

"There is no pie that cannot be remedied
by a scoop of ice cream."

-BETH

PIE IS NOT ABOUT PERFECTION.

Pie is like life: it's messy. It should look homemade, handmade, and real, and not like it's been molded from a machine, manicured like Parisian topiary, or airbrushed like a Victoria's Secret supermodel. Imperfections, blemishes, bad dough days (like bad hair days and bad moods) are all part of life. We compare ourselves to others and think we—or our pies—are not good enough. But we are all unique, we each have something beautiful to offer. There is no need to worry about burnt edges, holes in the crust, soggy bottoms, or any of that, because people will inevitably say, "That looks delicious!" They will know your pie was not store-bought, and that it was made with the best, most important ingredients: enthusiasm, care, and love.

PIE IS AN EXPRESSION OF YOUR INDIVIDUALITY.

Styles and tastes are subjective. Different people prefer different flavors. Some people swear by lard crusts. Some people are vegetarians and would turn their nose at the use of animal fat. Some like a plain, solid top crust, some like decorative lattice. Some roll their pie edges under, some roll them over. Some crimp with their fingers, some use a fork. Pies are a reflection of our personalities, our feelings. They are our own personal signatures.

PIE IS ABOUT IMPROVISING.

When you don't have one ingredient, substitute something else. If you don't have the right tools, find something that will work. No rolling pin? Use a wine bottle. No pie plate? Use a cake pan. Better yet, make it freeform (see page 194). Just fold in the sides of the dough to hold the filling in. You get the idea. Or at least you will after reading this cookbook.

PIE IS NOT COMPLICATED.

The pilgrims made pie. The pioneers made pie. Did the pilgrims and pioneers fuss the way chefs are suggesting we should? Did they fret and agonize and berate themselves about their pies not being perfect? Did they refrigerate their bowls and utensils? Did they use food processors? No! They didn't have refrigerators, let alone electricity. They were living out of covered wagons and cabins with no power. They were baking their pies over open fires.

Our grandmothers and great grandmothers made pie. Did they come up with elaborate concoctions using umpteen exotic ingredients, instructions for adding extra steps to the baking process, and the need to dirty five pans? No! When my Grandma Ida made her peach pies, she didn't add ginger, amaretto, caramel sauce, grated dried orange peel, and God-knows-what-else. She just used peaches. Fresh, ripe ones. Period.

Between the cooking shows on TV, food websites, and blogs, and the proliferation of cookbooks and culinary schools, the foodie trend has turned pie-making into a competition. No offense to chefs and all their professional training, but it's as if bakers are making their recipes more and more complicated to prove that they have something new or special to offer. But pie has been around for at least 4,000 years. It has a proven track record, staying power. Why do we need to reinvent it? Worse, complicate it? Life is already complicated enough! When it comes to pie, my motto is "the simpler, the better." Less is more. Don't let today's fussy recipes intimidate you. Stick to the basics. Skip steps if you want. Make your own rules. It's your pie. Make it however you like. And if you like it complicated, well, that's your choice.

PIE RECIPES ARE GUIDELINES, NOT GOSPEL.

The recipes in this book—and in any other cookbook, for that matter—offer what I call "guidelines" and not absolutes for ingredient amounts. For starters, every pie dish is different. Though most recipes call for a 9-inch pie plate, I have a wide range of dishes that vary in size, from width to depth to shape. It would be impossible for me to have recipes to accommodate the exact amount of filling for each of these sizes. That's why I suggest—no, *insist*—that these recipes not be taken too literally. Learn to scale your recipe to fit the dish by understanding and aiming for ratios instead of a specific measurement. A pinch of this for a small pie, an extra pinch of that for a larger one. Allow yourself to work outside of the numbers. It will set you free. And your pie will still be amazing.

PIE IS NOT ABOUT PRECISION.

My goal is to take the fear out of making pie—especially pie dough. The recipes in this book should only be used as a starting point. Among the many things I preach (or rant about, depending on how you see it) is that pie is not about precision. I want to empower people to make their own decisions about how much water, flour, fruit, sugar, and spice to use. You like a lot of cinnamon in your apple pie? Go ahead. Add as much as you like. You want to use nutmeg even though I don't include it in my recipes? Just do it. My approach to pie-making is so relaxed, I don't even own measuring spoons. "You're just like your Grandma Nona," my mom scolds me when she watches me take the salt and just shake it straight onto the apples. "She didn't measure either." I take that as a compliment.

My best advice is to simply pay attention to what's in front of you and troubleshoot accordingly. Is your dough crumbling when you try to roll it? It needs more water. "But I added the exact amount the recipe called for," you explain. That's the problem! Moisture content varies based on climate and ingredients. Is your cream-pie filling too runny? Try adding more thickener next time. Use your own judgment. Rely on your own instincts. Trust yourself. And above all, just relax and have fun.

IF YOU CAN GET PAST YOUR FEAR OF PIE DOUGH, YOU CAN GET PAST OTHER, BIGGER FEARS.

I've seen so many people take my pie class who came in saying, "I can't do it." By the time they leave, they are saying, "I can't believe I did this!" They leave confident and proud, oozing with a sense of accomplishment. This is what I love about teaching pie. Because it's not about the pie. It's about pushing past your self-limiting beliefs and being open to just trying. And when you see how easily you succeeded—and how much fun you had doing it—the experience will get you thinking: I will try tackling some of those other things on my "I can't/I don't know how" list. If life is not about stretching and growing, then I'm not sure what the point is.

PIE MYTHS, BUSTED

1. YOU NEED TO REFRIGERATE YOUR DOUGH FOR AT LEAST 30 MINUTES BEFORE ROLLING IT. FALSE!

Really? Has anyone ever questioned this old-school method? If you start with chilled ingredients and don't overwork your dough, it will be as soft as a baby's bottom and therefore very supple and easy to roll. Old bakers say refrigerating the dough will help it "rest." Yeah, whatever. Refrigeration makes dough hard and actually more difficult to roll. So unless it's like 110 degrees in your kitchen, feel free to skip this waiting period. You'll see. Your pie will be great and you will have saved yourself precious time.

2. YOU SHOULD ONLY USE UNSALTED BUTTER FOR YOUR CRUST. FALSE!

This one kills me. Can you really taste or tell the difference? I say use whatever butter you have in your fridge. You use salted butter for your toast? Trust me, it works for pie dough too. The argument against using salted butter is that salted butter has a different density and moisture content and makes it more difficult to gauge how much extra salt to use. If you want to get your microscopic measuring tools out, be my guest. The way I see it is that if I use salted butter that's one less ingredient (salt) that I have to remember to add.

3. YOU MUST USE A PRECISE NUMBER OF TABLESPOONS OF ICE WATER FOR YOUR DOUGH. FALSE!

I've had so many pie students tell me their dough has never turned out because they followed a recipe, adding *exactly* the amount of water the recipe called for. Their dough wouldn't hold together and was impossible to roll and that if it wasn't a big crumbling mess, it was too tough. Here's the thing: Too little water causes people to force the dough to bind, and force—such as kneading—will cause your dough to become tough. Let the water do the work of holding your dough together. Don't worry about too much moisture. It's the big almond-sized chunks of butter you leave in your dough that will ensure a flaky and tender crust.

4. USING YOUR HANDS TO MIX THE DOUGH WILL MAKE YOUR DOUGH TOUGH. FALSE!

While your hands conduct heat and can conceivably "melt" the butter and shortening, it is the process of overworking the dough that makes it tough, not the touch of the hands themselves. And I don't care how "woo woo" it sounds, but I believe that the physical, sensual, tactile experience of mixing your dough with your bare hands makes for a better pie.

There is a sort of transference of energy that takes place, connecting you with your food, adding an unseen ingredient of love. Besides, there is a certain instinctual feel you will get for knowing when your dough is done, a feel you cannot get with the blade of a food processor or pastry blender.

5. USING TOO MUCH FLOUR ON YOUR ROLLING SURFACE WILL MAKE YOUR DOUGH TOUGH. FALSE!

Repeat after me: Overworking your dough is what makes it tough. Sprinkling your rolling surface with flour is necessary to ensure your dough doesn't stick and become a big, frustrating mess. Sticky dough is what sends people running to the store to buy pre-made pie crust. Consider that flour is your friend. It's like an insurance policy. You don't need to go overboard with it, but you will need it. So don't be afraid to use it.

6. YOU SHOULD ROLL YOUR DOUGH ON WAXED PAPER OR A ROLLING CLOTH. FALSE!

Um, no you shouldn't. I roll my dough right on my kitchen counter made of Caesarstone (it's like granite) or on my butcher-block table. Just sprinkle flour to keep the dough from sticking. (See busted myth above.) Sometimes, however, I will roll on a silicone baking mat. The advantage of this is that if your dough won't come off the surface in one piece, you just pick up the mat and flip it into your dish! I made this discovery on a very hot, dough-melting day.

7. YOU NEED TO COVER YOUR EDGES WITH FOIL TO KEEP THEM FROM BURNING. FALSE!

I have one simple answer to this: If your edges are burning, your oven is too hot. Don't bother fussing with foil, just turn the temperature down!

8. YOU CAN ONLY BAKE ONE PIE IN THE OVEN AT A TIME. FALSE!

You can bake more than one pie in the oven at a time. I cram as many as 12 at a time into my domestic GE Profile oven. Contrary to common belief, they do not take longer to bake. I do keep a close eye on them to make sure they bake evenly. The crust closest to the back or the sides of the oven walls tends to brown first, but a little quarter turn of the pie plates—or rearranging, if need be—solves this.

FREQUENTLY ASKED QUESTIONS

1. WHAT IS THE RIGHT TEMPERATURE FOR BAKING PIES?

Every oven is different. If you're concerned about precision, invest in an oven thermometer so you can be certain of your settings. I just keep a watchful eye on my pies. For my fruit, custard, and savory pies, I start hot (425 degrees) to set and brown the crust. While recipes suggest this stage will take 20 minutes, my oven bakes hot and my crust can turn dark within 10 minutes. I set my timer and check the progress in 5-minute increments. And adjust the temperature accordingly.

2. WHY IS IT IMPORTANT TO START WITH A HOT OVEN?

Starting your pie in an oven that is not hot enough will cause your crust to melt rather than "set." You'll see how your beautifully crimped edges simply sag until they're limp and falling over the edge of the pie dish.

3. HOW LONG WILL MY PIE KEEP?

That depends on what kind of pie. I like to think apple pie has the longest shelf life. I will keep an apple up to one week in the refrigerator (okay, I've kept them longer). I freeze a lot of my pies, particularly the fruit ones. I think the quality suffers a little (I swear I can taste freezer burn a mile away), but with a slow thaw and a quick re-heat in the oven, your pie should appear to be freshly baked.

4. DO I NEED TO REFRIGERATE MY PIE?

If it has eggs or cream or milk in it, yes, you do. And if it's a berry or peach pie in a hot summer, refrigerating your pie will keep it from molding.

5. HOW DO I KEEP MY BOTTOM CRUST FROM GETTING SOGGY?

As for me, I don't mind a soggy bottom. Some people say you can pre-bake your crust a little to help set it. I don't bother. Making sure your filling has enough thickener in it will keep juice from saturating your bottom crust.

6. HOW DO I KEEP MY MERINGUE FROM WEEPING?

I'm told that high humidity is what causes a weeping meringue, those little brown tear drops that form on top. Well, Iowa is humid as hell and I don't control the weather. So, first of all, I say, who cares?! Besides, the solution is simple: Eat it faster and you'll never notice it. My Eldon, Iowa, neighbor Pat Hancock swears that using cornstarch and powdered sugar in her meringue solves this. (For Pat's Coconut Cream pie, see page 155 in "Pies to Seduce.")

7. WHAT KIND OF FLOUR DO YOU USE?

I only use all-purpose white flour, unless I'm making a gluten-free crust (see page 33). It's, as the name suggests, all-purpose.

8. DOES IT MATTER WHAT BRAND OF SHORTENING YOU USE?

I do notice a difference in the consistencies of vegetable shortening. I like Crisco for its texture, but I buy 50-pound boxes of a different brand from the local culinary school and it works perfectly well. Keeping your shortening in the refrigerator and using it chilled in your pie dough is helpful no matter what the brand.

9. DO YOU EVER USE LARD?

When I worked at Mary's Kitchen in Malibu, I used half butter, half lard in my pie dough. But since being a judge at the Iowa State Fair and sampling too many pies that tasted like stale bacon grease, my opinion about the stuff has become more negative. I'm not opposed to it. It's your pie, use whatever fat you want!

10. HOW DO YOU KEEP YOUR PEELED APPLES FROM TURNING BROWN?

For the pie stand, we peel 100 pounds of apples every weekend. By hand. This takes a long time, so of course the apples end up sitting a while. But do I care if they turn brown? They are going into an apple pie. And what color is cinnamon? Right. I rest my case. That said, I do keep them in an airtight tub if I'm not using them immediately. And while it's an option, I don't bother with lemon juice or salt water to "preserve" them.

11. DO YOU EVER SPRINKLE SUGAR ON TOP OF YOUR PIES?

I almost never do this. I try to keep my sugar usage to a minimum. But I do like how it looks. And I like the texture. It's just not a habit or a tradition.

12. HOW MANY VENT HOLES DO I NEED?

There are no rules on the number of holes. I don't count, I just carve big pitchforks into the tops of my pies. It's my signature, or logo if you will. But I'd say at least four. And make them big enough so you can stick a knife through, in case you need to prod your pie to test for doneness.

13. WHAT'S THE BEST ROLLING SURFACE FOR DOUGH?

I roll directly on my butcher-block kitchen table or my Caesarstone countertop, making sure to sprinkle enough flour to keep my dough from sticking. I do not roll on waxed paper because it inevitably crumples up underneath my dough. I hate it when that happens! Sometimes I roll on a silicone baking mat. This works well because I can gauge the size of my dough when rolling it toward the edges of the mat, and if my dough is crazy-sticky, I can pick up the whole mat and flip the dough right into my pie dish.

14. WHAT'S THE BEST KIND OF ROLLING PIN?

The "best" kind of rolling pin is the pin that feels best to you. This is a personal preference kind of thing, like having a favorite kind of pen or baseball bat. I prefer the wooden kind with ball bearings so it spins freely. I roll so much dough that the French pin (no handles) makes my wrists sore after a while. I don't care for the marble rolling pins, as they are heavy, not to mention expensive.

15. WHAT'S THE BEST KIND OF PIE DISH?

This question gives me a headache. I have all kinds of pie dishes: metal, glass, Pyrex, disposable aluminum—in all shapes and sizes. And I use them all, indiscriminately, without judgment. Go ahead, make your arguments for which material bakes best, but I just want to get on with making my pie.

16. WHAT'S YOUR FAVORITE KIND OF PIE?

Every pie in this cookbook is my favorite. But if pressed, I would have to say apple crumble (see page 88). I love the softness and comfort-food feeling of the filling combined with the crunchy, brown sugar and butter topping.

17. HOW DO YOU EAT SO MUCH PIE AND STAY SO THIN?

I had to include this question only because I get asked this so often. The answer is that I don't eat that much pie. I certainly make a lot of it, but when I'm baking both hands are busy and I don't even have a chance to drink a cup of coffee, let alone eat lunch. I haul 50-pound bags of flour and sugar in and out of my car and up and down my stairs every single week. I also get "real" exercise, mostly biking, hiking, and yoga. And, yes, I do love eating pie. When I get the chance to actually sit down and enjoy a slice.

KEY INGREDIENTS:

Unless otherwise stated, when a recipe in this book calls for…

Flour, it means all-purpose white flour.

Sugar, it means granulated white sugar.

Eggs, it means large eggs (but if you have medium or extra-large eggs, just use those).

Butter, it means that either salted or unsalted is okay. (If using salted, just cut back on any salt you're adding to the recipe.)

Brown sugar, it means light brown and firmly packed.

Spices such as cinnamon, ginger, cloves, etc., it means ground spices.

Corn syrup, it means light corn syrup (even when a recipe specifically calls for dark, I still end up using light, so don't sweat this one).

Vanilla, it means vanilla extract. Use the real stuff. It tastes better.

Tapioca, it means minute tapioca, the finest granules possible.

But after saying all that, really, it doesn't matter what you use. If you only have dark corn syrup, so what? Go ahead and use it. You only have medium eggs? It won't matter. Just make do with what ingredients you have on hand. Pie is, after all, about improvising! (And a reminder: It is also not about precision.) The pioneers did not have grocery stores they could run to when they needed the "right" ingredients, and they still made pie. A lot of pie. So think like a pioneer and give yourself permission to be flexible.

PIE DOUGH:

CRUSTS THAT QUESTION AUTHORITY

Fear of making pie dough is the number one reason people run to the store for pre-packaged pie dough and frozen pie. I feel it's my personal mission to help these would-be bakers by sharing some of my confidence-building guidelines. It's just pie. You don't need a culinary school degree or any kind of degree at all to make it. All you need is desire, a few pointers, and some encouragement to break the rules! (Also see "Pie Myths, Busted" on page 19)

DOUGH POINTERS FOR THE NERVOUS PIE-MAKER

These are the basics I teach in my pie classes:

LEAVE IT CHUNKY.
It's the big chunks of fat that make for a flaky dough. So when you're working the fat into the flour, leave pieces of butter the size of almonds and peas. Brazil nuts are a bit too large. You can't go back once you've worked fat too fine, so err on the side of super chunks.

ADD AS MUCH WATER AS THE DOUGH NEEDS.
Every recipe known to mankind says to add as little water as possible and only one tablespoon of it at a time. I completely disagree with this! I say, better to add more water and let water be the glue rather than use brute force to get your dough to hold together. Working your flour and butter too much is what makes dough tough, not water.

FORGET WHAT THE RECIPE SAYS, JUST PAY ATTENTION TO WHAT'S IN FRONT OF YOU.
For example, if your dough is dry and crumbly, add more water.

TAKE THE TIME TO BE A PROBLEM SOLVER.
If your dough is rolling out to an uneven shape, stop, take stock of the situation, and figure out what you need to do—and what areas you need to roll—to get your dough the shape and thinness you want. If your rolling surface or rolling pin is gunked up, take the time to clean it. If your dough isn't holding together, add more water. If your dough is melting, refrigerate it for a while. There is a solution to every problem, even if the solution is to throw out the dough and start over.

PIE CAN BE FORGIVING.

What? You dumped in too much water? Add some flour to compensate. That won't ruin your dough. Overworking it—like trying to knead it or force it together without enough water—that is what will ruin your dough.

PIE *SHOULD* LOOK HOMEMADE.

Do not worry about what it looks like! A crack? A hole? Who cares? You don't want your homemade creation to look like it was made by a machine.

YOUR TWO HANDS ARE YOUR BEST TOOLS.

Forget what the recipes say about how your hands hold heat and that heat will make your dough tough. Overworking the dough will make it tough, true. But if you keep a light touch, leave big chunks of butter, toss the water in lightly, and use enough water (instead of force!) to hold the dough together, you will love using your hands. Just remember to be quick. Get those hands in, then out, and all will be well.

ROLLING PIE DOUGH IS LIKE HORSEBACK RIDING.

Pie dough is like a horse and knows when you're scared. You have to take the reins and show that horse you are in charge! Take the rolling pin and tell that dough where *you* want it to go. Always keep in mind the shape you are aiming for. When the shape gets out of control—like turning into a map of Africa—stop and assess the situation. Figure out how you are going to solve the problem and roll your pin around the edges of the dough to coax it back into a round shape—as if you were riding your horse around an arena.

THE PIONEERS DID NOT HAVE REFRIGERATORS.

What's that? The recipe says you should refrigerate your flour, your bowls, and your utensils? Do you want a rectal thermometer to go with all that? Sheesh. Just chill your butter and shortening (or fat of your choice), and use ice water, and your ingredients will be cold enough. Really, when did pie-making turn into this overly (and unnecessarily) detailed contest-like activity? Just relax.

TOOLS FOR MAKING BASIC PIE DOUGH:

Your two best tools are your hands. But you'll need a few other essentials too.

Large bowl.

1-cup measuring cup: to measure flour. I have a 2½-cup measuring cup, ideal for this recipe. In a pinch, when traveling, I just use a coffee cup.

Paring knife: to cut butter into manageable-sized chunks, and later to trim dough edges and poke ventilation holes.

Small pitcher: for ice water. Or a simple glass will work too.

Small bowl: for extra flour to sprinkle on rolling surface.

Rolling pin.

Pastry scraper: for lifting dough off the rolling surface.

Pie dish.

Scissors: to trim excess dough from rim of pie dish.

Aluminum foil for a blind-baked crust.

Pie weights (such as dried beans, rice, etc.) for a blind-baked crust.

CRUSTS

BASIC PIE DOUGH (FOR A SINGLE-CRUST PIE)

¼ cup (½ stick) butter, chilled and cut
  into large chunks
¼ cup vegetable shortening, chilled
1¼ cups flour, plus at least ¼ extra
  for rolling
Dash of salt
Ice water (fill a ½ cup but use only
  enough to moisten dough)

To make your single-crust pie dough, simply follow the instructions below for the double-crust pie dough. It's the same exact method!

BASIC PIE DOUGH (FOR A DOUBLE-CRUST PIE)

½ cup (1 stick) butter, chilled and cut
  into large chunks
½ cup vegetable shortening, chilled
2½ cups flour, plus at least ½ cup extra
  for rolling
Dash of salt
Ice water (fill a full cup but use only
  enough to moisten dough)

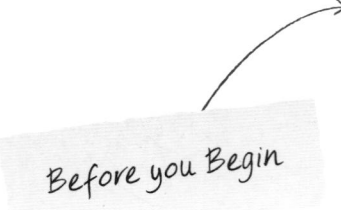

Before you Begin

★ Flour is your friend when it comes to rolling dough. It's what I like to call your "insurance policy." Contrary to what other cookbooks will tell you, extra flour will not make your dough tough. Adding flour to your rolling surface will keep your dough from sticking—and will keep you from running to the store in frustration to buy pre-made pie crust.

★ That said, always start from the center and roll out to the edges, rolling in one direction. You can push, you can pull, but don't roll back and forth like a crazy person. I like to think of rolling dough as a dance; stay fluid in your motions. Also, put a little body weight into it so you can really stretch your dough. Too little pressure won't get your dough to roll thin; too much pressure will mangle your dough. Try it out, get a feel, don't be afraid to experiment.

★ Keep your workspace clean. Take the time to scrape the gunk off your rolling surface as well as your rolling pin. This is another one of those "insurance policies" to keep your dough from sticking.

★ When rolling dough, use your pie dish to calculate how big you'll need it. Allow for enough extra width to account for the depth of the dish and make sure the extra inch or two of overhang from the dish has enough bulk for crimping the edge.

★ Size isn't the only goal when rolling dough. You want to aim for a certain "thinness." My pie teacher, Mary Spellman, taught me what her mother taught her: Roll it thin enough so you can just start to see the stripes of the tablecloth through the dough. I always think about this transparency, even if there are no stripes on my rolling surface.

l. In a deep, large bowl, work the butter and shortening into the flour and salt with your hands until you have almond- and pea-sized lumps of butter.

2. Then, drizzling in ice water a little at a time, "toss" the water around with your fingers spread, as if the flour were a salad and your hands were the salad tongs. Don't spend a lot of time mixing the dough, just focus on getting it moistened. Translation: With each addition of water, toss about four times and then STOP, add more water, and repeat.

3. When the dough holds together on its own (and with enough water, it will), do a "squeeze test." If it falls apart, you need to add more water. If it is soggy and sticky, you might need to sprinkle flour onto it until the wetness is balanced out. The key is to not overwork the dough! It takes very little time and you'll be tempted to keep touching it, but don't!

4. Now divide the dough in two balls (or three, if your pie dishes are smaller) and form each into a disk shape.

5. Sprinkle flour under and on top of your dough to keep it from sticking to your rolling surface. Roll to a thinness where the dough almost seems transparent.

6. Measure the size of the dough by holding your pie plate above it. It's big enough if you have enough extra width to compensate for the depth and width of your dish, plus 1 to 2 inches overhang.

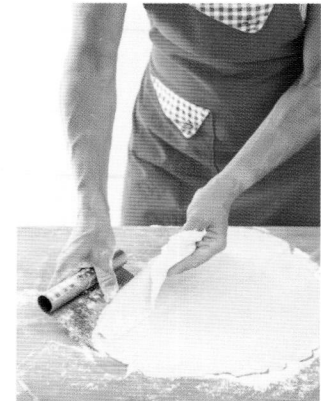 

7. Slowly and gently—SERIOUSLY, TAKE YOUR TIME!—lift the dough off the rolling surface, nudging flour under with the scraper as you lift, and fold the dough back. When you are sure your dough is 100 percent free and clear from the surface, bring your pie dish close to it and then drag your dough over to your dish. (Holding the folded edge will give you a better grip and keep your dough from tearing.)

8. Place the folded edge halfway across your dish, allowing the dough of the covered half to drape over the side. Slowly and carefully unfold the dough until it lies fully across the pie dish.

9. Lift the edges and let gravity ease the dough down to sit snugly in the dish, using the light touch of a finger if you need to push any remaining air space out of the corners as you go.

10. Trim excess dough to about 1 inch from the dish edge (I use scissors), leaving ample dough to make crimped, fluted edges.

BLIND-BAKED CRUST

A blind-baked crust is used for cream pies, where you cook the filling over the stove and thus the pie crust doesn't get a chance to bake in the oven unless you bake it by itself first.

―――――――――――――

BASIC PIE DOUGH FOR SINGLE-CRUST PIE

1. Prepare Basic Pie Dough (see page 28) recipe for a single-crust pie, then roll and crimp the edges.

2. Prick the bottom and sides of the pie crust with a fork.

3. Lay a large piece of foil over the top and fill with pie weights (or beans, rice, coins, chains, screws—anything to weight down the crust to keep it from puffing up or shrinking.)

4. Bake at 425 degrees for 15 to 20 minutes.

5. Remove the weights and foil, turn oven down to 375 degrees, and continue baking for another 5 minutes or more, to brown the bottom of the crust.

NOTE: The weights hold the crust in place as it bakes, keeping it from shrinking as the moisture evaporates. If it does shrink, it will rattle around in your pie dish, and though it will be smaller than you had hoped, it will still taste good.

You don't want to roll the dough more than once (okay, maybe twice) as it will toughen it, so if you don't have the shape or size just right, it's better to cut and piece the dough into the pie dish rather than wad it up and start over. Tough dough is not only hard to roll, it's hard to chew.

GRAHAM CRACKER CRUST

I love how a graham cracker crust with its buttery, crumbly texture melts in your mouth. For added flavor, you can throw some cinnamon and sugar into the mix. (I don't use sugar because graham crackers are already sweet.) If using a large, deep-dish pie plate, be sure to increase the amount of crackers in your recipe.

1½ cups crushed graham crackers
(about 9 to 12 crackers, at least one
sleeve)
5 to 6 tbsp butter, melted

OPTIONAL INGREDIENTS
1 tsp cinnamon
¼ cup sugar

1. To crush crackers, place in a ziplock plastic bag, push out all the air, and roll over them with a rolling pin.

2. In a bowl—or directly in the pie dish to avoid washing more dishes—mix melted butter into cracker crumbs. If you like, mix in cinnamon and/or sugar.

3. Press crust mixture into pie plate with your fingers or the bottom of a glass.

4. Bake at 350 degrees for 10 minutes.

CHOCOLATE COOKIE CRUST

You can use Oreo® cookies or any chocolate sandwich cookies for this recipe. Good luck not eating some in the process.

24 chocolate sandwich cookies
(or more if your dish is large)
4 to 6 tbsp butter, melted

1. To crush cookies, place in a ziplock plastic bag, push out all the air, and roll over them with a rolling pin. It's easier to crush them if cookies are laid flat in a single layer to start.

2. In a bowl or directly in the pie dish, mix melted butter into cookie crumbs.

3. Press crust mixture into pie plate with your fingers or the bottom of a glass.

4. If you are using a filling you're going to bake, you don't need to bake the crust first. If you're using this crust for a refrigerated pie, bake at 350 degrees for 10 minutes.

GLUTEN-FREE RICE FLOUR CRUST (FOR A DOUBLE-CRUST PIE)

This type of gluten-free dough doesn't hold together like "normal" pie dough. You will likely have to piece it together to make a solid crust. Don't worry, you can smooth out the dough once it's in the pie plate, and you can still make it pretty by crimping the edges. (No one will see what the bottom looks like!) For the top crust, use cookie cutters to make decorative dough pieces to either cover up any blemishes like cracks or holes, or to make a purely unique and artistic pie top. Pie is about improvising.

---

2 cups rice flour, plus more for rolling surface
½ tsp baking powder
½ tsp salt
½ cup (1 stick) butter, cut into chunks
   (I add an extra few tablespoons)
2 beaten eggs
¼ cup cold water (use more if needed)

1. In a large bowl, mix together rice flour, baking powder, and salt.

2. Work the butter into the dry ingredients, then mix in the eggs and water. Dough will be sticky.

3. To take the stickiness out of the dough when handling it, rub rice flour on your hands like "flour mittens." Divide the dough into two balls, then flatten into disks.

4. Roll the dough on a silicone baking mat or a large piece of waxed paper. Sprinkle the surface with extra rice flour when rolling dough to keep it from sticking.

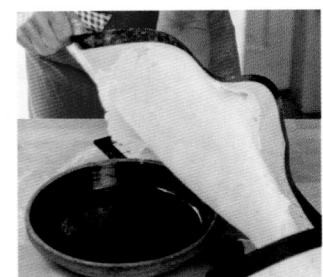

5. Flip the mat or waxed paper upside down into the pie pan.

6. Trim excess dough to about 1 inch from the dish edge, as you would with Basic Pie Dough, leaving ample dough to make crimped, fluted edges.

7. Assemble pie as you would with Basic Pie Dough, then brush with a beaten egg before baking.

8. Bake as directed for Basic Pie Dough.

BETH'S TIP: For a gluten-free filling, use tapioca instead of flour as a thickener for fruit.

CRUST-CRIMPING TECHNIQUE

Rolling the top and bottom crusts together serves a practical purpose: it creates a seal that keeps the juices inside. Crimping your edges afterward adds a pretty decorative touch to your pie. If you choose not to finger-crimp your edges, you can use a fork instead—just press down along the pie's rim for a textured edge. Or simply roll your edges closed and leave the pie plain, uncrimped.

TIP: Dip your fingers in a small bowl of flour to coat them. This keeps the dough from sticking to your fingers and pulling apart. Continue dipping your fingers in flour as needed.

1. Roll the edges of the top and bottom crusts (for a double crust pie) or the edge of the bottom crust (for a blind baked pie, see photos below) in an underhand direction. Don't pinch or fold yet; this is just the prep stage for the crimping). Make sure the rolled part sits on top of the pie dish rim. Run your fingers around the underside of the rim to ensure there's no dough hanging below. Stray dough as such will fall off in the oven.

2. Hold your thumb and forefinger in the shape of a clothespin, keeping a little more than a fingertip's worth of space in between them, and place your set of fingers on the **inside rim** of your pie dish. Note: This is your static hand. Your fingers do not move, they do not pinch; they are just placeholders.

3. On the **outside rim** of the pie dish, just opposite the "clothespin" fingers on the inside rim, hold your other forefinger in a vertical position and give the dough a push with the side of your fingertip to create a deep groove between the "clothespin" fingers.

4. Pick up your set of "clothespin" placeholder fingers, keeping them in position, and repeat the crimp around the dish. Rotate the dish as you work your way around it, instead of contorting your body. I like to work between 2 and 4 o'clock on my dish.

NOTE: The ruffled edge will soften in the oven, so make sure you give it a firm, seemingly extreme pinch. Try to keep your edge a little "chubby" because thinner dough is prone to overbrowning when baking.

LATTICE TECHNIQUE

1. Roll out dough as you would for a top crust, but take it slightly wider than usual.

2. With a paring knife or a lattice cutter (like a mini pizza cutter but with a zigzag wheel), cut strips even in width. The measure of width is up to you: Sometimes I make wide ones, sometimes skinny ones.

3. Slowly and carefully, pick up one of the longer strips from the center (use the dough scraper to help you), and lay it across the middle of your pie.

4. Now take a second long strip and lay it in the opposite direction across the top of your pie, so you have a cross on top.

5. Pick up another of the longer strips, and lay it parallel to one of the others already on top of the pie.

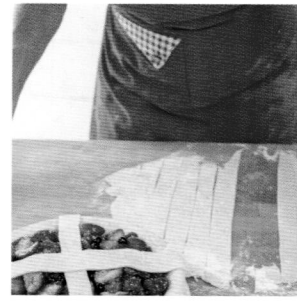 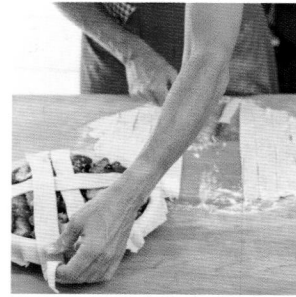 

6. Still working with your longer strips, lay another in the opposite direction of the last one, parallel to its neighbor strip.

7. You will now see the need to begin weaving, so take stock and understand the pattern. Pull back one of your strips on the pie halfway across its diameter, lay down the new strip, then pull the folded strip back into place. You will now have created an "over, under" system.

8. Continue folding strips on the pie halfway back as you place a new one on top. Once you have several strips on top, you will have to fold all of them back to get each new strip into place. Then return the folded strips to their full laid-out position afterward.

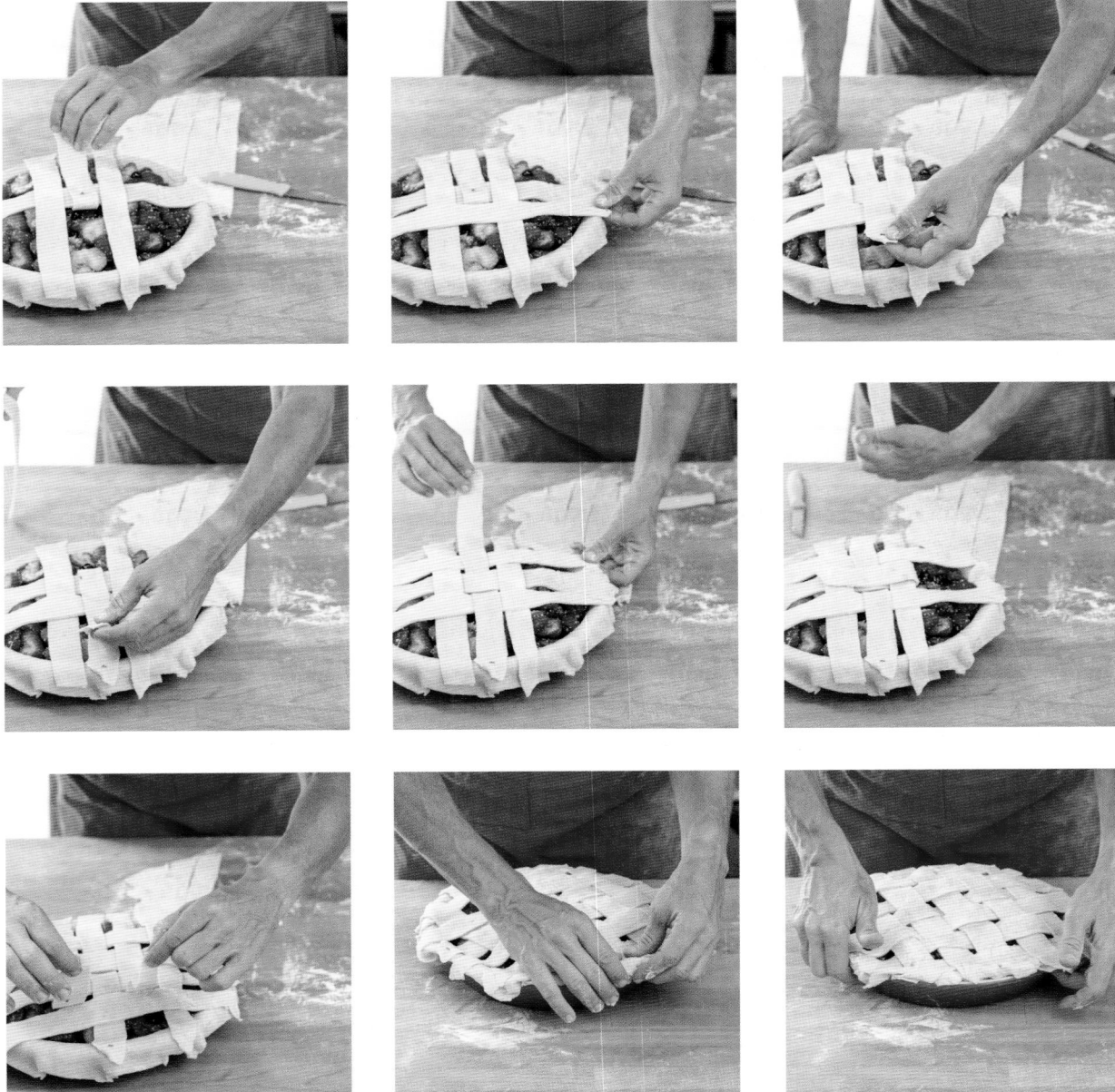

9. Trim the excess edges of the strips and bottom crust, leaving enough extra dough to roll the strips and bottom crust together in an underhand direction. This will give you a smooth edge.

10. As with the crimping technique, run your fingers under the pie dish rim to ensure there is no dough hanging beneath it. You can crimp the edge for added effect, but I like mine just rolled.

11. Brush with beaten egg. And no need to poke vent holes as the lattice gives the filling plenty of breathing space.

NOTE: If any strips break, no worries! Just hide the broken part under the strip that lays across it.

 # Pies to Heal

I learned over the years that pie has many magical powers. Pie can seduce, cajole, boost your confidence, calm your nerves, initiate marriage proposals, and impress even the most jaded of human beings. But the most important thing pie has done for me is to help me heal. Specifically, heal from the grief of losing my husband, Marcus.

My first and most lasting discovery of this was five months after Marcus died. I had traveled in the 24-foot RV that Marcus left behind, driving from Portland where I was living, down to Los Angeles where I was collecting my belongings from a storage unit. It was adventure enough to drive that damn camper. I had never driven it when Marcus was alive, but when I inherited it, I needed to either face my fears and learn to drive it or sell it. I didn't want to sell it because we had shared many good times in "The Beast," as we affectionately called it. So there I was, white knuckling my way down Interstate 5 over two mountain passes straight into the heart of America's worst traffic.

I was parked at my friend Melissa's house, where her friend Janice Molinari was staying. Janice was a TV producer whom I had met a few times, and when she saw the RV her face lit up under the brim of her "Life is Good" baseball hat. "I want to go on a road trip," she announced. "We could drive around and make a pie documentary."

I had nothing else going on in my life at that time, except for my weekly sessions with my grief counselor. So I said, "Okay."

We drove through California for two weeks, interviewing pie makers and orchard owners, and sampling pies at diners.

Our shoot coincided, as we had learned, with National Pie Day. Yes, there really is such a thing. It's an official holiday registered in Chase's Calendar of Events—created because it was the birthday of a man named Charlie Papazian who wanted to ensure that he would be served pie and not cake on his special day, which is January 23. The holiday has grown and is now sponsored by the American Pie Council. It was Janice's idea to gather several of my closest friends and make 50 apple pies and hand them out by the slice—for free—on the streets of LA to commemorate the event.

Thus, we spent the entire day of January 22 in Melissa's kitchen, mixing dough, peeling 150 pounds of apples, and rolling out 100 individual crusts. I agree with the proverb that states, "Many hands make light work," but my friends' hands made work feel like play. With Nan, Jane, Melissa, Janice, and a few other helpers, we baked, we peeled, we rolled, we crimped, and we exchanged stories. And we laughed. What I remember most is the laughter. The camaraderie was therapeutic, indeed, but this was only just the beginning of the pies' healing powers.

The next day, we loaded up The Beast with 50 bakery boxes. The scent of apples, butter, and cinnamon permeated the space. The RV had never smelled so good. Instead of oxygen, we were breathing in comfort and calm. We also loaded folding tables, paper plates, plastic forks, and a large, foam homemade sign that read "Free Pie."

We began our Great Pie Giveaway at Fire Station 39 in Van Nuys, slicing up the first of our pies and passing them out to the crew of firefighters and first responders. If anyone deserves free pie, it's these kind of hard-working Good Samaritans who risk their lives to help make the world a safer place. Janice moved around the room with her camera, filming them as they scooped vanilla ice cream on top and proceeded to gobble up the pie, the gooey apples, flaky crust and all. I stood by watching quietly, feeling the room fill with palpable joy.

Next we set up a table on Ventura Boulevard, the main corridor of LA's San Fernando Valley. But a shortage of foot traffic—it's true that everyone drives in LA—convinced us to move to another location. We drove down to Venice Beach and, putting my gradually improving parallel-parking skills to the test (I had only dented the rear ladder and cracked the plastic air-conditioning cover on top due to a low tree branch), secured a spot for the RV on the trendy shopping street Abbott Kinney Way.

Here, we set up a folding table on the sidewalk and it didn't take long for pedestrians to stop and gawk at the abundance of crusty triangles oozing out their filling onto the paper plates.

"Would you like a slice?" we asked. Most of my pie crew from the previous day, Nan, Melissa, and Janice, were there to help, along with another friend named Jeff. "It's free," we added.

The passersby were incredulous. "Free?" they asked. "Free" was inconceivable. "Who's sponsoring you?" they persisted, unable to accept that there were no strings attached.

"No one," we replied.

"Then why are you doing this?" they wanted to know.

"We're just doing this to make the world a better place."

I spent most of the day hovering in the background. Five months after Marcus's death, I was still vulnerable, raw, and crying—no, I was *bawling*—daily. But I was taking it all in. I watched the people lifting their forks to their lips, their eyes closing with pleasure as the taste of childhood filled their mouths, their heads involuntarily nodding in approval. I heard men and women alike say, "This reminds me of my grandmother's pie." And then I heard them say, "This pie is so good, and what you've done is so nice, it makes me want to do something nice for someone else."

I had made that pie. I had put my time, my energy, my hands, my heart into that pie. All 50 of those pies. And now I was witnessing the effect that pie was having on others, a positive, pay-it-forward kind of response. I was at the lowest point in my entire life and I was able to see first-hand that I still had something left to give. I had always believed that giving to others helps you feel better yourself. What I learned that day—National Pie Day—is that in spite of the weight of my grief, the constant pain from my shattered heart, the darkness of knowing I would spend the rest of my life without Marcus in it, I could actually feel better.

I've baked—and given away—more than a thousand pies since then. My grief is still there—it never ever really goes away—but I know just what to do when it rears its head. There is always someone, somewhere who is in greater need than me, someone who could use a homemade pie to remind them that life still holds some hope, promise, and a little taste of happiness. And so I get busy baking.

Pie Recipes to Heal

Apple

Homemade Caramel

Marionberry

Peach Crumble

Cherry

Pumpkin

Brownie

Cinnamon

Lemon Chess

Chocolate Cheesecake

APPLE

This is my signature pie. Apple is the first pie I ever learned how to make—when caught stealing apples from an orchard in Washington State and the owner turned out to be a retired pastry chef. It's the first pie that Mary Spellman taught me to make when I worked for her at Mary's Kitchen in Malibu. (I still make it her way and think of her every single time I make it.) Apple is one of the most universally loved pies. It was the first pie I made for Marcus and then it became the pie I made to heal from the loss of him. It's the pie I teach in my pie classes. And it continues to be the pie I share with others in need, to help in their healing.

CRUST

Basic Pie Dough for double-crust pie (see page 28).

FILLING

7 to 10 large Granny Smith apples, peeled (see tip on page 46)

½ tsp salt (you'll sprinkle this on so don't worry about precise amount)

1 to 2 tsp cinnamon (use however much you like, but remember it's a powerful spice)

¾ cup sugar (more or less, depending on your taste, tartness of apples, and number of apples)

4 tbsp flour (to thicken the filling)

1 tbsp butter, to pat on top of filling

1 beaten egg, to brush on top crust

The pie is "assembled" in two layers, which is not only a nice shortcut, it saves you from having to wash an extra bowl!

Prepare the Basic Pie Dough for a double-crust pie (see page 28).

Prepare the Filling: Slice half of the peeled apples directly into the pie, arranging and pressing down gently to remove extra space between slices. Fill the dish enough so you don't see through the first layer to the bottom crust.

Cover with half of salt, cinnamon, sugar, and flour.

Slice the remaining apples into the pie, arranging and pressing down gently on top of first layer, and cover with second half of ingredients.

Add a pat of butter on top, then cover with the top crust.

Trim the edges with scissors, leaving about 1 to 2 inches overhang, and then roll the top and bottom crust together underhand so that it's sealed and sits on the rim of your pie plate.

Crimp the edge with your fingers or a fork, then brush with a beaten egg. (The egg gives the pie a nice golden-brown shine. Do be careful not to let egg pool in crevices. You will use about half an egg per pie.)

continued overleaf

**VARIETY IS THE SPICE OF LIFE...
AND PIE:** It's okay to use a variety of apples. Try Braeburn and Royal Gala. I don't use Fuji (they are too juicy) or Red Delicious (they have no taste). Tart apples work best for pie. The number of apples you use will depend on the size of apple and the size of pie dish, but the general amount is about 3 pounds per 10-inch pie.

Use a knife to poke vent holes in the top (get creative here with a pattern), then bake at 425 degrees for 15 to 20 minutes to set and brown the crust.

Turn oven down to 375 degrees and bake for another 30 to 40 minutes, until juice bubbles. Keep an eye on it as it bakes. If it gets too dark, turn down the temperature.

To be sure it's done, poke with a knife through the vent holes to make sure apples have softened. Do not overbake or apples will turn mushy.

BETH'S TIP:
Slicing your apples too thick will mean your pie takes longer to bake. But slicing them too thin will translate in filling that's like applesauce. I don't like to suggest numbers, but think ¼ inch thick. Also, keeping your slices a consistent size will help the pie bake more evenly.

KEEP CALM!
Don't worry about your apples turning brown. I mean, think about it: what color is cinnamon? Exactly! No one will ever know.

HOMEMADE CARAMEL

A little added gooeyness to an already warm and luscious apple pie can't hurt. I mean, we're talking pies to heal, so why not take the comfort level up a notch and add some homemade (not from a jar!) caramel sauce? To turn an apple pie into a caramel apple pie, simply follow the recipe above and add a drizzle of caramel sauce in between each layer, including on the top and bottom of the pie.

HOMEMADE CARAMEL SAUCE
1½ cups brown sugar, firmly packed
⅓ cup light corn syrup
6 tbsp (¾ stick) butter
½ tsp salt
½ cup heavy cream

Over medium heat in a saucepan, cook the brown sugar, corn syrup, butter, and salt until the mixture is almost boiling.

Gradually stir in the cream.

Cook for about 10 minutes.

MARIONBERRY

I love this pie. It reminds me of when Marcus and I lived in Portland, Oregon, one of the happiest times in our marriage. Marionberries, a cross between a raspberry and blackberry, are native to Oregon and I used to pick them myself on Sauvie Island, just outside of Portland. Marionberry pie also reminds me of my Year of Grief, when I returned to Portland after Marcus died. My best pal there, Alison Kauffman, would take me out to Sauvie Island, where we picked berries in the quiet of nature. Filling my bowl with the finger-staining fruit reminded me of the seasonal nature of life—and the thorns from the bushes reminded me of life's occasional harsh sting! I credit both the friendship of Alison and the making of pie from this fruit as instrumental in my healing.

CRUST
Basic Pie Dough for double-crust pie
    (see page 28)

FILLING
5 cups marionberries (see tip below)
1 cup sugar
3 tbsp tapioca
½ tsp salt
¼ tsp lemon juice (optional)

1 tbsp butter, to pat on top of filling
1 beaten egg, to brush on top crust

Prepare the Basic Pie Dough for a double-crust pie (see page 28).

Prepare the Filling: Mix the ingredients in a large bowl. Let sit for 20 minutes to activate the tapioca. Spoon into the bottom pie crust.

Dot with a pat of butter and cover with top crust.

Trim the dough edges as needed, then roll top and bottom crust together in underhand direction until it sits on the rim of the pie plate.

Crimp the edge with your fingers or a fork, then brush with beaten egg.

Poke ventilation holes in the top, then bake at 425 degrees for 15 to 20 minutes.

Turn temperature down to 375 degrees and bake for another 30 minutes, or until filling bubbles and thickens.

KEEP IT SIMPLE! If you can't get marionberries, you can substitute with blackberries.

PEACH CRUMBLE

I dubbed this pie "Peach Grumble" after making it for a grumpy landlord I had during the year I was working at Mary's Kitchen in Malibu. I had to break my lease since I couldn't afford the tiny studio on my even tinier pie baker's salary. Well, my landlord didn't like that. He said he was going to hold me accountable for the entire year's rent and even threatened to sue me. In turn, I baked him a peach crumble pie and delivered it with a note of apology for any trouble I had caused him. A few days later I saw him in the driveway. He rolled down the window of his old Porsche and muttered, "The pie was, um, good." I found a new tenant for him, he didn't sue me, and I moved on. But I still think of him and how that pie might have softened his heart a little.

CRUST

Basic Pie Dough for single-crust pie (see page 28), crimped

FILLING

8 to 10 ripe peaches, peeled and sliced (number of peaches depends on size of fruit and size of your pie dish, but have at least 3 pounds on hand)

1 cup sugar

¼ cup tapioca

½ tsp cinnamon (optional, but I love it)

CRUMBLE TOPPING

1 cup flour

½ cup (1 stick) butter, chilled and cut into large chunks

½ cup brown sugar, firmly packed

CRUMBLE FIX! Overworking the crumble topping will turn it into a melted mush. To remedy this, either add more flour or refrigerate it. You can then break it into a crumbly texture. Underworking the crumble however will result in a texture that is too fine. In this case, just keep picking up handfuls and roll it between your hands until the desired texture is achieved.

Prepare the Basic Pie Dough for a single-crust pie (see page 28).

Prepare the Filling: In a large bowl, combine peaches, sugar, tapioca, and cinnamon. Let sit for 15 to 20 minutes to let tapioca activate, then pour into pie shell.

Prepare the Crumble Topping: In a large bowl, rub together the flour, butter, and brown sugar—and rub and rub and rub—until the texture feels like various sizes of marbles.

With both hands, distribute the crumble topping over the top of the pie. Do not press down on it, as you don't want your crumbs to look flat. It's a good idea to place a cookie sheet or oven liner under this pie when baking, as a few bits of the crumble topping may roll off into the oven.

Bake at 425 degrees for about 15 to 20 minutes, until browned.

Turn down the heat to 375 degrees and continue baking another 30 minutes, or until the filling bubbles, the peaches soften, and the juice thickens.

BETH'S TIP:
For a chunky crumble topping, rub the flour, butter, and brown sugar in your hands as if you were rolling ball bearings. It's the circular motion that will create the little round chunks. Pick it up in handfuls, rub, rub, rub, let it fall back into the ball, and keep repeating.

CHERRY

For some people—er, me—apple pie is a favorite. For others, it's unquestionably cherry that rocks their world. I get asked every weekend at the Pitchfork Pie Stand if I have cherry pie. My response is a quick one: "Who's going to pit all those cherries?!" But cherry pie is bred deeply in the American DNA, and for that, and its bright and cheery appearance, there is a place for it when offering gifts of healing to others.

CRUST
Basic Pie Dough for double-crust pie
   (see page 28)

FILLING
5 to 6 cups pitted fresh cherries (sweet,
   tart, or a combo of both)
1½ cups sugar (or less if cherries are
   sweet)
3 tbsp tapioca, or 4 tbsp cornstarch
Pinch of salt

1 tbsp butter, to pat on top of filling
1 beaten egg, to brush on top crust

SWITCH IT UP? If you use cornstarch instead of tapioca to thicken, and you don't mind doing an extra step—and having another dish to wash—you can pre-cook the cherries in a saucepan over the stove, stirring in the sugar, cornstarch, and salt, and heating, stirring constantly, until thickened.

Prepare the Basic Pie Dough for a double-crust pie (see page 28).

Prepare the Filling: Mix cherries, sugar, tapioca, and salt together in a large bowl. Let sit for about 20 minutes to let tapioca activate, then pour into pie shell.

Add a pat of butter on top, then cover with the top crust.

Trim and crimp edges, brush with beaten egg, then poke vent holes.

Bake at 425 degrees for 15 to 20 minutes.

Turn oven down to 375 degrees and bake for another 30 minutes or more. Filling should be bubbling.

NOTE: Go for the lattice top on this pie! Those cherries will look so pretty poking out from underneath with all their messy, delicious-looking juice oozing out.

BETH'S TIP:
If you use frozen cherries, you don't need to thaw them first, but you will need to let them sit longer in the tapioca before baking—about an hour. You will also need to increase the baking time by about 30 minutes so they cook fully.

PUMPKIN

I've found that the best, most reliable recipe for pumpkin pie is the one straight off the Libby's® canned pumpkin label. And for this pie, I do use canned pumpkin. When I lived in Germany with Marcus, I couldn't buy canned pumpkin so I cooked my own pumpkins to get the purée. I could not taste the difference, and thus even when I grew pumpkins in my first garden at the American Gothic House, I didn't feel there was any taste or texture difference to justify the effort of the baking, scraping, and sieving to get a great pie. What makes this one a good healing pie is the ease of eating (and making) it. It's moist and goes down easily. And if it reminds you of happy family gatherings at Thanksgiving, even better—nostalgia is good for the soul.

CRUST

Basic Pie Dough for single-crust pie, crimped (see page 28)

FILLING

¾ cup granulated sugar
1 tsp cinnamon
½ tsp salt
½ tsp ground ginger
¼ tsp ground cloves
2 eggs
1 can (15 ounces) pumpkin purée
1 can (12 ounces) evaporated milk

Prepare the Basic Pie Dough for a single-crust pie (see page 28).

Prepare the Filling: Mix sugar, cinnamon, salt, ginger, and cloves in a small bowl.

Beat eggs in a large bowl, then stir in pumpkin and sugar-spice mixture.

Gradually stir in evaporated milk. Pour into pie shell.

Bake at 425 degrees for 15 minutes.

Turn temperature down to 350 degrees and bake for another 40 to 50 minutes or until knife inserted near center comes out clean. If you don't eat it all immediately, then refrigerate.

BROWNIE

My best friend since age 12 is Nan. She lives in New York City. Our mutual love of brownies is one of the many things that bonds us. Every time I stay with her in NY she has a pan of brownies waiting for me. Nan rushed to my side when Marcus died—even when I told her she didn't have to come. She wasn't able to bring brownies with her, but she brought her love and support, and I wouldn't have survived those days of despair without her. She is due to visit me soon—she still hasn't been to the American Gothic House—and when she does I will have brownie pie waiting for her.

CRUST
Basic Pie Dough for single-crust pie
(see page 28) or Chocolate Cookie
Crust (see page 32)

FILLING
½ cup butter (1 stick), melted
2 eggs
1 cup sugar
1 tsp vanilla
½ cup cocoa powder
½ cup flour
½ tsp baking powder
½ tsp salt
½ cup nuts, walnuts, or pecans
(optional)

Prepare the Basic Pie Dough for a single-crust pie (see page 28) or the Chocolate Cookie Crust (see page 32).

Prepare the Filling: Combine melted butter, eggs, sugar, and vanilla in a large bowl.

Stir in cocoa powder and other dry ingredients, then spoon into pie shell.

If using Chocolate Cookie Crust, bake at 350 degrees for about 30 to 40 minutes. If using Basic Pie Dough, start oven hot at 425 degrees and bake for 10 to 15 minutes to set the crust, then turn oven down to 350 degrees to continue baking the filling without scorching it!

CINNAMON

I sampled this pie when Eldon, Iowa, resident Diana Ostrander Harness helped me with my Pitchfork Pie Stand one summer weekend, and, when I wasn't looking, she whipped one up with some leftover pie dough. It's an uncomplicated pie that is very simply a creamy, syrupy layer of butter, milk, sugar, and cinnamon poured over scraps of crust. The recipe came from Diana's grandmother, Kathryn Schiller of Donnellson, Iowa, who raised dairy cows so they had their own butter and milk readily available. It's been a family favorite ever since and continues to get passed down through the generations of the pie-loving Ostrander Family. Now that's a comforting thought.

CRUST
Basic Pie Dough for single-crust pie
    (see page 28), crimped

FILLING
½ cup sugar
¼ cup milk
3 to 6 tbsp butter
Cinnamon, to taste

Prepare the Basic Pie Dough for a single-crust pie (see page 28).

Prepare the Filling: Mix the sugar and milk together, and pour into unbaked pie shell.

Dot generously with butter.

Sprinkle cinnamon to taste over the custard, then bake at 400 degrees for 15 to 20 minutes or until crust is done.

LEMON CHESS

When life gives you lemons...yada, yada, yada. But there is something helpful and true about that cliché. Healing is about taking what is bitter (death of a spouse, car trouble, tax audits, lemons, you get the picture) and adding something sweet, like two whole cups of sugar. Or, to put it in more definitive terms, as my friend and cancer survivor Colleen Sommers in Austin, Texas, says, "Pie fixes everything." Well, almost.

CRUST
Basic Pie Dough for single-crust pie
    (see page 28), crimped

FILLING
2 cups sugar
2 tbsp flour
1 tbsp corn meal
5 eggs
⅔ cup buttermilk (or whole milk)
¼ cup butter, melted
2 tsp vanilla
3 tbsp lemon zest
¼ cup lemon juice, fresh squeezed,
    seeds removed

Prepare the Basic Pie Dough for a single-crust pie (see page 28).

Prepare the Filling: In a large bowl, combine sugar, flour, and corn meal. Beat in the eggs and buttermilk (or milk) until blended.

Stir in the melted butter, vanilla, lemon zest, and lemon juice. Pour into the pie crust.

Bake at 425 degrees for 10 to 15 minutes to set the crust.

Turn oven down to 350 degrees and bake for at least 30 more minutes or until filling is set. Center will puff up a little, though may still be a bit jiggly.

CHOCOLATE CHEESECAKE

There are a lot of ways (and fussy ones at that) to make chocolate cheesecake. Triple chocolate this, decadent fudge that. I say, if this is a pie to heal, then the point is not how fancy the cheesecake (or complicated the recipe)—it is to deliver the healing powers of chocolate in as quick and painless a way as possible. So if you can't hook up to a chocolate IV, make this super-easy cheesecake instead!

CRUST
Chocolate Cookie Crust (see page 32) or
    Graham Cracker Crust (see page 32)

FILLING
¼ cup (½ stick) butter, melted
½ cup cocoa powder
3 packages (8 ounces each) cream
    cheese, softened
1 can (14 ounces) sweetened
    condensed milk
4 eggs
1 tbsp vanilla

Prepare the Chocolate Cookie Crust (see page 32) or Graham Cracker Crust (see page 32), then pat into a 9-inch spring-form pan and bake at 350 degrees for 10 minutes.

Prepare the Filling: Mix melted butter and cocoa powder, stirring until smooth.

In a large bowl, beat cream cheese, then add cocoa mixture and beat well.

Mix in sweetened condensed milk, eggs, and vanilla, and beat until smooth. Pour into crust.

Bake at 325 degrees for an hour or until set. The middle may be soft.

Cool before removing from spring-form pan. Refrigerate for an hour or more before serving. And by all means, store this in the fridge.

 # Pies to Compete in the Iowa State Fair

I was born and raised in Iowa, and while I had an idyllic "Brady Bunch" childhood, I always felt there was a bigger world out there beckoning me to explore it. I grew increasingly restless during high school, to the point it was "suggested" that I graduate a semester early so I could begin my world travels. I left Iowa at 17, proclaiming I was "never coming back," and set off for college in Olympia, Washington, as far away from my home state as I could get without leaving the country.

I did see the world, many corners of it. My list of countries where I haven't been is shorter than the ones where I have lived or traveled. In keeping with my adventurous ways, I married Marcus, who was German. He worked for an international automotive company, which involved several transfers. We lived in Germany for the first two-and-a-half years of our marriage, then in Portland, Oregon, for a year and a half, and then in Saltillo, Mexico, for 10 months. After Mexico, he was then transferred back to Germany for what would have been a yearlong assignment, but that was cut short—as was his life—when he died suddenly and unexpectedly of a ruptured aorta. He was 43.

I spent a full year mired in debilitating grief. I allowed myself the time to rest, read, walk with my dogs, cry, and get a whole lot of grief counseling. When that year was up, I knew I needed to move out of the place where I had been in mourning. I also, instinctively, knew I needed to be somewhere grounding on the one-year anniversary of my

husband's death, the date of which was August 19. The idea came to me strongly, deeply, like a repressed longing I didn't know I had. Some inner voice instructed me clearly. It said: *Go to Iowa.* Just thinking about it, I could feel the nurturing embrace of the open landscape, see the puffy white clouds against a blue sky, breathe in the scent of freshly cut grass, sense the comforting weight of humidity on my bare skin—and get a whiff of hog manure. Not just go to Iowa, but to the Iowa State Fair, whose dates coincided with Marcus's anniversary.

I arrived in Iowa, and driving across the state alone would have been enough to fulfill my nostalgic sensory desires. But once I crossed the threshold of the Iowa State Fair—as in, showed my all-access wristband at the ticket booth—I entered a whole new world of food (everything fried and served on a stick), of farm implements (tractors resembling supersized alien destroyers), and of fashion (teenage girls in *de rigueur* cutoffs and cowboy boots).

Preferring to attend the state fair with a purpose, I had volunteered to be a pie judge. Not only was I accepted, I was assigned to all 17 categories of competition. This translates as approximately 1,020 bites of pie (not all good) and God knows how much lard and sugar or how many calories.

If you thought the Super Bowl or March Madness was tough competition, you have not entered or even observed the pie competition at the Iowa State Fair. These bakers take their blue ribbons very seriously, discussing their strategy and developing new recipes all year and then hovering around during the contest to see how their pie fares. The pie judges take the judging seriously, too. Some of them have food science degrees from the 1950s and they put the contenders through extreme scrutiny, examining the top crust, bottom crust, and every detail in between. I'm surprised they don't bring laboratory instruments to measure moisture content, rulers to calculate crust thickness, and thermometers to take the pie's temperature. And all of this competing is conducted in front of a live audience. Long before there was the Food Network, there was the Iowa State Fair.

Of all the pie categories—apple, French silk, pecan, cream cheese, Keebler crust, pot pie—my favorite is peach. Not because peach is my favorite pie, though I do love it (of course I love it, I love *all* pie), but because the sponsor of this particular category, Neal Rhinehart, a local businessman, gives slices of the leftover pie away to the audience afterward. Think about all those people, tired from walking all around the fairgrounds, sitting on metal folding chairs, and gazing upon a panel of judges who examine, cut, then taste bite after bite of some very flaky, fruity, and often nicely decorated pies. What do they do with all that pie where sometimes only one slice has been cut out? Does it go to food banks? Does it go back home with the contestants? The answers remain ambiguous, but with Neal's peach contest, the pies are happily and appreciatively devoured on site. After the judging (by a panel made up of Neal's family members plus me), Neal pulls out his bag of paper plates, plastic forks, and napkins, and the line forms. I help slice and serve, the audience's hungry hands reaching for the plates so fast I don't have time to look up from the pie plates. All I see is the pie disappearing. And I hear a lot of comments, mostly, "Mmmm, ohhh, this is very good."

As a pie judge, and not the kind who looks for the minutiae, I have some simple advice for competitors. Taste matters more than appearance. You can spend a lot of time arranging Martha-Stewart-like cutout shapes on your crust, or you can weave a magazine-cover-worthy lattice crust, but if your pie doesn't taste good it won't win. For example, in a peach pie contest, your pie should be all about the peaches. Try to get all "fancy" by adding dried orange zest or macadamia nuts or, god forbid, peach Jell-O, and your pie is no longer a classic peach pie. My number-one rule for judging comes down to one question: Do I want another bite? If yes, good. If I can't stop eating it, it's a sure winner.

Long before there was the Food Network, there was the Iowa State Fair.

I spent 12 days at the Iowa State Fair that summer. I made it through the anniversary of Marcus's death without falling apart into a sobbing mess. I didn't make it through the fair without having to admit that, yes, I was a little tired of eating pie. But the real crux of the story is that after the state fair, I went down to visit my birthplace of Ottumwa, saw a highway sign for the American Gothic House, fell in love with the place, and moved in two weeks later. Four years later, I'm still living in Iowa. T. S. Eliot said, "We shall not cease from exploration and the end of all our exploring will be to arrive where we started... and know the place for the first time." To which he should have added, "And make pie."

Pie Recipes to Compete in the Iowa State Fair

Peach Pie with Lard Crust

Toffee Pecan

Fresh Apricot

Black Raspberry

Butterscotch

Chai-Spiced Pumpkin

Pumpkin Goat Cheese

Mississippi Mud

Veggie Pot Pie

Pulled-Pork Hand Pies

PEACH PIE
WITH LARD CRUST

One of my favorite pie contests—actually the only pie contest I like—is Neal Rhinehart's "Oh My! It's Peach Pie" at the Iowa State Fair. The reason I like it is that Neal sets a mandate that the pie be shared with the audience after the judges are done deliberating over it. Yes, that's right—pie is meant to be shared! Carole Permar has entered her pie for the past three years and each year it seems to get honorable mention, when I think it should get first place. Her lard crust is the best I've ever tasted, and I like how the cinnamon is balanced with the peaches. I bite into this and think, "This is a classic grandma pie." And then I can't stop eating it. If comfort has a taste, this is it. (Thank you, Carol. I'm so grateful to finally get your recipe.)

LARD CRUST
(MAKES 3 DOUBLE-CRUST PIES)
5½ cups flour
1 pound lard (2 cups)
2 tsp salt
2 tbsp vinegar
2 beaten eggs

NOTE: If you don't want to use lard in your crust, just use my Basic Pie Dough recipe (see page 28).

FILLING (MAKES I PIE)
6 cups fresh, peeled, sliced peaches
¾ cup sugar
2½ tbsp cornstarch
½ tsp cinnamon
1 tbsp lemon juice

1 tbsp butter, to pat on top of filling
1 to 2 tsp sugar, to sprinkle on top crust

Prepare the Lard Crust: Combine flour, lard, and salt until blended. (Keep a light touch. Do not knead.) Mix in vinegar and beaten eggs to moisten and bind the dough. Form into 6 separate disks (to make 3 double-crust pies) and roll out dough.

Prepare the Filling: Combine all ingredients in a large bowl, then place in pie crust.

Dot with butter, then cover with top crust.

Trim and seal edges, then crimp.

Sprinkle sugar on top crust before baking. (Carol doesn't brush hers with beaten egg.)

Bake at 425 degrees for 40 minutes. Turn oven temperature down if crust gets too brown.

TOFFEE PECAN

When I talk of friendships being formed through pie, I am specifically thinking of friends like Kathleen Beebout. A resident of Des Moines and a regular competitor in the Iowa State Fair, Kathleen has a passion for pie that matches her warmth, her savvy, and her sense of humor. After just becoming acquainted, we met for lunch one winter day at a café near her house, and she brought one of her award-winning toffee pecan pies for me. I was so touched. It's a treat for me to get other people's pies. So besides this pie being sinfully good—and a first-place winner at the state fair—it holds a special memory for me.

CRUST
Basic pie dough recipe (Kathleen's recipe makes two single-crust pies, so use the double crust recipe to make enough dough for two single crusts, page 28.)

FILLING
¾ cup (1½ sticks) butter
1½ cups brown sugar (Kathleen uses dark, I use only light)
1 tsp salt
1⅓ cups corn syrup
6 eggs
2 tbsp vanilla
2 cups whole pecans
2 cups chopped pecans
2 cups Heath Bar bits

Prepare the Basic Pie Dough for two 10-inch single-crust pies (see page 28). You'll still make the double-crust recipe, but for two separate pies!

Prepare the Filling: In a saucepan over medium to low heat, melt the butter, then add the brown sugar, salt, and corn syrup. Continue to stir until fully heated. (Kathleen uses a double boiler for this stage, but she knows me and said, "You can change the instructions, simplify them if you want." To which I answered, "Oh, I already did.")

Beat the eggs slightly. Add some of hot mixture to the eggs, then mix the egg mixture back into the saucepan, stirring so as not to curdle the eggs. (Remember, no one likes scrambled eggs in a pie!)

Continue heating, stirring well until thick, then add vanilla.

Combine hot mixture with nuts and toffee bar bits and pour into pie shells.

Bake at 350 degrees for 45 minutes or until set.

FRESH APRICOT

When I think of fruit pies, apricot is not one that comes to mind. Maybe just because apricot pie wasn't part of my childhood lexicon. (In my house, it was all about banana cream.) But in Iowa, and surely in other parts of the USA—if not the world—apricot is one of those pies that people go gaga over. Kathleen Beebout (once again!) generously shared her blue-ribbon-winning recipe, since I don't have one. Well, I do now.

CRUST
Basic Pie Dough for double-crust pie
  (see page 28)

FILLING
5 cups apricot halves (pits removed!)
¾ cup sugar
½ tsp almond extract
1 tsp orange zest (optional)
3 to 4 tbsp cornstarch
4 tbsp (½ stick) butter, cut up

2 tbsp half-and-half or 1 beaten egg,
  to brush on top crust
2 tbsp coarse (or sanding) sugar,
  to sprinkle on top crust

Prepare the Basic Pie Dough for a double-crust pie (see page 28).

Prepare the Filling: Combine all ingredients and pour into pie shell.

Cover with top crust, then trim, seal, and flute the edges.

Brush with half-and-half (or a beaten egg, like I do), and sprinkle with sugar.

Bake at 425 degrees for 20 minutes.

Turn oven down to 375 degrees and bake another 30 to 35 minutes, until golden brown.

BLACK RASPBERRY

Lana Ross has won more ribbons at the state fair than anyone else I know. She is one of my favorite pie makers, not only because of her show-stealing pies but for her bubbly personality. She would make a killing if she opened up a pie shop. Instead, she spends her days working as a lobbyist for community action, fighting to end poverty. I'm convinced it's not just her recipes that make her pies so good. I think it's because she adds the extra ingredients of herself, her good heart, and happy soul. If a person could be anointed into Pie Sainthood, it would be Lana. (See her French Silk recipe on page 156 in my "Pies to Seduce" chapter. Not sure what extra ingredient she adds to that one, but it is powerful!)

CRUST
2 cups flour
½ tsp salt
⅔ cup lard
⅔ cup ice water (use as little as
   it takes)

FILLING
4 cups black raspberries
¼ cup flour
1 cup sugar
2 tbsp lemon juice

2 tbsp butter, to pat on top of filling
2 tbsp milk, to brush on top crust
2 tbsp coarse (or sanding) sugar,
   to sprinkle on top crust

Prepare the Crust: Mix the flour and salt. Cut in the lard.

Gradually add the ice water until the crust sticks together.

Wrap in plastic wrap and place in the refrigerator for at least 2 hours to keep it cold. (This is Lana's style, not mine!)

When you're ready to prepare the pie, divide the crust into two equal parts. Roll out bottom crust and place into a 9-inch pie pan.

Prepare the Filling: Mix berries, flour, sugar, and lemon juice and pour into shell.

Dot berry mixture with butter.

Roll out remaining crust and place on top of the pie. Crimp the edges to seal.

Brush pie top with milk and sprinkle with sugar.

Bake at 350 degrees for about an hour or until lightly browned and berries are bubbly.

BUTTERSCOTCH

My pie mentor, Mary Spellman, always told me, "You can't go wrong with brown sugar and butter." She's right. The caramel taste and creamy texture make everything seem right in the world. Maybe that's why butterscotch pie is such a popular category at the Iowa State Fair.

CRUST
Blind-Baked Crust, single crust pie
(see page 31)

FILLING
1½ cups brown sugar, firmly packed
⅓ cup cornstarch
2 cups whole milk (for a richer pie,
use half-and-half or mix in some
heavy cream)
4 egg yolks (save whites for meringue)
2 tsp vanilla
4 tbsp (½ stick) butter

MERINGUE
4 egg whites (6 egg whites for a
bigger meringue)
¼ tsp cream of tartar
¼ cup sugar
1 tsp vanilla

Prepare the Blind-Baked Crust (see page 31).

Prepare the Filling: In a saucepan over medium heat, stir together the brown sugar and cornstarch, then gradually stir in the milk. Cook until thick and bubbling. Remove from heat.

Beat egg yolks in a separate bowl.

Add about a cup of the hot mixture to the eggs, stirring quickly so the eggs don't curdle. Then add this egg mixture back to the saucepan and continue cooking and stirring until it comes to a gentle boil again.

Continue cooking for 2 more minutes, stirring the entire time. (I hope you like stirring because that's what it takes to make these cream pies!)

Remove from heat and stir in vanilla and butter.

Pour into a blind-baked pie shell.

Prepare the Meringue: In a clean, grease-free bowl, beat egg whites until foamy.

Add cream of tartar and beat until peaks start to form.

Beat in sugar a little at a time. Add vanilla. Beat on high speed until peaks become stiff.

Spread the meringue over the pie filling, all the way to the edge of the pie crust to create a seal. Dab at meringue with the back of a large spoon, pulling up to create curlicue effect.

Bake at 375 degrees for about 10 minutes or until meringue peaks turn brown. Keep a close eye on it while the meringue is baking!

CHAI-SPICED PUMPKIN

This recipe was adapted from that of the overall 2010 pie winner Christina Montalvo of West Des Moines. She is an outstanding pie maker, and she is far more patient and precise than I am. I guess that explains what it takes to be Number One, not only at the Iowa State Fair, but also at the National Pie Championships. She's won there, too. I took some liberties with her recipe, simplifying it and eliminating a few steps so I could make it without kvetching. Anyway, I'm not going for a ribbon, I just want to eat it. I've been craving this pie ever since those few bites I took as a judge. Obviously, it's a winner.

CRUST

Basic Pie Dough for single-crust pie
(see page 28), crimped

FILLING

2 teabags black chai spice tea,
or 2 to 3 tsp loose tea
1½ cups pumpkin purée
(canned is okay)
3 eggs
⅔ cup brown sugar
½ cup sugar
½ tsp salt
1 cup heavy cream
1 tsp vanilla

TOPPING

1 cup heavy cream
1 tbsp sugar
½ tsp ground ginger

Prepare the Basic Pie Dough for a single-crust pie (see page 28).

Prepare the Filling: If you're using teabags, open up the sachets and grind up the contents.

Mix all ingredients and pour into pie shell.

Bake at 425 degrees for 15 minutes, then turn oven down to 350 degrees and bake about 40 minutes or until center is set. Set aside to let cool.

Prepare the Topping: Using an electric mixer (or by hand!), beat cream, sugar, and ginger until peaks form.

Once pie is completely cooled, top with ginger whipped cream. Keep the pie chilled. But you'll eat it so fast it probably won't ever make it back to the fridge after that first—and second, and third—slice.

BETH'S TIP:
While I love the black pepper and cardamom punch you get from the ground-up tea, you can instead look for Chai Tea Latte Mix (try Oregon Chai brand). It comes in 1.1-ounce packets. Use two packets of the powder mix instead of the teabags, but you will also need to add ⅛ tsp each of ground allspice, ground cloves, and ground ginger.

PUMPKIN GOAT CHEESE

I got this recipe from my friend Nan who makes it every year for Thanksgiving. But given the categories of the Iowa State Fair, I think this would make a good contender for a blue ribbon. If I believed in pie competition, that is.

CRUST
Graham Cracker Crust (see page 32)
1 tsp each cinnamon and ground
    ginger (for added spice)

FILLING
8 ounces goat cheese
2 packages (8 ounces each)
    cream cheese
1½ cups sugar
1¼ cups canned pumpkin purée
    (one 15-ounce can minus ½ cup)
1 cup sour cream
3 eggs
2 tsp vanilla

Prepare the Graham Cracker Crust (see page 32), adding cinnamon and ginger to the mix. Press into the bottom of a 9-inch spring-form pan. Bake at 350 degrees for 10 minutes.

Prepare the Filling: In a large bowl, beat the goat cheese, cream cheese, and sugar together with a mixer (hand, stand-up, or old-fashioned spoon—you choose).

Add the pumpkin, sour cream, eggs, and vanilla and mix very well until smooth. (This takes a while, like at least 10 minutes. Ugh!)

Pour into the spring-form pan and bake at 350 degrees for 1 hour 15 minutes.

Cool and then refrigerate for several hours to help it set.

MISSISSIPPI MUD

Given that the Mighty (and muddy) Mississippi flows along the eastern border of Iowa, this pie is a no-brainer representative for the State Fair. The variations on this pie can be wildly different, but basically you just throw in anything chocolate. My version—and the version I know from my Iowa upbringing—is the one with fudge-covered mocha ice cream in a chocolate crust. It's not one I would enter in a pie contest, because this recipe doesn't really qualify as "original" given the already-prepared ingredients. But who cares? I believe in shortcuts. And anyway, it's amazing. So. Bring. It. On.

CRUST
Chocolate Cookie Crust (see page 32)

FUDGE SAUCE
1 jar of hot fudge, heated enough to
    liquefy and pour into pie shell

OR MAKE YOUR OWN FUDGE:
2 cups milk
4 tbsp (½ stick) butter
2 tbsp corn syrup
2 tsp vanilla
2 cups sugar
⅔ cup cocoa powder
2 tbsp flour

FILLING
2 pints (1 quart) mocha ice cream,
    slightly softened

TOPPING
1 cup heavy whipping cream
3 tbsp sugar
1 tsp vanilla
Chocolate shavings, slivered almonds,
    and/or toffee bits, for garnish
    (optional)

Prepare the Chocolate Cookie Crust (see page 32).

Prepare the Fudge Sauce (if using homemade): In a saucepan over low to medium heat, combine the milk, butter, corn syrup, and vanilla, stirring until it's all melted together.

Mix in the dry ingredients, stirring constantly, and bring to a boil. Cook until it thickens. Set aside to cool.

Prepare the Filling: Soften the ice cream.

Pour a layer of fudge on the bottom crust, if you like.

Spread ice cream into pie shell. Place the pie in the freezer to re-harden the ice cream before covering it with top layer of fudge.

Pour layer of fudge on the top, then place pie back in the freezer.

Prepare the Topping: Beat cream, sugar, and vanilla until peaks form.

When you're ready to serve, spread whipped cream over top of pie. To take it up a notch, drizzle more fudge and sprinkle chocolate shavings, slivered almonds, and/or toffee bits on top of the whipped cream.

NOTE FROM BETH: Use whatever ice cream you like—mocha almond fudge, coffee, coffee chip... oh, don't get me started. They're all good.

VEGGIE POT PIE

Upon arrival at the Iowa State Fair during my first year there in 2010, the very first category I judged (out of 17!) was Pot Pie. It was the ideal way to kick off a full day of pie eating, by filling my belly with something savory instead of sweet. Mmm, just thinking about it, I would happily go back and judge this one again. All that buttery crust overflowing with thick, warm gravy. All those colors of mushy, miniature vegetables. This pie is so hearty, (relatively) healthy, and hospitable, it should be declared the State Pie of Iowa. Then again, it would be oxymoronic to choose a vegetarian pie in the pork-producing capital of America. In that case, the Pulled Pork overleaf should be nominated for the title. Since pie is not about politics or about competition, I say pick both.

CRUST

Basic Pie Dough for double-crust pie
(see page 28)

FILLING

1 small onion, diced

2 garlic cloves, chopped

1 to 2 tbsp olive oil

1 cup (or more if needed) vegetable
broth

3 carrots, diced

2 potatoes, diced

1 tsp salt

1 tsp pepper

¼ tsp thyme

¼ tsp dried basil

CREAM SAUCE

¼ cup flour

½ cup heavy cream

4 tbsp (½ stick) butter

1 cup peas (frozen but thawed and
heated, or canned)

1 beaten egg, to brush on top crust

Prepare the Basic Pie Dough for a double-crust pie (see page 28).

Prepare the Filling: In a small skillet on medium heat, sauté onion and garlic in olive oil.

In a saucepan over medium heat, add the vegetable broth, carrots, and potatoes. When veggies are cooked and softened, add onion, garlic, seasoning and herbs.

Prepare the Cream Sauce: Mix flour into cooked veggies in saucepan, distributing and stirring well to dissolve lumps.

Add cream and butter and cook over low heat until sauce thickens. Stir in peas.

Taste to check seasoning and add more of whatever you want based on your preferences.

Spoon filling into pie shell(s) and cover with top crust. Crimp and brush with beaten egg.

Poke vent holes in the top, then bake at 425 degrees for 15 minutes.

Turn oven down to 375 degrees and bake until crust is golden brown and filling bubbles.

NOTE FROM BETH: You can make this either as a double-crust pie or with a single, top crust only. You can also make this as mini pies for adorable individual servings.

PULLED-PORK HAND PIES

Pork is the mainstay of Iowa, so no State Fair would be complete without this "other white meat" in a competition. Seeing as I like to shake things up a little, sprinkle some magic fairy dust here and there, if I were going to enter a pork dish, I would make this cute variation, serving it up in little hand pies. Maybe I'd get bonus points for the fact that these are easy to eat while driving a tractor. PS: Thank you to my Eldon neighbor Priscilla Coffman for the recipe. She dropped off the recipe card on my back porch when I first moved in, along with a bag of all the spices I needed. Iowa hospitality never ceases to amaze me.

MARINADE
1 tsp cayenne pepper
½ cup apple cider vinegar
¼ cup lemon juice
1 tsp crushed rosemary
1 tsp whole coriander seeds
½ tsp whole black peppercorns
1 tsp salt

FILLING
6 lbs butt pork roast, fat trimmed
¼ cup olive oil, enough for searing
   roast
1 can Rotel green peppers

DRY RUB
½ tsp cinnamon
1 tsp cardamom
1 tbsp dry mustard
¼ cup brown sugar
1 tsp ground cumin
1 tbsp smoked paprika

SAUCE
Juices and spices from roasting pan
Worcestershire sauce, to taste
Brown sugar, to taste
Dry mustard, to taste

CRUST
Basic Pie Dough for double-crust pie
   (see page 28)
1 beaten egg, or more if necessary,
   to brush on top crust

Prepare the Marinade: Combine all marinade ingredients in a bowl.

Place roast in a separate large bowl and pour marinade over it. Cover and let marinate for an hour, occasionally turning over roast. When done, reserve marinade.

Prepare the Dry Rub: Combine all rub ingredients in a small bowl.

Dry the roast and press the dry rub into it.

Brown the roast in a cast-iron skillet over medium heat with a little olive oil. Sear all sides and ends.

Transfer to a Dutch oven or any heavy roasting pan with a lid. (Priscilla's recipe says, "You can borrow mine." I still smile at the offer.)

Add 1 cup of the reserved marinade and 1 can Rotel green peppers.

Cover and roast at 315 degrees for 3 hours. Roast is done when it falls apart while pulling at it.

Let it rest and cool, then pull the whole thing apart using two forks.

Prepare the Sauce: Scoop up the juices and spices left in the roasting pan and combine with Worcestershire sauce, brown sugar, and dry mustard to taste. (My interpretation of "to taste" amounts to 1 tbsp Worcestershire, ¼ cup brown sugar, and 1 tsp mustard.) Pour this over the pork.

Prepare the Crusts: Follow the Basic Pie Dough instructions on page 28 up to step 5. After rolling out the dough, cut it into "hand size" rectangles or circles. (See page 190 in "Novelty Pies" for instruction.)

Place several spoonfuls of pork in the center of the dough and cover with top crust (a corresponding rectangle; or if round, fold dough over to enclose). Gently press fork around the edges to seal.

Brush with beaten egg and bake at 425 degrees until crust browns and appears fully baked. (Inside is already cooked, and small pies bake faster, so oven time will be short.) Turn oven down to 375 degrees if browning happens too fast.

Pies will be hot, so cool slightly before eating.

BETH'S TIP:
These hand pies are the perfect way to use leftover meat. I will often serve the pulled pork by itself for a meal and make what's leftover into hand pies.

Pies of the Pitchfork Pie Stand

I've had numerous people ask me for advice on how to start a pie stand or home-baking enterprise of some kind. "You've simplified your life and are making a living doing what you love," they all surmise. "How can I quit my job and start a pie stand?"

I smile and say nothing.

"Just a little weekend business," they continue. "How hard could it be?"

I try to hide my grimace before breaking into laughter, the kind of laughter where something is so excruciating all you can do is laugh through the pain.

I am the first person who would encourage others to give up life in a cubicle. And I am the last person who would dissuade others from pursuing their dreams. But let me share with you what it takes to channel your inner Girl Scout—or Amish farm wife—and run a pie stand.

Step one is to simplify your life, cut your expenses way back to a minimum. You won't get rich making pie! You will be working so hard you won't get fat either. Besides, you are *selling* that pie, not eating it.

I've pared down my life to the basics. For starters, I moved to rural Iowa where my rent is $250 a month. Really, it would be hard to find a place much cheaper than that. But with the low rent comes sacrifice. I'm not talking about giving up my privacy to live in a tourist attraction, about how people look in my windows because they don't realize there is someone actually *living* in the American Gothic House. I'm referring to the fact

that I live 100 miles from the nearest Starbucks (Starbucks being my definition of "civilization") and 20 miles from the nearest grocery store. My town, Eldon, Iowa (population 928), has two gas stations, both at which you can get take-out pizza, and two bars, one deemed rough enough that I won't set foot in it and the other where you can get breaded pork tenderloin sandwiches so large the meat hangs off the sides of a dinner plate. There is a post office, a library, and a thrift store, the thrift store created as a fundraising effort to restore the opera house upstairs from it. There is a grain elevator, a fertilizer business, and a handful of churches. And that is it. Oh, and there's a certain little pie stand, but it's only open on summer weekends.

I don't enjoy shopping, so I don't really miss having stores nearby. When I moved to Iowa I went straight to the Tractor Supply Company, where I purchased one pair of denim overalls for $26 and a pair of tall rubber farm boots for $19, and this now pretty much makes up my entire wardrobe. Well, overalls and my collection of pie T-shirts. In winter, I simply layer long underwear under the overalls and T-shirts. Having a "uniform" definitely makes getting dressed in the mornings easy.

So, yes, first pare down, make sacrifices, get your expenses to a minimum, and then you can pursue "doing what you love for a living."

I love making pie and the pie stand does bring in some income—"grocery money," I call it—but I make my living as a writer (which, given that isn't the most lucrative career choice, also requires paring down and keeping my expenses to a minimum). I love writing, crafting tales of life's adventures—and misadventures—and typing my way toward a happy or at least hopeful ending.

Pie—and the making of it—provides an ideal counterbalance to the solitude and technical aspects of writing. Pie-making is a tangible act that engages the senses. I love the soothing rhythm of rolling dough, the meditative trance I enter when peeling apples, and the sense of pride and accomplishment when lifting my bubbling and browned beauties out of the oven.

But making one pie at a time is different from making 100 every weekend. And running a pie business is still, well, running a business. It comes with all the risks, expenses, and headaches that any entrepreneurial endeavor entails. With one additional caveat: You will work harder than you have ever worked in your life.

"Just a little weekend pie stand," you had thought, right? "It can't be that difficult."

Consider that when you run your own home-baking business you will not enjoy the luxuries of a full-fledged bakery. You will not have a commercial dishwasher, let alone a dishwashing staff. You will instead have your hands in sink water more often than you ever dreamed. You will also spend countless hours on your hands and knees scrubbing your kitchen floor. Usually late at night when all you want to do is kick back with a glass of wine or soak in a hot bath.

You will be pulled in way too many directions all at once, simultaneously trying to fold bakery boxes, get pies in—and then out—of the oven, wait on customers, peel more apples or peaches, get more dough made, answer the phone to take orders, and, oh, so much more.

You will not need to go to a gym because you'll get in good shape hauling 50-pound bags of flour and

sugar in and out of the car (and up and down the stairs). You will also be carting crates of whatever ripe fruit you can possibly find within an hour's driving range of your rural location, burning not only calories but precious time, money, and gas on this weekly scavenger hunt for produce.

You will run out of supplies and find yourself at Wal-Mart on a Saturday night, crying in the parking lot, on the phone with your mother, whining about how your quiet country life has become so hectic. "This isn't what I had envisioned," you will tell her or whoever will still listen to your increasingly frequent rants.

You will be frustrated that you can't make enough pies to satisfy the demands of the customers, and then frustrated that there aren't enough customers to buy all those extra pies you made. You will fantasize about how you can renovate your kitchen to get more much-needed counter space. You will be swearing as jars, bottles, pints of berries, and blocks of butter fall

out of your refrigerator as you fight to make space for pie dough made in bulk.

> If you dream of something, then just do it. Don't let it take a tragedy to get you moving.

You will need—but not get—days off in between marathon baking sessions to let your hands and arms heal from the paring knife gashes and the oven burns. You will be surprised at how fast the week goes and how, even though you scaled your pie-stand hours back to just Saturday and Sunday, your "free" time is filled with catching up on emails and updating your pie-stand website.

You will be putting every cent you make on pies back into the business—for ingredients and for gas for all those trips to the store, for bakery boxes, pie tins, paper plates, plastic forks, napkins, business cards, signage, etc.—while simultaneously dipping into your savings account for the rest of your living expenses. (Because, life, no matter where you live, is expensive.)

Some days you will be wishing you still had that job in a cubicle where you could sit in front of a computer and drink coffee. Because you will never actually be able to finish a cup of coffee while running a pie stand, as your hands are constantly busy doing something else.

That said, my advice is—be it starting a pie stand, writing a novel, getting a dog, going sky diving, or leaving a loveless marriage—if you dream of something, then just do it. Don't let it take a tragedy (like the sudden death of your 43-year-old husband) to get you moving.

I tell you all this because not only is life short, but because on closing day of your pie stand, you will already be thinking about next year and what improvements you're going to make: Hire extra help, get a second refrigerator, put a folding table on the back porch for extra work space. And even though on this last sweltering day of the summer, when you're feeling tired and burned out, you still need to scrub your kitchen floor, scrape the dough out of your cupboard handles, and do your umpteenth load of laundry (of aprons, hand towels, and overalls), you will not only be thinking about next year's pie stand, you will be looking forward to it.

3 SECRETS FOR A SUCCESSFUL PIE STAND

1. KEEP IT SIMPLE.

A pie stand, like pie itself, is about simplicity, so keep the pie choices to a minimum. The more types of pie you offer, the harder it is for customers to decide. And when they ask why you don't offer their favorite pie, gently remind them that it's a pie stand, not a bakery. Or, for a win-win, offer them the recipe for that particular pie and suggest they make their own.

2. MAKE SURE IT'S LEGIT.

Home-baking licensing varies state by state and can also vary by town. Some areas don't offer them at all. Some have limits on the types of food products you can sell, as well as rules about consuming the food on the premises. Contact your local city hall, health department, or business affairs office to find out what your area allows.

3. FRESH SELLS.

When baking pies in bulk, avoid labor-intensive recipes. Stick with what is freshest, ripe, affordable, and available—look for what's in season—but also easy to clean and cut.

Pie Recipes of the Pitchfork Pie Stand

Peach

Strawberry Rhubarb

Strawberry Crumble

Blueberry

Apple Crumble

Shaker Lemon

Chess

Shoofly

PEACH

My peach pie didn't used to turn out very well. I had been using flour to thicken the filling and because the peaches were so juicy I just kept adding more and more flour until I ended up with a gluey, mealy, inedible mess. What was I thinking?! When I moved to Eldon, Iowa, the mayor of the town, Shirley Stacey, brought me a slice of her peach pie. It was not gluey or mealy. It was so incredibly tasty and perfectly thickened, I had to learn her secret. In one word, it was this: tapioca. I've dubbed tapioca the Super Power of Thickeners because it always saves the day—and the pie.

CRUST
Basic Pie Dough for double-crust pie
    (see page 28)

FILLING
8 to 10 ripe peaches, peeled and sliced
    (number of peaches depends on
    size of fruit and size of your pie
    dish, but have at least 3 pounds
    on hand)
1 cup sugar (if your peaches are
    super ripe and sweet use less)
¼ cup tapioca
½ tsp cinnamon (optional, but
    I love it)

1 tbsp butter, to pat on top of filling
1 beaten egg, to brush on top crust

THE PERFECT COMBINATION...
I have three words for you:
Vanilla. Ice. Cream.

Prepare the Basic Pie Dough for a double-crust recipe (see page 28).

Prepare the Filling: In a large bowl, combine peaches, sugar, tapioca, and cinnamon. Let sit for 15 to 20 minutes to let tapioca activate, then pour into pie shell.

Place pat of butter on top, then cover with top crust.

Trim, crimp, brush with egg, and poke vent holes.

Bake at 425 degrees for 20 minutes to set and brown crust, then turn oven down to 375 degrees and bake for another 30 minutes. Filling should be bubbling and thickened.

ALLEN'S TIP:
My neighbor, Allen Morrison (the same adorable guy who supplies me with rhubarb), brings me crates of peaches from the Dutchman's Store in Cantril, about 45 minutes away from the American Gothic House. He's the one who insisted—and, as it turns out, rightly so—that blanching the peaches helps tremendously in removing the skin. Instead of peeling the peaches, the skin slides right off in one layer! To blanch, boil the peaches in a pot of water for just a few minutes to loosen the skin, then dip in cold water to cool them enough so you can handle them.

STRAWBERRY RHUBARB

I first started making this pie when I worked at Mary's Kitchen in Malibu. It was Dick Van Dyke's favorite and he ordered it every week. Once his wife (sadly, now late wife) called and told Mary, "Dick said the pie wasn't sweet enough." The next time I made it Mary watched me and, sure enough, I wasn't putting enough sugar in it. One weekend at the pie stand we made it with no sugar at all. Uh, yeah, sometimes these things happen. But I tasted it and the strawberries were so ripe and so naturally sweet that we didn't miss the sugar at all. And if the sugar was missed, well, that's what ice cream is for!

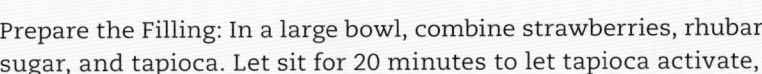

CRUST

Basic Pie Dough for double-crust pie
(see page 28)

FILLING

2 pints whole fresh strawberries,
cleaned, de-stemmed, and cut into
halves or quarters (about 3 cups)
3 cups (about 1 lb) sliced fresh rhubarb
(1 inch per slice) (about 8 medium
stalks)
1 cup sugar
¼ cup tapioca

1 tbsp butter, to pat on top of filling
1 beaten egg, to brush on top crust

Prepare the Basic Pie Dough for a double-crust recipe (see page 28).

Prepare the Filling: In a large bowl, combine strawberries, rhubarb, sugar, and tapioca. Let sit for 20 minutes to let tapioca activate, then pour into pie shell.

Add a pat of butter on top, then cover with top crust. (Feeling adventurous? Go for a lattice top so you can see the pretty red and green filling underneath.)

Trim and crimp edge of crust, brush with beaten egg, then poke vent holes (no need for vent holes if making a lattice top.)

Bake at 425 degrees for 15 to 20 minutes to set and brown the crust, then turn oven down to 375 degrees and bake for another 20 to 30 minutes, until filling is bubbling and thickened.

BETH'S TIP:
I go a little heavier on the strawberries than the rhubarb, mostly because rhubarb is hard to come by. You can shift the balance of fruit to your taste or your availability. I'll say it again: Pie is not about precision!

STRAWBERRY CRUMBLE

Strawberries tend to be available and affordable and getting them at optimal ripeness is fairly dependable. That said, occasionally my local source, Aldi Grocery, has a two-per-customer limit. Which is why I have had to bribe the store manager with pie to get an exception. (Just kidding.) I started making this for the pie stand when I ran out of rhubarb but still had a truckload of strawberries to use. The crumble topping gives it that je ne sais quoi in the form of more texture and taste. What started off as "making do" by improvising the recipe has become a staple—and much coveted pie—in my repertoire.

CRUST
Basic Pie Dough for single-crust pie
    (see page 28), crimped

FILLING
2 to 3 pints whole fresh strawberries,
    cleaned, de-stemmed, and cut into
    halves or quarters (6 to 7 cups)
1 cup sugar
¼ cup tapioca
Pinch of salt

CRUMBLE TOPPING
1 cup flour
½ cup (1 stick) butter, chilled and cut
    into large chunks
½ cup brown sugar, packed

Prepare the Basic Pie Dough for a single-crust pie (see page 28).

Prepare the Filling: Place the strawberries in a large bowl. Stir tapioca, sugar, and salt into the strawberries and let sit for 20 minutes to let tapioca activate. Pour into the pie shell.

Prepare the Crumble Topping: In another large bowl, rub flour, butter, and brown sugar together until the texture resembles marbles. (**NOTE:** Not enough rubbing and your crumble topping will be too powdery and fine. So keep rubbing. Too much rubbing and it will become one big melted, sticky glob. In this case, you can add a little more flour, or refrigerate until it gets cold and break it apart into manageable crumb size.)

With both hands, distribute the crumble topping over the top of the pie. Do not press down on it, as you don't want your crumbs to look flat. It's a good idea to place a cookie sheet or oven liner under this pie when baking, as a few bits of the crumble topping may roll off into the oven.

Bake at 425 degrees for 15 to 20 minutes to brown the top, then turn oven down to 375 degrees and bake for another 30 minutes, or until the strawberry filling is bubbling and thickened.

BETH'S SHORTCUT: For quick tips on cleaning and de-stemming strawberries, see page 150 in "Pies to Seduce."

BLUEBERRY

Are you a pie novice? Start with this one. It is the easiest of all pies to make. The filling is absolutely no fuss. You just rinse the berries, leave them a little damp, and then in a large bowl toss them with the sugar and cornstarch. (The dampness helps the cornstarch coat and stick to the berries.) It's so damn easy that if I could (i.e.: if blueberries were always in season), I would only make blueberry pie for the pie stand. Besides, it's just really, really good.

CRUST
Basic Pie Dough for double-crust pie
(see page 28)

FILLING
3 pints blueberries (I pile them high!)
1 cup sugar (I tend to use less)
¼ cup cornstarch

1 tbsp butter, to pat on top of filling
1 beaten egg, to brush on top crust

THE GIFT OF PIE: Blueberries make an ideal filling for mini pies or pies in a jar (see pages 187 and 188). Their naturally small size helps them pack easily into a small pie dish without having to be cut or diced.

Prepare the Basic Pie Dough for a double-crust pie (see page 28).

Prepare the Filling: Mix blueberries, sugar, and cornstarch in a large bowl. Toss the berries around until they are coated with the dry ingredients, then pour into pie shell.

Add a pat of butter on top, then cover with top crust.

Trim and crimp edges, brush with beaten egg, and poke vent holes.

Bake at 425 degrees for 15 to 20 minutes, then turn oven down to 375 degrees and bake for another 20 to 30 minutes. Blueberry filling should be bubbling and baked long enough for the juice to thicken. A cloudy, liquid filling indicates it's not yet done.

BETH'S TIP:
So many fruit pies, blueberry included, call for lemon juice or lemon zest. I don't really see the point. No one ever notices it's missing. Besides, if I'm having blueberry pie I want to taste the blueberries. Period. Lemon can be overpowering. And it's just one more thing to remember. Or, in my case, forget.

APPLE CRUMBLE

This one is sometimes referred to as "Dutch apple," and you'll build this pie in two layers, the same way I make my double-crust Apple pie (see page 45) Regardless of what you call it, this is a pie-stand favorite, as well as a favorite of mine. I love it for the soft, cinnamony comfort of the apple filling combined with the crunchy, buttery topping. I always use my apples when teaching pie classes (pictured is one of my students, left) to convey the technique and rhythm of peeling and the shortcut of slicing the apples directly into the pie dish. Really, can pie get any better than this?

CRUST
Basic Pie Dough for single-crust pie
(see page 28), crimped

FILLING
7 to 10 Granny Smith apples, peeled
and sliced (number depends on
size of your apples, as well as size
of your pie dish)
½ tsp salt
1 to 2 tsp cinnamon
¾ cup sugar
¼ cup flour

CRUMBLE TOPPING
1 cup flour
½ cup (1 stick) butter, chilled and
cut into large chunks
½ cup brown sugar, packed

Prepare the Basic Pie Dough for a single-crust pie (see page 28).

Prepare the Filling: Slice half of the apples directly into your pie shell. Fill it enough so you can't see through to the bottom crust, and press down gently on the apples to get slices to lay snugly against each other.

Sprinkle half of the salt, cinnamon, sugar, and flour on top.

Slice a second layer of apples, pressing down gently on top of first layer and filling pie dish to a mounded height.

Sprinkle remaining salt, cinnamon, sugar, and flour on top. (For this pie, I don't add a pat of butter on top as the crumble topping has a full stick of the stuff.)

Prepare the Crumble Topping: In a large bowl, rub flour, butter, and brown sugar together until the texture resembles marbles. (**NOTE:** Not enough rubbing and your crumble topping will be too powdery and fine. So keep rubbing. Too much rubbing and it will become a melted, sticky glob. In this case, you can add a little more flour, or refrigerate until it gets cold and break it apart into manageable crumb size.)

With both hands, distribute the crumble topping over the top of the pie. Do not press down on it, as you don't want your crumbs to look flat. It's a good idea to place a cookie sheet or oven liner under this pie when baking, as a few bits of the crumble topping may roll off into the oven.

Bake at 425 degrees for 15 to 20 minutes to brown the top, then turn oven down to 375 degrees and bake until bubbling and apples have softened. (Test doneness by prodding with a paring knife. There should be little or no resistance from the apples.)

SHAKER LEMON

People come back year after year just for this pie. I love this recipe. The ingredients are so few and so simple you don't even need a recipe to remember them. And I am ALL about simplicity! Plus, since this pie uses the entire lemon—rind, pith, pulp, juice, and all (except the seeds and stems)—it is like eating vitamin C. Or, as I say in my pie-stand sales pitch, "Lemonade in a pie crust."

CRUST
Basic Pie Dough for double-crust
    pie (see page 28)

FILLING
2 lemons
2 cups sugar
Pinch of salt
4 eggs
3 tbsp flour

1 beaten egg, to brush on
    top crust

FREEZE IT AND FORGET IT:
This pie freezes very well. And you can actually serve it frozen. In fact, frozen—or at least very chilled— is the ideal way to serve it on a sweltering summer day. It's more refreshing than lemonade and even better because it's pie!

Prepare the Basic Pie Dough for a double-crust pie (see page 28).

Prepare the Filling: Wash and dry lemons, then slice off the stem and nib on the ends.

Using a mandoline or serrated knife, slice the lemons paper thin and place in a bowl, making sure to include any juice. Pick out and discard the seeds as you work.

Add the sugar and salt to the lemons and stir.

Cover the bowl and let it set overnight at room temperature. This macerates—or softens—the lemons.

When ready to prepare the pie, beat the eggs, whisk in the flour, then stir into the lemon-sugar mixture.

Pour into pie shell, then cover with top crust.

Trim, seal, and crimp the edges, then brush with beaten egg and poke vent holes in the crust. (Be careful here as the liquid filling makes the crust exceptionally pliable.)

Bake at 425 degrees for 15 to 20 minutes to set and brown the crust. Turn oven down to 375 degrees and continue baking for another 30 minutes or so. Definitely bake until the middle doesn't jiggle. I like to let this one bake until the middle puffs up a little.

NOTE FROM BETH: You will find variations of this recipe calling for Meyer lemons. A Meyer lemon is a cross between a lemon and an orange. These can be hard to find—it's almost impossible to get them in rural Iowa—and naturally they are more expensive. You know what I'm going to say: Use whatever lemons you can get! You can also substitute oranges for lemons. For that recipe, see Natalie Galatzer's Shaker Orange pie recipe on page 118.

BETH'S TIPS:
* This one can be hard to cut and serve because of the lemon slices.
* Use a serrated knife and really saw through the filling until your slice is cut free.
* The key to this pie is PAPER-THIN lemon slices. Thin, thin, thin. Use a mandoline. I also advise investing in a Kevlar slicing glove so you don't end up with skin in your pie. Don't say you weren't warned.

CHESS

I have a dear friend and former co-worker named Holly Hollingsworth, from my dot-com days (when I was held hostage in front of a computer monitor for 16 hours a day—but was paid handsomely for it). Holly got wind of my pie-making ventures through that other dot-com phenomenon, Facebook, and sent me her Granny Heck's recipe for this most wondrous and delicious of all pies. Granny Heck was born in Arkansas in 1896, but lived most of her life in Central Oklahoma. Says Holly of this pie, "It's simple, rich, and best served with strong coffee." It's so rich I cut the butter in half. Sorry, Granny.

WARNING: This is one of those pies where you say, "Oh, just one bite," and then you cannot stop eating it until it's gone. You will LOVE this pie. You will CRAVE this pie. This pie will become an addiction and may cause you to seek out psychotherapy to overcome your obsession with it. Thank you, Granny Heck.

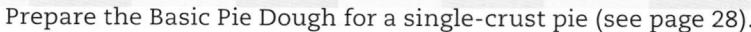

CRUST

Basic Pie Dough for single-crust pie (see page 28), crimped

FILLING

2 cups sugar
2 tbsp flour
1 tbsp cornmeal
5 eggs
⅔ cup buttermilk
¼ cup butter, melted (Granny Heck's calls for ½ cup—that's a whole stick! Go for it if you want, but it pools in the center.)
2 tsp vanilla (I added an extra teaspoon to the recipe. I don't think Granny would mind.)

Prepare the Basic Pie Dough for a single-crust pie (see page 28).

Prepare the Filling: In a large bowl, combine sugar, flour, and cornmeal.

Beat in the eggs and buttermilk until blended.

Stir in the melted butter and vanilla, then pour into the pie crust.

Bake at 350 degrees for at least 45 minutes, or until filling is set.

NOTE: By the way, true to my reckless, lazy baking style, I just mix everything in no certain order—and it still comes out the same.

BETH'S TIP:
I bake this until the middle puffs up before taking it out of the oven. It will "sink" as it cools, leaving you with a crusty top reminiscent of crème brûlée.

SHOOFLY

This recipe for a "Wet Bottom" Shoofly pie comes from my pal Sue Sesko in Pennsylvania. Sue and I met on Facebook through our mutual love of pie and, taking a leap of faith as we had never met before, she flew out to Iowa to help me with the pie stand for a week. She made a delicious, molasses-rich Shoofly pie for the pie stand. The customers—the ones who actually knew what it was—went crazy for it. Better yet, Sue arrived a stranger and left a lifelong friend.

NOTE: Sue says this recipe makes two pies because, as she points out, "Pennsylvania Dutch never make only one." But when I use my beautiful 10-inch ceramic pie dishes, I only have enough filling for one.

CRUST
Basic Pie Dough for two 9-inch single-
    crust pies (see page 28)

FILLING
1 cup brown sugar
1 cup molasses, light or dark
    (Sue suggests dark)
1 egg
1 tsp baking soda
1 tbsp flour
2 cups boiling water

CRUMB MIXTURE
2 cups flour
1 cup brown sugar
½ cup shortening
1 tsp baking soda
Pinch of salt

Prepare the Basic Pie Dough for two 9-inch single-crust pies (see page 28).

Prepare the Filling: Mix brown sugar, molasses, egg, baking soda, and flour in a large heat-safe bowl, then add boiling water and let cool.

Prepare the Crumb Mixture: Using a spoon or fork, mix all crumb mixture ingredients in a bowl.

Fill unbaked pie crusts by gently pouring in 1½ cups liquid mixture, then 1½ cups of the crumbs.

Repeat with remaining liquid, then sprinkle remaining crumbs evenly over the top.

Bake at 400 degrees for 10 minutes, then turn oven down to 350 degrees and bake for 50 minutes. Test with a toothpick; it should come out clean when done.

Pies to Keep
an Open Mind

Rhubarb used to grow in the backyard of the American Gothic House, so I'm told. Yep, grew right there, around the base of the clothesline poles. The stuff apparently grows like a weed and, like the moles digging tunnels on my two acres, it can be hard to control. Which is why, I suppose, the plants were dug up and removed, and why my pie stand has been deprived of rhubarb pie. Rhubarb takes two years to mature, and because I never dreamed I would be living in the American Gothic House long enough to be able to use it, I just didn't bother planting it. I kept meaning to. But then I read up on all these rules about optimal planting time, which exact part of the roots you can plant, where to plant it, blah, blah, blah—God, I hate rules!—and so I guess I just gave up on it. Besides, Bob, my 85-year-old neighbor, grows rhubarb so I figured I could get a supply from him. Every spring and into early summer, I walk over to his garden and check on its progress, teasing him that I am going to come back and pick it when he's not around. But Bob is a baker himself and he uses it for his own pies and there is never enough for me, and certainly not enough for my pie stand.

Other friends in town, Allen and Rosie Morrison, told me of another local source. Allen gave me directions to where I would find said rhubarb patch, but when I rode my bike the eight miles up the road I couldn't find it. I called Allen to ask how I could have missed the place and had him point me to the exact location. Instead of getting a satisfactory answer, I got something better. He came over a few hours later with two huge plastic bags full. Allen's face, barely visible behind the bounty of red and green stalks sticking out over the tops of the sacks, was beaming with an impish grin. I didn't just smile back, I broke into laughter.

> I never had a taste for the stuff, ever…But now rhubarb has a permanent place in the Top Five list of my favorite pies.

My Grandma Genny grew rhubarb in her backyard in Ottumwa, Iowa, just 15 miles from the American Gothic House. Her house is still there, but I don't know about the garden or the rhubarb. As an eight-year-old, I remember standing among the sunflowers and rows of green beans, swatting at bugs while biting into a freshly picked stem of rhubarb, thinking it might taste like celery. But no, rhubarb bears no resemblance to celery other than its texture and its long, stringy stalk. The taste is so bitter your body nearly convulses in a spontaneous reaction. There is no stopping your brow from furrowing, your eyes from squeezing shut, and your lips from puckering in response to the sensation in your mouth. Grandma Genny used to dip the stalks in sugar making it more palatable to eat it raw, but when she offered me some to try I just shook my head in a vigorous "No, thanks!"

I never had a taste for the stuff, ever. Rhubarb was not even in my vocabulary until I spent a summer living in Texas. Yes, summer, when daily temperatures reach 115 degrees. (Don't ask.) I was staying in the ghost town of Terlingua, population 200. (And I thought Eldon, Iowa's population of 928 was small!) Terlingua, popular among rafters and retirees, sits on the Mexican border near Big Bend National Park.

When I first arrived in the Texas town, I was introduced to Jim Carrico, a retired superintendent at the national park and investor in an adventure sports outfitter. We only met once on a daylong rafting trip on the Rio Grande. We were in different boats and even when we all stopped to have lunch together we had barely talked.

But old Jim had heard I was a pie maker, and about two months later the woman I was renting a house from, Betty, knocked on my door. "Jim called," she said. "He wants to know if you want some rhubarb from his garden."

Naïvely, I said, "Sure, should we drive over there together?" Naïve, I say, because rhubarb couldn't possibly grow in the scorching heat of the Chihuahua Desert. Nothing grows there except rattlesnakes and scorpions. Oh, and tarantulas. Really, it's quite a place.

"He is at his summer house in Colorado Springs," Betty replied.

I couldn't believe Jim remembered me. Even more incredibly that he was thinking of me from 700 miles away and how I could use the rhubarb from his Colorado garden to make pie.

I didn't actually expect him to follow through on the offer. I mean, what was he going to do, mail it? But a few days later, the promised rhubarb showed up at my door, hand-delivered by a young woman who had just driven through the Rocky Mountains on her way back to Texas.

I rummaged through a neighbor's old cookbook, the classic *Better Homes and Gardens* red-and-white checkered one, until I found an easy, no-fuss rhubarb pie recipe. It was called Rhubarb Cream Pie (though more of a custard than a cream because of the eggy filling) and it was a cinch to make.

I chopped the rhubarb stalks into thumbnail-size green and red chunks, careful not to cut my own thumbs off in the process, while simultaneously wondering who ever came up with the idea that this weird, tough vegetable would taste good in a pie. Then I mixed several cups of these crunchy cubes into the liquid mix of three beaten eggs, sugar, and a little cinnamon, and filled the pie plate of dough with the whole lot.

Perhaps because the adventure of making this pie in my 100-year-old cabin with no air conditioning was bringing out my pioneer spirit—or because the afternoon was so ungodly hot that my dough was melting and I couldn't lift the top crust off the countertop in one piece—I covered the top in an old-fashioned way, by weaving strips into lattice.

After the pie had baked, I cut myself a slice. As the fork touched my tongue the words, "Oh! My! God!" spontaneously tumbled out of my mouth before I even swallowed the first bite. What pie

rock had I been living under to be missing out on this tangy, juicy, tender filling? It wasn't bitter at all. In fact, oddly, the flavor resembled the sweetness and tartness of apples. Now rhubarb has a permanent place in the Top Five list of my favorite pies.

It's too late to plant rhubarb in the backyard of the American Gothic House, even if I don't live in it long enough to reap the rewards in the coming years. Besides, if I ever do leave, I'll make sure another pie maker moves in after me. But in some ways I don't really want my own crop. I like walking over to Bob's garden and teasing him about stealing his. And I love seeing Allen's smiling face when he surprises me with a batch at my backdoor. And now that I think about it, as a backup, I might drop ol' Jim Carrico a line and give him my Iowa address.

Pie Recipes to Keep an Open Mind

Rhubarb Custard

Double-Crust Rhubarb

Gooseberry

Apple Sour Cream Walnut

Lemon Meringue

Sweet Potato

Avocado

Goat Cheese & Spinach

BLT

Venison

RHUBARB CUSTARD

This is the first version of rhubarb pie I ever made and I loved it. The egg base gives it some added sweetness and texture. If you're not a fan of eggs, try the double-crust straight rhubarb recipe below. Come on. Just try it. And open up your mind.

CRUST
Basic Pie Dough for double-crust pie
    (see page 28)

FILLING
1½ cups sugar
¼ cup flour
1 tsp cinnamon
3 eggs
5 cups rhubarb (about 2 lbs) chopped
    fresh rhubarb (1 inch per slice)
    (about 14 stalks)

1 tbsp butter, to pat on top of filling
1 beaten egg, to brush on top crust

Prepare the Basic Pie Dough for a double-crust pie (see page 28).

Prepare the Filling: Combine sugar, flour, and cinnamon in a large bowl.

Beat the eggs and mix with dry ingredients.

Mix in about 5 cups (give or take) rhubarb. Pour into pie shell.

Place a pat of butter on top, then cover with top crust (lattice is nice for this one) and brush with a beaten egg.

Bake at 425 degrees for 15 to 20 minutes to set and brown the crust, then turn temperature down to 375 degrees and bake for another 30 to 40 minutes. Filling should bubble and be thickened.

FARM →
RHUBARB

· DOUBLE-CRUST RHUBARB ·

Really want to embrace the taste of rhubarb? Go for the pure, unembellished version. You couldn't have convinced me when I stood in my Grandma Genny's garden at age eight that I would ever say this, but I adore this pie. It's tangy but sweet, unusual and yet down to earth. And when a filling gets picked from the garden and goes straight into a pie, well, that earns it automatic bonus points.

CRUST
Basic Pie Dough for double-crust pie
    (see page 28)

FILLING
6 to 7 cups (at least 2 lbs) chopped
    fresh rhubarb (1 inch per piece)
    (about 16 stalks)
1 cup sugar
3 tbsp cornstarch
Dash of salt

1 tbsp butter, to pat on top of filling
1 beaten egg, to brush on top crust

Prepare the Basic Pie Dough for a double-crust pie (see page 28).

Prepare the Filling: Toss all ingredients together in a large bowl to coat fruit. Pour into bottom crust.

Place a pat of butter on top of rhubarb filling and cover with top crust, gently pressing down dough to fit snuggly over fruit.

Lifting the edges of top and bottom crusts, roll together in an underhand motion all the way around the pie dish.

Crimp edges by pinching between thumb and forefinger to create a fluted pattern, or, for another style, press edge down with a fork. (The point is to create a seal so the juice doesn't run out while baking.)

Brush top crust with beaten egg, then poke holes on top for ventilation.

Bake at 425 degrees for 20 minutes to set and brown the crust.

Turn oven down to 375 degrees and bake for another 30 minutes or so, depending on the size of your pie and temperament of your oven. Fruit should be bubbling and filling should appear thickened.

BETH'S TIP:
I don't believe in waste, so if you have extra rhubarb and extra dough, make some mini pies!

GOOSEBERRY

I get requests for this pie all the time at my pie stand. I've only tried it once and it's not my kind of pie. I would never order it off a menu, but if it was being served at someone's house I wouldn't refuse a slice. I mean, who would ever turn down a slice of pie, regardless of the flavor?! My point is, the people who love this pie WORSHIP it, live for it, crave it, demand it. This is a pie with roots deeply based in nostalgia. This is most definitely your grandmother's pie. Good luck finding those gooseberries. They grow wild in some parts of the country, but they're tiny and it takes a while to pick enough for a pie—and then you have to de-stem them. But remember, keep an open mind! This could be your new favorite, the way rhubarb became mine.

CRUST

Basic Pie Dough for double-crust pie
(see page 28)

FILLING

5 cups gooseberries
1½ cups sugar
½ tsp salt
2 tbsp tapioca
2 tbsp cornstarch
1 tsp cinnamon (optional)

1 tbsp butter, to pat on top of filling
1 beaten egg, to brush on top crust

Prepare the Basic Pie Dough for a double-crust pie (see page 28).

Prepare the Filling: Wash the gooseberries and remove stems. (Put on some good music and settle into the task because this will take for-freakin'-ever.)

In a saucepan, cook the berries, sugar, and salt over medium heat until the sugar has dissolved and the berries plump up so much they burst. (Starting to like this pie already?)

Stir in the tapioca, cornstarch, and cinnamon, if using, and cook until thickened, about 5 minutes.

Try to have patience (what's that?!) and let it cool—at least until it is cool enough to touch. Then pour the berry mixture into your pie crust.

Place the pat of butter on top, then cover with your top crust.

Trim, roll, and crimp edges, brush with egg (you know the drill by now), and poke vent holes on top.

Bake at 425 degrees for 20 minutes to set and brown the crust, then turn the temperature down to 375 degrees and bake another 20 to 30 minutes, until the filling bubbles.

This pie reflects the reality of life—a little sour at times, a little bitter, and yet, luckily, the sweetness wins out in the end. But why ruin a perfectly good apple pie with something like the sourness of the cream and bitterness of the walnuts in the first place? Because it tastes good. I had this pie at a dinner party in Los Angeles about 15 years ago and I still remember how much I loved it. You know a pie is good when you haven't eaten it for that many years and yet you still think about it—even when you can't for the life of you remember whose house you were at. And with that, it's time to expand my repertoire and make it myself. Finally.

CRUST
Basic Pie Dough for single-crust pie
(see page 28), crimped

FILLING
1 cup sugar
¼ cup flour
2 tsp cinnamon
¾ cup sour cream
1 beaten egg
7 to 10 apples (about 3 lbs, depending
on size of pie dish), peeled, cored,
and sliced

CRUMBLE TOPPING
1 cup flour
½ cup (1 stick) butter, chilled and
cut into large chunks
½ cup brown sugar, packed
1 cup chopped walnuts

Prepare the Basic Pie Dough for a single-crust pie (see page 28).

Prepare the Filling: In a large bowl, mix together sugar, flour, cinnamon, sour cream, and egg. Add apples and stir until they are coated. Pour apple mixture into pie shell.

Prepare the Crumble Topping: Rub the flour, butter, and brown sugar together until the texture resembles marbles. Be patient, it takes a while to achieve this crumbly consistency (see tip below).

By hand, mix in the walnut pieces until fully blended.

Cover the top of the pie with the crumble mix. With both hands, distribute the crumble topping over the top of the pie. Do not press down on it, as you don't want your crumbs to look flat. It's a good idea to place a cookie sheet or oven liner under this pie when baking, as a few bits of the crumble topping may roll off into the oven.

Bake at 425 degrees for about 15 minutes, until the top starts to brown.

Turn oven down to 375 degrees and continue baking for about 40 minutes, until filling bubbles and apples feel soft when jabbed with a paring knife.

BETH'S TIP:

Not enough rubbing and your crumble topping will be too powdery and fine. So keep rubbing. Too much rubbing and it will become a melted, sticky glob. In this case, you can add a little more flour, or refrigerate until it gets cold and break it apart into manageable crumb size.

LEMON MERINGUE

I used to make this pie at Mary's Kitchen in Malibu. I made it for Barbra Streisand once when she ordered it at the last minute for a dinner party she was hosting. That pie, however, never made it to her table, as she sent her driver to pick it up and when returning to her house he drove over the speed bumps too fast, and the meringue stuck to the top of the box. I still think she should have served the pie. People would have loved it regardless of how it looked. Oh well.

CRUST
Blind-Baked Crust (see page 31)

FILLING
2 cups sugar
¾ cups flour
¼ cup cornstarch
½ tsp salt
1½ cups fresh-squeezed lemon juice
   (from roughly 12 lemons)
¾ cup water
6 eggs yolks (reserve whites for
   meringue topping)
2 tbsp lemon zest
4 tbsp (½ stick) butter, softened

MERINGUE
6 egg whites
½ tsp cream of tartar
¾ cup sugar

Prepare the Blind-Baked Crust (see page 31).

Prepare the Filling: In a heavy saucepan, whisk together the sugar, flour, cornstarch, and salt.

Mix the lemon juice with the water, then add 2 cups of this liquid to the dry ingredients in the saucepan. Heat over low to medium heat until well thickened, stirring constantly.

Beat the yolks in another bowl. Add a few spoonfuls of the hot lemon mixture to the eggs, stirring quickly so the eggs don't curdle. Then stir the yolks into the saucepan and continue cooking for 2 minutes.

Add the remaining lemon-water liquid (¼ cup), the lemon zest, and the butter to the saucepan. Stir and cook for another few minutes.

Remove from heat and pour into baked pie shell.

Prepare the Meringue: Mix all ingredients in a clean bowl with an electric mixer until stiff peaks form.

Spoon on top of lemon filling and dab at the meringue with the back of a large spoon, pulling back with each stroke to create curlicue peaks.

Bake at 375 degrees for about 10 minutes, but keep a close eye on it to prevent over-browning.

SWEET POTATO

This pie dates back to the Colonial days in American history. It used to be served as a side dish before it became popular as a dessert. Still, you wrinkle your nose at the taste and texture of sweet potatoes? Well, just think of all those A-vitamins you could be getting—and now, you can get them in a pie. Still need something more to sweeten the deal? Cover it in a layer of mini marshmallows and pretend it's Thanksgiving.

CRUST
Basic Pie Dough for single-crust pie
   (see page 28), crimped

FILLING
2 cups mashed sweet potatoes (about
   3 medium whole potatoes),
¼ cup (½ stick) butter, softened
1 cup sugar
½ cup milk (evaporated or whole milk,
   your choice)
2 beaten eggs
1 tsp cinnamon
½ tsp nutmeg
2 tsp vanilla

Prepare the Basic Pie Dough for a single-crust pie (see page 28).

Prepare the Filling: Mix all ingredients with a whisk or electric mixer until well blended and smooth. Pour into pie crust.

Bake at 375 degrees for 50 minutes to an hour, until filling sets.

AVOCADO

I am a huge fan of avocados. Admittedly, it took years to acquire a taste for this healthy protein-packed superfood, but now they are a staple in my diet. I eat them plain or sliced on a toasted and buttered baguette. But avocado pie? Ewww! I was first alerted that such a (strange, weird-looking) pie even existed by my good friend John Primeau. In the throes of stage 4 esophageal cancer, John still had the wherewithal and energy to send me this recipe to include in my cookbook. Don't think guacamole. It's sweet, a little like a Key lime pie. I am going to make avocado pie on a regular basis so I can remember my dear friend and honor his beautiful but sadly short-lived life. Thank you, John.

CRUST
Graham Cracker Crust (see page 32)

FILLING
2 ripe avocados
1 package (8 ounces) cream cheese, softened
1 can (14 ounces) sweetened condensed milk
2 tsp lime zest
2 tbsp fresh lime juice

TOPPING
1 cup heavy whipping cream
3 tbsp sugar
1 tsp vanilla

Prepare the Graham Cracker Crust (see page 32).

Prepare the Filling: Scoop out avocado flesh from skin (removing pit) and then mash in a large bowl.

With an electric mixer, blend in cream cheese, sweetened condensed milk, lime zest, and lime juice with the avocados.

Pour—or, more realistically, spread—into crust. Chill until set, preferably overnight.

When you're ready to serve, top with whipped cream. (With an electric mixer or whisk, whip cream with sugar and vanilla until peaks form.) You'll need to eat this within a day or two, before the avocado turns brown. Don't worry if filling is lumpy. It will still taste good.

GOAT CHEESE & SPINACH

This one is a nod to the origins of pie. What? You thought pie was American? Guess again. Pie hails back to ancient times, when the crust was inedible and used merely as a way to preserve and transport the meat held inside it, like the Tupperware of its time. Not open to goat cheese? You can switch up this recipe by using feta instead, or Cheddar instead of Swiss, etc. And if you really want to go authentic Greek—albeit "modern" Greek—use phyllo dough instead of regular pie crust.

CRUST
Basic Pie Dough for single-crust pie
   (see page 28), crimped

FILLING
4 cloves garlic, chopped or crushed
   in press
1 small onion, diced
2 tbsp olive oil (or butter)
1 lb fresh spinach, washed and dried
1 tsp salt
1 tsp pepper
1 tsp chopped fresh basil (or ½ tsp
   dried basil)
1 tsp thyme
¾ cup (about 6 ounces) goat cheese
1½ cups grated Parmesan cheese
   (or shredded mozzarella, Cheddar,
   or Swiss)
2 beaten eggs
1 cup half-and-half (or milk)

Prepare the Basic Pie Dough for a single-crust pie (see page 28).

Prepare the Filling: In a heavy skillet over medium heat, sauté garlic and onion in olive oil.

Add the spinach, salt, pepper, basil, and thyme, then cook until spinach softens.

In a large bowl, combine the cheeses, then mix in the beaten eggs and half-and-half.

Add the cooked spinach and stir well. Scoop into the pie crust.

Bake at 375 degrees for about 40 minutes or until the filling is set in the middle. (If it gets too brown, turn oven down to 350 degrees.)

BETH'S TIP:
To vary the flavor, you can use nutmeg instead of basil and thyme.

BLT

I got this recipe from a local Iowa pal, Marie Zoromski, who is really from Wisconsin. Which may explain the extra cheese. She says it should really be called a BBT pie—Bacon, Basil, and Tomato. But her friends who also love this recipe say it's more like a decadent deep-dish bacon pizza. Either way, though it may sound odd, this chapter is all about being open minded, so it's well worth giving it a try.

CRUST
Blind-Baked Crust (see page 31)
¼ cup grated Parmesan cheese

FILLING
4 large tomatoes (Romas are okay), sliced and de-seeded but not peeled (see tip below)
½ to 1 lb bacon (or more if you love it), fried till crisp, drained, and chopped
½ cup chopped fresh basil (see shortcut below)
3 green onions (i.e., scallions), thinly sliced
½ tsp garlic powder
1 tsp dried oregano
½ tsp crushed red pepper
¾ cup Parmesan cheese
2 cups shredded Cheddar cheese
¼ cup mayonnaise

TOPPING
Shredded lettuce (optional)

Prepare the Blind-Baked Crust (see page 31). Before baking, poke bottom of crust with a fork, then sprinkle Parmesan on the bottom and bake uncovered at 350 degrees for 15 minutes.

Prepare the Filling: In the pre-baked pie crust, layer the tomatoes, fried bacon pieces, basil, green onions, garlic powder, oregano, red pepper, and ½ cup Parmesan.

In a small bowl, mix the Cheddar and mayo, then spread over top of pie.

Sprinkle remaining Parmesan on top.

Cover loosely with aluminum foil and bake at 350 degrees for 30 minutes.

Remove foil and bake an additional 30 minutes.

Serve warm or cold. For the real BLT experience, top with shredded lettuce.

BETH'S TIP:
De-seeding your tomatoes will help reduce sogginess, but if you don't feel like doing this step, don't worry about it. Also, if you don't have fresh tomatoes, a large can of Italian-spiced chopped tomatoes will work.

VENISON

When you live in rural Iowa, venison is part of the local diet. (And, sadly, a huge source of roadkill.) Before you dis this one, think about it: Eating wild game is about living off the land. It's natural. It's how our species survived before there were grocery stores—or cattle confinements or slaughterhouses. It may have a slightly stronger taste than beef but it's leaner and organic. Sorry, Bambi.

CRUST

Basic Pie Dough for double-crust pie
(see page 28)

FILLING

1 tsp salt

½ tsp black pepper

2 pounds venison stew meat, cut into
1-inch cubes

¼ cup flour

3 tbsp butter

1 medium onion, diced

2 to 3 carrots, diced

3 garlic cloves, chopped or crushed
with press

1 bottle red wine—1 cup for the pot pie,
save the rest for drinking!

1 cup peas (canned or frozen)

½ cup beef broth (chicken or vegetable
broth is okay too)

2 bay leaves (I always forget these.
I never miss them either.)

Prepare the Basic Pie Dough for a double-crust pie (see page 28).

Prepare the Filling: Sprinkle salt and pepper on the venison, then coat with flour.

Melt butter in a large skillet over medium heat, then add the venison and brown on all sides.

Cook for about 5 minutes, then add onion, carrots, and garlic. Stir and cook until softened. Add wine, peas, broth, and bay leaves. Cover and simmer for about 20 minutes.

Pour "stew" into pie shell. Cover with top crust, trimming, sealing, and crimping the edges.

Bake at 400 degrees for about 25 minutes, until top browns and filling bubbles.

BETH'S SHORTCUT: Cut basil leaves with kitchen scissors. (An old boyfriend taught me this and it makes cutting up herbs so easy!)

 # Pies to Lift Your Spirits

NOTE: This chapter should be titled Pies to Keep You From Being Jealous of Your Friends Who Are on Spring Break in the Bahamas *or* Pies to Get You Out of a Bad Mood When It's Still Snowing in April. *Then again, the applications for this pie-making method are much farther-reaching.*

One of the best things about pie, besides eating it, is making it. When I get into bad moods, when I get frustrated or irritated or impatient with life and I want to crawl out of my skin to get away from all that unsettled energy—and when calling my sister to vent just isn't enough—I go to the kitchen. I don't reach for the pint of Ben & Jerry's to snuff out my feelings. I don't wolf down a bag of Oreos. I grab my best weapon of defense—my rolling pin—and make pie.

A reminder of how therapeutic pie-making can be came after looking at my friend's spring break pictures of her beach vacation in the Bahamas. White, sandy beaches. Light turquoise ocean water. Bright, bronzing, skin-penetrating sunshine.

I was sitting at my desk in rural Iowa. It was April. And it was snowing. After five months of sub-zero weather, it was incredibly, maddeningly, relentlessly still snowing. As I clicked through the pictures—my friend smiling at the camera in her bikini, my friend sailing on a catamaran, my friend holding up a coconut with a straw sticking out of it—pangs of jealousy surged through my cold, pale, winter-saturated body. Searing, boiling, unabashed jealousy.

"Don't be jealous!" I scolded myself. "Just go there yourself." Or, to put it in the words of my friend Alayne, "There is no problem that cannot be solved by throwing money at it."

I spent not only hours, but days, searching for good deals on Caribbean vacation packages, but everything was just too expensive. My jealousy simmered; my discontent swelled. It got so bad that I was completely unproductive. Until another idea occurred to me; if I couldn't go to the Caribbean, then I could at least try to make myself feel like I'm there.

I knew just where to start. I headed to the store to buy the ingredients for a Key lime pie. What better pie to inspire a tropical sensation? And what better way to channel that aggression than to get busy doing the thing that always seems to help me find my way back to balance?

I hadn't made a Key lime pie in 12 years, not since I had worked at Mary's Kitchen in Malibu, the place I spent a year on a "pie-baking sabbatical" after quitting a stressful dot-com job. Mary Spellman is my pie mentor. It had been so long I couldn't remember if the pie was supposed to have a blind-baked crust made from flour or with graham crackers. The answer, when I called Mary to ask, was graham crackers.

Once I unloaded my grocery bags, I got straight to work.

I had read a tip somewhere to put the graham crackers in a ziplock bag before crushing them.

(I trust you know by now that I do not own, nor do I ever plan to own, a food processor.)

Oh, and crush I did. I took my rolling pin and beat them, pounded on them, rolled over them with force, taking out all my frustration on these innocent little crackers, the post-nap snacks of my childhood. "Take that, snow!" I grunted. "I swear I will never spend another winter in the Midwest," I grumbled in between the smackdowns of my rolling pin. It was a good start, but then the texture of the crackers changed as they crumbled, and soon they resembled sand, and that reminded me that my friend was still on a sandy beach sunning herself. And that didn't help my mood.

I carried on, melting the butter and mixing it with the crushed crackers. Then I pressed the mixture into the pie dish. I had to work a little more gently in this phase, as pressing too hard on the crackers was pushing the crumbly mixture right out of the dish. I baked it for 10 minutes, until it came out looking browned, like it had a suntan. A tan?! What was I thinking making this pie?!

Next I squeezed about 20 little Key limes. Oh that smell! That tropical smell. That smell of summer. That memory of drinking gin and tonics on the back porch on those hot and humid evenings. That friend who is probably squeezing a lime into her margarita right now. "Waahhh!"

The last thought just made me dig the fork deeper into the pulp of each lime, turning and twisting harder, wringing every last drop of juice out of their little green necks. "Take that! And that!"

Once I had extracted half a cup—and it takes a while with those miniature limes, so long that my fingers pruned—I cracked and separated the eggs. This was a more soothing task, giving my dark mood a respite. Mary taught me to separate my eggs in my bare hands, letting the whites run through my separated fingers while cupping the yellow yolk delicately in the palm of my hand. The cool, soft feel of the eggs brought my bitterness into check and hinted that somewhere in me I was still capable of tenderness and peace.

The respite was temporary. This Key lime pie recipe called for beaten egg whites to add some lightness to the filling. Lightness. Yes, I need more of that. Instead of using my hand mixer, I intentionally beat the egg whites by hand, with a whisk. It took longer but it was infinitely more satisfying to my current state of mind. I beat and beat and beat that whisk against the eggs. The wires clanged with each stroke against the metal bowl, the sound so intense my dogs came to see what was happening. I didn't hold back. I beat faster and harder until the muscles in my arm burned. I wanted—needed—to get all that pent-up energy out of my body!

I set the egg whites aside and whipped the egg yolks, then mixed in the sweetened condensed milk. It is always a marvel when baking to watch textures and colors come together—in this case, the thick, sticky yellowish milk; the viscous, vibrant orange egg yolks; then the watery green lime juice. And how miraculous, really, the way just a few simple ingredients can merge to create an unlikely harmony of tangy, sweet, and creamy.

This smells way better than Coppertone…

This little revelation inspired another idea. Why hadn't I thought of it before? I practically ran to my computer and changed the Pandora station from Adele to Jimmy Buffett. "Changes in Latitudes" started playing. And when he sang about changing your attitude, I thought it must have been a sign from God.

Gentleness was required again when folding in the egg whites, another opportunity to tone down the energy, to let go of that anger, to find that equilibrium, to—as Jimmy was crooning—change that attitude. This need to alter the pace reflected how closely the process of making pie reflects life, its ever-changing tides, its ups and downs, its yin and yang requiring constant adjustments to one's approach.

As I spooned the filling into the pie dish, the sweet, brown-sugary, toasted crust wafted its way through the kitchen. "This smells way better than Coppertone," I murmured to myself.

While the pie baked for 20 minutes, I ran a bath, turning the faucet as high as it would go until the temperature was nearly scalding. I figured the heat might trick me into thinking I was lying in the sun. I added Epsom salts to make it seem more like seawater. My skin turned so bright and pink from the hot water, it almost looked like I had a sunburn. I soaked, and I sweated, and I burned. But I was still in Iowa.

When the pie was done, there was something I hadn't factored into my tropical fantasy. It had to cool—first on a wire rack, then for at least three hours in the refrigerator—before I could cut into it.

So instead of eating it, I took pictures of it. And then I emailed those pictures to several friends, including the one in the Bahamas, as well as to my mother, who lives on the beach and is always calling me with her weather reports ("It's so cold here today; it's 65 degrees," she imperviously writes to me in January and February). Because what better way to rid oneself of jealousy than by making others jealous! I spread that jealousy like malaria and then, like a wicked character in a Roald Dahl story, wrote a little caption to accompany my photos: "I just made a Key lime pie. Doesn't it look good? I am so looking forward to having a slice."

That pie did lift my spirits, both the making of it and eating it. And while it did transport me to a tropical world in my mind, I made a vow that the next winter I would pack up my bags and head south for real. Someplace where I could pick the limes myself to make more Key lime pie.

Pie Recipes to Lift Your Spirits

Key Lime

Shaker Orange

Strawberry Margarita

Macadamia Nut

Atlantic Beach

Fresh Strawberry

Coconut Custard

S'more

Grasshopper

Tomato Basil

KEY LIME

Besides the fabulous, zesty taste, I love this pie for the fact that its ingredients are so few and so simple. It's a super-easy, no-fuss pie—if you let it be. There is some "controversy" about the authenticity of using a meringue topping versus a whipped-cream topping. According to David L. Sloan, author of The Ultimate Key Lime Pie Cookbook *and Key West resident, the answer is, "Neither. The original Key lime pie didn't have any topping." Of course, if you're David Sloan you will come up with your own embellishments, like pouring a shot of tequila over your slice. Sloan also explains how this pie came about with the invention of sweetened condensed milk in 1856. It was shipped to the Keys in lieu of fresh milk, and men who fished the seas for sponges poured the sweet, thick milk over their stale bread to soften it, mixed in whatever eggs they could find, and squeezed lime juice on top to "cook" it. The next thing you know, in a Darwinian style of evolution, this ingenuity gave birth to a now-beloved pie. As well as a means to restore sanity to Iowans suffering from the winter blues.*

CRUST
Graham Cracker Crust (see page 32)

FILLING
4 egg yolks (reserve 2 egg whites)
1 can (14 ounces) sweetened condensed
    milk
½ cup fresh-squeezed lime juice (about
    20 Key limes or 6 Persian limes),
    or bottled juice (see tip below)
2 tsp fresh lime zest (optional but zesty!)

TOPPING
1 cup heavy whipping cream
3 tbsp sugar

BETH'S SHORTCUT: You can use bottled lime juice for this recipe. Recommended brands are Nellie and Joe's or Manhattan (unsweetened). It's a lot faster and easier than squeezing those mini Key limes and will keep your fingers from pruning. That said, I always prefer using fresh fruit with no preservatives.

Prepare the Graham Cracker Crust (see page 32).

Prepare the Filling: Whisk 4 egg yolks in a large bowl, then add condensed milk, lime juice, and lime zest.

Beat 2 reserved egg whites until stiff and fold into mixture. This will make your filling lighter. (This is an optional step, but one that I always do.)

Pour filling into prepared crust.

Bake at 350 degrees for 20 minutes or until filling is set. Let cool, then chill for at least 3 hours. (Waiting is the hardest part!)

Prepare the Topping: Beat cream and sugar until peaks form. Spread over top of pie. Alternatively, use your leftover egg whites to make a meringue topping. I prefer the whipped cream over the meringue for its sense of freshness.

BETH'S TIP:
Instead of little Key limes, you can also use "regular" limes, known as Persian limes. They are bigger and juicier and thus easier to squeeze, but are said to be less tangy than Key limes. However, I did a taste test with a few Key lime pie aficionados in Key West, people who swear by using Key limes, and they all voted for the pie made with the Persian limes. Even the experts were fooled. Go figure. (This is why I insist on questioning authority and thus dispelling myths.)

SHAKER ORANGE

I had this pie while on a video shoot in San Francisco. I was traveling in my RV (a.k.a.: The Beast) with my TV producer friend Janice Molinari and we were making a pie documentary, a project that has yet to be completed. We were interviewing Natalie Galatzer, who was running a little cottage industry called Bike Basket Pies, delivering, as the name suggests, pies on her bicycle around San Francisco's Financial District. Her business was a great success. Why? Because office workers need pie! She delivered a mini pie to the door of my RV. I remember it vividly, which is a marvel given the way I inhaled the thing in three bites. I always say pie is meant to be shared. But not this pie! This was all mine. Janice didn't get any. I wouldn't have thought to order this one off a menu, but having tried it, it is now one of my very favorites. Maybe it was the bicycle. Or the butter crust. Or because Natalie is such a good pie maker. Well, here's her recipe so now you can make it too. Bicycle not required.

CRUST (FOR DOUBLE-CRUST PIE)
¾ cup (1½ sticks) butter
4 tbsp shortening (Natalie uses
    Earth Balance non-hydrogenated
    shortening sticks)
2½ cups flour
4 tsp sugar
1½ tsp salt
2 tbsp apple cider vinegar
5 to 10 tbsp ice water

FILLING
2 to 4 tangerines, mandarins,
    or clementines (4 if small, 3 if
    medium, or 2 if large)
2 cups sugar
Pinch of salt
4 eggs

1 beaten egg, to brush on top crust
    (optional)
2 tbsp coarse (or sanding) sugar, to
    sprinkle on top (optional)

Prepare the Filling: Slice the oranges paper thin, discarding seeds.

Place in a bowl (capturing the juice run-off), and add sugar and salt. Cover and let sit overnight.

Prepare the Crust: Cut your butter and shortening into cubes. Throw them into the freezer in an airtight container for at least 15 to 20 minutes while you assemble and prep the rest of the ingredients.

Combine flour, sugar, and salt in a large bowl.

Cut in cold butter and shortening until the butter is in pea-sized chunks.

Mix the vinegar and 5 tablespoons ice water together in a separate bowl.

Slowly add the liquid to the butter-flour mixture, working it in by hand quickly, until all the dough sticks together and is tacky but not too sticky. If necessary, add more ice water to get the right consistency.

Split the dough into two balls, and form each into a disk shape.

Wrap in plastic and put the dough in the fridge. Let chill at least 1 hour before rolling out, though Natalie says chilling overnight is best. (I don't chill my dough.)

When you're ready to assemble the pie, beat eggs in a large bowl, then stir in the orange-sugar mixture.

Pour into the pie shell. Cover with top crust and crimp edges, then poke vent holes on top. I make this with my usual beaten-egg wash on top. Natalie simply sprinkles her top crust with sugar.

Bake at 425 degrees for 20 minutes. Turn temperature down to 350 degrees and bake for another 30 to 40 minutes, until crust is golden and a knife inserted into a vent comes out fairly clean. Let cool before serving.

BETH'S TIP:

When selecting tangerines, mandarins, or clementines to use in your pie, try to pick ones that are thin-skinned, juicy, and with a thin pith.

· STRAWBERRY MARGARITA ·

I judged this pie at the Iowa State Fair and I will never forget it. I wrinkled my nose at the first bite and made that lip-smacking sound you make when you're tasting something and not quite sure if you like it or not. Okay, so my first impression was that I didn't like it. But then, my fork went in for another bite. And then another. And the next thing you know, I had broken my two-bite tasting rule and I gobbled the entire slice down. You know a pie is a winner if you can't stop eating it. I couldn't stop. And now I'm sharing a variation of the recipe with you. If this pie doesn't make you feel like you're on a tropical vacation, well…

CRUST
Graham Cracker Crust (see page 32)

FILLING
4 cups halved or quartered fresh
   strawberries, plus a few for garnish
   (optional)
1 tbsp fresh lime zest
¼ cup fresh lime juice (from 2 or
   3 limes)
1 can (14 ounces) sweetened
   condensed milk
2 tbsp tequila
2 tbsp Triple Sec (or any orange-
   flavored liqueur)
1½ cups heavy cream, chilled

Lime slices, for garnish (optional)

Prepare the Graham Cracker Crust (see page 32).

Prepare the Filling: In a blender, purée strawberries, lime zest, lime juice, sweetened condensed milk, tequila, and Triple Sec until smooth.

In a large bowl, beat cream with an electric mixer (or with a whisk if you want to get a workout!) until the cream forms peaks.

Slowly and gently fold the strawberry mixture in with the whipped cream.

Pour filling into the crust and then freeze for about 4 hours. If you have the patience, allow it to soften for 30 minutes in the refrigerator before serving.

If you like, garnish with strawberries and lime slices (this is how I had it at the state fair).

When I was 27, I lived on the Big Island of Hawaii, where I could buy macadamia nuts for next to nothing. Hell, I could have even picked them off the trees had I wanted. Alas, I now live in Iowa where the only plentiful crop is corn. Hmm, corn nut pie? I don't think so. It's worth spending the extra bucks for the rich and buttery macadamias. You can almost taste the tropical sun in them. And that's cheaper and faster than a flight to Hawaii.

CRUST

Basic Pie Dough for single-crust pie (see page 28), crimped

FILLING

2 cups macadamia nuts, whole or chopped (I use salted, roasted nuts, but you can use raw too.)

3 eggs

¾ cup corn syrup (preferably dark, if you have it)

¾ cup brown sugar

2 tbsp butter, melted

2 tsp vanilla

Prepare the Basic Pie Dough for a single-crust pie (see page 28).

Prepare the Filling: Place nuts in the bottom of the pie crust.

Mix all remaining ingredients in a large bowl, then pour over the nuts in the dish.

Bake at 350 degrees for 45 minutes to 1 hour. Filling should puff up in the middle.

ATLANTIC BEACH

I heard about this pie on NPR, coincidentally, during the time I was lamenting my endless Iowa winter. Or was it coincidence? Maybe it was another sign from God telling me I needed a dose of the beach. Regardless, I love the surprising element of the salty crust that complements the tangy citrus filling. Chef Bill Smith of Crook's Corner in North Carolina doesn't take credit for the origin of the recipe, but I do like how he touts it as the world's easiest and fastest pie to make. I'm all for simplicity!

CRUST (FOR ONE 8-INCH PIE)
60 saltine crackers
3 tbsp sugar
½ cup unsalted butter, softened

FILLING
4 egg yolks
1 can (14 ounces) sweetened
    condensed milk
½ cup fresh-squeezed lime juice (or
    lemon, or a combination of both)

TOPPING
Fresh whipped cream
Coarse sea salt, to sprinkle on top

Prepare the Crust: Using a rolling pin, crush the crackers finely but not to dust.

Mix with sugar in a large bowl, then work in butter until crumbs hold together like dough.

Press into an 8-inch pie pan.

Chill 15 minutes, then bake at 350 degrees for 18 minutes or until crust browns a little.

Prepare the Filling: While crust is cooling (it doesn't need to be cold), beat egg yolks into condensed milk, then beat in citrus juice until completely combined.

Pour into pie shell and bake at 350 degrees for 15 minutes or until filling has set. Chill completely before slicing.

Serve with fresh whipped cream and a sprinkling of sea salt.

FRESH STRAWBERRY

This fresh and juicy pie is irresistible. So much so, I once made it on a Saturday afternoon for a Sunday brunch. I kept spying it in the refrigerator and couldn't stand the agony of waiting until the next morning to try it. The problem with pie is that it needs to be presented whole, and thus you don't get to taste it like you can with cookies or snitching a cupcake. Looking at those bright red, juicy strawberries, I couldn't hold back. I cut myself a slice and then cleverly covered the entire pie in whipped cream so no one would notice the missing piece! It was so good, it was worth the teasing I got when my friends discovered the empty spot under the cream.

CRUST
Blind-Baked Crust (see page 31)

FILLING
7 cups (about 3 pints) whole fresh
   strawberries, cleaned, dried, and
   de-stemmed
1 cup sugar
¼ cup cornstarch

TOPPING
2 cups heavy whipping cream (for
   serving—and hiding missing pieces!)
½ cup sugar
1 tsp vanilla
Additional strawberries for garnish
   (optional)

Prepare the Blind-Baked Crust (see page 31).

Prepare the Filling: In a saucepan, combine half of strawberries with sugar and cornstarch and cook over medium heat until the sugar dissolves.

Reduce heat, mash up the berries, and continue cooking over low heat for about 3 to 5 minutes, simmering until the mixture thickens.

Place the remaining whole strawberries in the pie crust, arranging with the tips pointing up (to make it look pretty).

Pour the cooked filling over the berries and refrigerate.

Prepare the Topping: Whip the heavy cream with sugar and vanilla and either serve as a dollop on the side or, if you've stolen a slice, cover the whole thing and garnish with more strawberries on top.

COCONUT CUSTARD

When I think of coconut, I think of Hawaii or the Caribbean. I think of my bones getting warmed by the tropical sun. I picture myself swimming in salty tepid ocean waters. I do not think of my Mini Cooper getting stuck in the icy mud behind the American Gothic House. And when my car does get stuck—oh, and it has many times—and my friend Patti sends her husband over to tow me out—and he has, many times—this is the pie to make as a thank you to my winter warriors who happen to love coconut as much as I do.

CRUST
Basic Pie Dough for 9-inch single-crust pie (see page 28), crimped

FILLING
2 tbsp flour
1 cup sugar
Dash of salt
3 eggs
1 cup milk
4 tbsp (½ stick) butter, melted
2 tsp vanilla
2 cups flaked unsweetened coconut, plus more for sprinkling on top

Prepare the Basic Pie Dough for a 9-inch single-crust pie (see page 28).

Prepare the Filling: In a large bowl, whisk together flour, sugar, and salt.

Add eggs, milk, butter, and vanilla, mixing thoroughly. Stir in coconut.

Pour filling into unbaked pie shell. Sprinkle the top with a light layer of coconut.

Bake at 350 degrees for 40 to 50 minutes or until set.

S'MORE

I don't know about you, but I have very fond memories of going to summer camp as a kid. So when I'm desperately in need of time-travel to sunnier, warmer, happy—and humidity-filled—days, this is the pie to make. It's as delicious and messy as when you're making s'mores around a campfire, but without the biting mosquitos and poison ivy!

CRUST
Graham Cracker Crust (see page 32)

FILLING
3 ounces (3 squares) unsweetened
   baking chocolate
1 cup heavy cream
1 cup sugar
3 eggs
1 tsp vanilla

TOPPING
4 to 6 cups mini marshmallows or a
   10-ounce bag of large marshmallows
   if you prefer a thick topping (I do)

Prepare the Graham Cracker Crust (see page 32).

Prepare the Filling: In a saucepan over low heat, melt the chocolate together with the cream and sugar, stirring until smooth.

Whisk in eggs and vanilla.

Pour into Graham Cracker Crust and bake at 375 degrees for about 40 minutes, until filling is set. (If crust starts to get too brown, turn oven down to 350 degrees.)

Prepare the Topping: Distribute the marshmallows over the top of the chocolate filling.

Place pie under the oven broiler until toasted. This is quick, so keep a close eye on it to keep it from burning!

GRASSHOPPER

With a combination of marshmallows, whipped cream, and minty-fresh alcohol nestled in a chocolate crust, this pie is sure to lift your spirits.

CRUST
Chocolate Cookie Crust (see page 32)

FILLING
30 large marshmallows (about ⅔ of 10-ounce bag)
¼ cup milk
¼ cup crème de cacao
¼ cup crème de menthe
1¼ cups heavy whipping cream, plus more for garnish

TOPPINGS (ALL OPTIONAL)
Chocolate shavings
Andes® after-dinner mints, crushed
Chocolate wafer cookies, crushed

Prepare the Chocolate Cookie Crust (see page 32).

Prepare the Filling: In a saucepan, heat the marshmallows and milk over low heat (the milk will keep the marshmallows from sticking as they melt).

Once melted, stir in the crème de cacao and crème de menthe. Refrigerate until cool.

Whip the cream, then fold it into the cooled marshmallow mixture.

Spoon into the Chocolate Cookie Crust and freeze for 3 to 4 hours before serving.

Garnish with more whipped cream, chocolate shavings, Andes after-dinner mints, or crushed chocolate wafer cookies (reserved from the pie crust).

PIE DYE? Because I refuse to add food coloring, I buy the green-colored crème de menthe instead of clear so the pie has some color.

PIE IN A JAR:
For an adorable dessert make the grasshopper pie in mini canning jars. With the layers of chocolate crust (pressed into the bottom only, not up the sides of the jar), fluffy light-green middle, whipped cream on top, and chocolate shavings for garnish, these make irresistible individual servings.

BETH'S TIP:
For a textured pie, you can stir the chocolate crumbs into the filling.

TOMATO BASIL

I grow mostly tomatoes and basil in my garden in the backyard of the American Gothic House, so of course just the thought of this pie puts me in a good mood. It reminds me of the bountiful produce I can pick right outside my door. When it's summer. When it's winter, however, I can still buy these ingredients in the grocery store. But the best thing is that no matter when I make this pie, it reminds me of my sunny, effervescent friend from Donnellson, Iowa, Esther Tweedy, who has graciously shared her family recipe.

CRUST
Blind-Baked Crust for 8-inch pie
   (see page 31)

FILLING
4 to 5 ripe tomatoes (Roma preferred)
1½ cups shredded mozzarella cheese,
   divided in half
½ cup fresh basil leaves
2 cloves garlic, chopped
⅓ cup mayonnaise
¼ cup grated Parmesan cheese
Salt and pepper, to taste

Prepare the Blind-Baked Crust for a 9-inch pie (see page 31).

Prepare the Filling: Slice tomatoes and drain.

Sprinkle ¾ cup mozzarella over crust.

Place tomato slices over cheese.

Sprinkle basil and garlic over tomatoes.

In a large bowl, stir together the remaining ¾ cup mozzarella, mayonnaise, Parmesan, and salt and pepper to taste.

Spoon this cheese mixture over top of pie.

Bake for 20 to 25 minutes at 350 degrees, until edges are brown and cheese is bubbly. Serve warm.

 # Pies to Comfort

Pie is the ultimate comfort food. What better way to soothe pain than with something creamy, sweet, and smooth nestled in between a rich, buttery crust? And I know I'm not the only one who shares this opinion.

I was visiting New York City last year when I had lunch with an old roommate of mine, Carol Barnett-Stark. I had lived with Carol in Manhattan when I was 25 years old. I had moved back to the U.S. from Nairobi, Kenya, and started a coffee import business I called Livingstone Provisions. (Back when I had that now-lost combo of big dreams and excess energy. How I miss those days.) I was trying to end a relationship with a long-term boyfriend and Carol, an aspiring actress at the time, was trying to escape a religious cult. We rescued each other by sharing a one-bedroom walk-up on the Upper East Side, solving all our problems by sitting on the fire escape and talking late into the night over steaming cups of chamomile tea and gingersnaps.

Fast-forward 25 years. Carol is still in New York with a darling nine-year-old daughter, and I'm in rural Iowa with two unruly terriers. In spite of the number of years that have passed, we have more in common now than we could have imagined. For starters, we both married German men. She is (amicably) divorced from hers and my husband is... well, deceased. (God, how I hate that word.)

When I went to meet her for lunch, taking the elevator up 20 floors to her office in a slick Times Square high-rise, I learned we now shared another bond in common: grief. Carol's dad, Frank, had died just two weeks earlier.

From our emails during the previous year, I knew Frank had been sick. He had been getting chemo and was doing much better than the doctors had predicted. He was living on his own, still meeting his friends for coffee every day, and then, out of nowhere, he had a stroke, his heart stopped, and he was gone.

Yes, I know what that feels like. To lose someone with no warning, no chance to say good-bye. Robbed of the opportunity to say "I'm sorry" or "I love you" or both. No time to say, to beg, "Please don't go! I don't know how I will survive without you." But they leave us—sometimes in an instant.

> Yes, I know what that feels like. To lose someone with no warning, no chance to say good-bye.

And thus, the day I happened to step into Carol's glass-walled office (with a million-dollar view of 42nd Street), I also stepped into her grief. Fresh and raw. I recognized it all too well.

"What should I do?" Carol asked me upon sharing her devastating news, forcing a half-smile as her eyes welled up with tears. "Make pie?"

I smiled back at her to mask my own sadness. "Well, it couldn't hurt," I said. "How about if you read my book? (I was referring to my memoir, *Making Piece*.) I mean, if you're ready. You will see all the ways pie helped me."

She nodded and said, "My dad loved pie. He was known for his pecan pie. Everyone loved it so much they always expected him to bring it to their picnics and parties."

"Are you serious? You never told me. I had no idea pie-making ran in your family."

She continued, "When we had to print the program for the funeral, we couldn't come up with any scripture or other quotes that fit my dad. The funeral director said sometimes people include other things, like a favorite recipe. So we included my dad's pecan pie recipe."

My jaw dropped. I couldn't believe I was sitting in the middle of Times Square talking about life, death, and pie recipes printed in funeral programs. But there it was, another example of the far-reaching powers of pie. I like to think that all those friends and family attending Frank Barnett's farewell service smiled at seeing the recipe in such an unlikely place, and that they all went home afterward to carry on his legacy by making his favorite pie.

When I returned to Iowa, I couldn't stop thinking about my lunch with Carol. Her dad remained very much on my mind. I wanted to tell others about Frank, about his pecan pie, and how his recipe played such a special role at his funeral. I asked Carol to send me the recipe and a picture of her with her dad. She sent both, along with this note:

With Thanksgiving approaching he would be getting requests and he would be so excited to whip up those pecan pies. He shelled the pecans himself. He was a salt-of-the-earth kind of guy. Content to sit on the porch and watch the grass grow. Or go into town to have breakfast with his buddies. Perhaps ride around on his tractor lawn mower, taking care of the grass. He was a simple man with a great sense of humor. The most patient person you'd ever meet. I can't tell you how many people came up to me at his funeral and said, "Your dad was my best friend." I thought, "Wow, my dad made everyone feel like they were his best friend…that's awesome." I too will make my first pecan pie in his honor this Thanksgiving—and be thankful for the amazing dad I had.

Carol is truly an inspiration and sets an example of dealing with grief with grace. She reminds me that I, too, have a lot to be thankful for. And to honor that, I scrapped my trusted pecan pie recipe (the one on the Karo Syrup label) and made Frank's recipe for Thanksgiving instead.

Twenty-five years after meeting Carol, we are still rescuing each other. Our wounds are much bigger than before, but we possess stronger weapons of comfort and healing now. We have a lifelong friendship to fall back on. And forget the chamomile tea and gingersnaps; now we have pie.

Pie Recipes to Comfort

Frank Barnett's Pecan

Amish Funeral

Sour Cream Raisin

Peaches & Cream Kuchen

Classic New York Cheesecake

Hot Fudge Sundae

Chicken Pot Pie

Shepherd's Pie

Ham & Cheese Quiche

FRANK BARNETT'S PECAN

I never got to meet Frank Barnett, but I know I would have liked him. He understood the spirit of pie, along with everything it embodies—generosity, sharing, creativity, and love. I am very honored to include his recipe in my book. And I'm equally honored to have his beautiful daughter as my friend.

CRUST
Basic Pie Dough for single-crust pie
    (see page 28), crimped

FILLING
1 cup brown sugar
½ cup white sugar
2 eggs, well beaten
½ cup (1 stick) butter
1 tbsp cornstarch
2 tbsp milk
1 cup pecans, chopped
1 tsp vanilla

Prepare the Basic Pie Dough for a single-crust pie (see page 28).

Prepare the Filling: Mix all ingredients well and pour into single crust.

Bake at 325 degrees for 50 minutes.

AMISH FUNERAL

Given that I live in southeast Iowa, where there are concentrations of Amish communities, it was inevitable that I would discover raisin pie. It is known in these parts as Funeral Pie because it's served so often at funerals. Not that I've ever been to an Amish funeral. But it's said that the ingredients are always easy to come by and, more important, the sweetness of the pie helps the grieving families forget their pain for a moment. Nice in theory, but given that I know what grief feels like, I'd say keep the Kleenex handy.

CRUST

Basic Pie Dough for double-crust pie
  (see page 28)

FILLING

2 cups raisins
2 cups water
½ cup brown sugar
½ cup white sugar
3 tbsp cornstarch
1½ tsp ground cinnamon
¼ tsp ground allspice
Pinch of salt
1 tbsp apple cider vinegar
3 tbsp butter

Prepare the Basic Pie Dough for a double-crust pie (see page 28).

Prepare the Filling: In a saucepan, cook the raisins and ⅔ cup water over medium heat for 5 minutes.

In a bowl, combine the sugars, cornstarch, spices, and salt.

Stirring constantly, gradually add the remaining 1⅓ cups water.

Add this mixture to the raisins in the saucepan. Continue stirring and cook until the mixture starts to bubble.

Add the vinegar and butter, stirring over heat until the butter is melted.

Pour filling into the pie shell, then cover with the top crust.

Trim and crimp the dough edges. Brush with beaten egg and cut decorative ventilation holes into the top crust.

Bake at 425 degrees for 15 minutes to set the crust, then turn oven down to 375 degrees and bake for another 20 to 25 minutes.

BETH'S TIP:

Don't be afraid to alter a recipe. Remember, it's just pie—your pie—and you can put anything at all between the crusts. For example, if an all-raisin pie isn't your thing, try adding some apples, pears, or other fruit, balancing out the flavor to suit your palate.

SOUR CREAM RAISIN

Joanne Maynard, the mother of Patti Durflinger, my BFF in Eldon, makes this pie. I had it—and fell in love with it—when said BFF hosted a pie auction fundraiser. What grabbed my attention—besides the fluffy meringue, the creaminess of the pudding, and the fact that I didn't mind the raisins—was the hint of orange zest. I found this compelling, a flavor that kept me coming back for more bites. Then again, maybe I just loved it because it was made with love by Patti's mom.

CRUST
Blind-Baked Crust (see page 31)

FILLING
2 cups sour cream
4 egg yolks (reserve egg whites for meringue)
1 cup sugar
4 tbsp flour
1 tsp orange zest
1½ cups raisins

MERINGUE
4 to 6 egg whites
¼ tsp cream of tartar
¼ cup sugar

Prepare the Blind-Baked Crust (see page 31).

Prepare the Filling: In a saucepan, combine sour cream and egg yolks. Stir in sugar, flour, orange zest, and raisins.

Cook over medium heat until the raisins plump up. Then pour into the pie shell.

Prepare the Meringue: Using a mixer on high speed, beat egg whites until frothy.

Add cream of tartar and slowly add sugar a little at a time. Beat until peaks form.

Spoon on top of the filling and dab at the meringue with the back of a large spoon, pulling back with each stroke to create curlicue peaks.

Bake at 350 degrees until the peaks turn brown, about 15 minutes.

BETH'S TIP:
Meringue can be like a sad person; sometimes it weeps. The cause—or at least the theory—for the formation of these little droplets is too much humidity in the air. And since, like many things in life that cause us grief, we cannot control the weather, the best solution is just to eat it fast!

PEACHES & CREAM KUCHEN

This is a pie from my childhood that my mom made when her fellow housewife friends came over for coffee. If the ladies left any scraps behind, we kids would pounce on them, devouring every last crumb of the sweet and rich dessert. My mom may not remember where she got the recipe, but I remember how much I loved it. Still love it. And by the way, kuchen is German for cake, but in Germany cake has a broad meaning and covers everything from traditional spongy cakes to tarts to pies.

CRUST
2 cups flour
2 tbsp sugar
½ tsp salt
¼ tsp baking powder
½ cup (1 stick) butter

FILLING
1 can (14 ounces) peach halves
(or 10 ounces frozen slices, or
4 medium fresh peaches, see
tip below)
½ to ¾ cup sugar
1 tsp cinnamon

TOPPING
2 egg yolks
1 cup heavy cream

Prepare the Crust: In a medium bowl, combine flour, sugar, salt, and baking powder.

By hand or with a pastry blender (go for the hands!), blend the butter into the flour until the mixture resembles coarse crumbs.

Pour into a pie plate and pat firmly against the bottom and sides.

Prepare the Filling: If you're using fresh peaches, cut them in half or slices, then drain the juice.

Arrange peaches in the pastry-lined pie plate. If using halves, place the cut sides down. If slices, arrange side by side in a single layer.

Combine sugar and cinnamon and sprinkle over peaches.

Bake at 400 degrees for 15 minutes.

Prepare the Topping: Beat the egg yolks and cream together and pour over peaches.

Bake for 30 minutes longer, until golden brown. Let stand 10 minutes and serve warm.

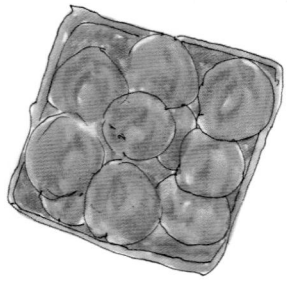

BETH'S MOM'S TIP:
My mom insists this is a "winter pie" and that canned peaches work best for this recipe. I made it once with fresh peaches, piled them high like I would for a double-crust pie, and—oh boy—that pie was one big scorched, soggy mess. Scorched because I baked it for an eternity in an unsuccessful attempt to get the filling to set. Whatever kind of peaches you use, keep them to a minimum and drain as much of their juice as you can. Or else you will hear it from my mother.

CLASSIC NEW YORK
CHEESECAKE

There is ongoing debate about whether cheesecake is cake or pie. The heated arguments over the question (on food blogs and Twitter in particular) provide great entertainment value. An irreverent women's website called Jezebel had a March Madness tournament duking out a battle for cake versus pie and I still laugh about the outrage and confusion when cheesecake won. Cheesecake is made up of filling held together with a crust, which by definition is pie. But who the hell cares? No matter what you call it, it's amazingly good.

CRUST
Graham Cracker Crust (see page 32)

FILLING
5 packages (8 ounces each) cream
 cheese, softened
1½ cups sugar
1 cup sour cream
2 tsp vanilla
3 tbsp flour
5 eggs

Fresh strawberries or raspberries,
 for garnish (optional)

Prepare the Graham Cracker Crust (see page 32), and press into a 9-inch spring-form pan (see tip below), pressing into the bottom and up the sides.

Bake at 350 degrees for 10 minutes.

Prepare the Filling: In a large bowl, beat cream cheese and sugar with an electric mixer until smooth and fluffy.

Add sour cream, vanilla, and flour and continue mixing at medium speed until combined.

Turn down the mixer to low and beat in eggs, one at a time.

Pour filling into crust.

Bake at 325 degrees for at least one hour. Filling should be slightly jiggly and moist in the center and slightly brown around the edge.

Cool completely in the pan on a wire rack, then refrigerate overnight.

Remove the outside of the pan to serve. Garnish with fresh strawberries or raspberries if you like.

BETH'S TIP:
If you don't have a spring-form pan, don't sweat it. Just use a regular pie plate (though you'll probably need two). It's still going to taste great.

HOT FUDGE SUNDAE

My dad always tells us kids, "When I go, don't cry over me. Just go out for a hot fudge sundae." Though he loves hot fudge sundaes as much as banana cream pie, he has been known to alter his statement and replace "hot fudge sundae" with "three-olive martini." I suppose when his time comes, I'll be drowning myself in both. Though not at the same time. Gratefully, my dad is still alive and well, and we can still enjoy indulging in his favorite things together.

CRUST
Chocolate Cookie Crust (see page 32)

FILLING
4 pints (1 quart) vanilla ice cream,
   slightly softened

TOPPING
1 jar hot fudge (see shortcut below)
1 cup heavy whipping cream
3 tbsp sugar
Maraschino cherries, for garnish
   (optional)

Prepare the Chocolate Cookie Crust (see page 32).

Prepare the Filling: Spoon ice cream into the crust and refreeze.

When ice cream has hardened and you're ready to serve, cut the pie into slices.

Pour heated fudge over the top of each slice and add a dollop of whipped cream (see page 107 for homemade whipped cream).

Cherry on top is optional. Gratitude for a life well lived is not.

BETH'S SHORTCUT:
I would say to make the homemade recipe on page 70, but I guarantee if I'm grieving or in need of instant comfort I'm taking the easy route and opening a jar.

CHICKEN POT PIE

I'm sorry to say this, but I think chicken pot pie is a pain in the rear to make. I don't like all those steps to cook all the ingredients separately, nor do I enjoy the resulting dirty pots and pans. Remember, I don't have a dishwasher in the American Gothic House. But, my goodness, this pie is a wonder to eat! My solution is to make several at once and freeze them. It's worth the effort to have comfort food ready at hand. Because, sadly, you'll need it eventually. You just never know when. Life is like that.

CRUST
Basic Pie Dough for double-crust pie
   (see page 28)

FILLING
1 lb chicken breast
2 cups chicken broth, plus more for
   Cream Sauce if needed
2 potatoes, diced
1 medium onion, diced
2 garlic cloves, chopped
1 to 2 tbsp olive oil
3 carrots, diced
10 ounces peas, canned or frozen
   (if frozen, thaw first)
1 tsp salt
½ tsp pepper
½ tsp dried sage
¼ tsp thyme

CREAM SAUCE
4 tbsp (½ stick) butter
¼ cup flour
½ cup heavy cream

Prepare the Basic Pie Dough for a double-crust pie (see page 28).

Prepare the Filling: Boil chicken in chicken broth. When chicken is cool enough, chop into cubes. Save the broth.

Boil potatoes in a separate pot until soft, then drain.

In a small skillet, sauté onion and garlic in olive oil.

Boil carrots until softened, then drain. Add the onion-garlic mixture, potatoes, peas, salt, pepper, sage, and thyme.

Prepare the Cream Sauce: In another pot, reheat the chicken broth.

Melt butter in the broth, then whisk in flour and cream. Cook until it thickens, adding more broth if it needs it.

Mix the vegetables, chicken, and thickened cream sauce until well combined, then pour into the unbaked pie shell.

Cover with top crust. Trim, crimp, brush with beaten egg, and poke vent holes.

Bake at 425 degrees for 15 minutes to set and brown crust.

Turn oven down to 375 degrees and bake until filling bubbles, about another 15 to 25 minutes, depending on the size of your pie.

SHEPHERD'S PIE

The illustrator of this book, Melissa Wood, not only has talent at the drafting table but also in the kitchen. I stayed at her artistically appointed abode outside of Chicago and was treated to some scrumptious, soul-satisfying meals, including this memorable Shepherd's pie. I just had to have the recipe. Now if I can get her to sketch an illustration of it! That and have her make it for me again.

FILLING (MAKES TWO PIES)

2 lbs ground beef

1 tbsp olive oil, plus more to coat
  pie pans

6 garlic cloves, crushed

2 small Vidalia onions, diced

5 tbsp parsley flakes

2 bay leaves

2½ cups V8 juice

1 can diced tomatoes

½ tsp thyme

8 rosemary leaves, chopped (yes, those
  tiny little needles on the sprig)

3 carrots, chopped and boiled

1½ cups peas (Melissa uses frozen)

1½ tsp salt

1 tsp pepper

TOPPING

6 large Idaho potatoes, peeled, boiled,
  and drained

1 cup half-and-half

½ cup (1 stick) butter

Salt and pepper, to taste

Paprika, to sprinkle on top

Prepare the Filling: In a large skillet or saucepan, cook beef, oil, garlic, onions, parsley, and bay leaves together, browning the meat.

Add V8, tomatoes, thyme, rosemary, boiled carrots, peas, salt, and pepper. Stir until combined and heat thoroughly.

Coat bottoms of two glass pie pans with olive oil.

Add meat-veggie mixture, mounding it up.

Prepare the Topping: Mash boiled potatoes with half-and-half, butter, and salt and pepper to taste.

Layer mashed potatoes on top of meat filling.

Top with remaining 1 tablespoon butter and sprinkle with paprika.

Bake at 350 degrees for 35 minutes or until potato layer is brown and crusty.

HAM & CHEESE QUICHE

To me, the ultimate comfort food—besides pie, I mean—is anything made with melted cheese. So why not go for the one-two punch and make a cheesy pie? Enter: Ham and Cheese Quiche. This is another one of those tasty, warm-your-insides recipes that's so easy you almost don't need a recipe. That's my kind of cooking! This is a good dish to deliver to a friend going through a hard time, who may not have the time or energy to cook.

CRUST
Basic Pie Dough for single-crust pie
    (see page 28), crimped

FILLING
6 eggs
1 cup heavy cream
1 cup cooked ham, diced
1 cup shredded sharp Cheddar cheese
    (I always add extra)
¼ cup onion, diced and sautéed
Salt and pepper, to taste

Prepare the Basic Pie Dough for a single-crust pie (see page 28).

Prepare the Filling: In a bowl, beat together eggs and cream, then stir in ham, cheese, sautéed onion, salt, and pepper.

Pour mixture into the pie crust and then bake at 375 degrees for 35 to 45 minutes.

 # Pies to Seduce

I often talk about how I was born because of banana cream pie, how when my parents were courting my mom invited my dad over for a romantic supper—of tuna casserole and Jell-O salad and his favorite pie—and how that made-from-scratch pie prompted my dad to propose to her. They had five kids and 50 years later they are still married. And my mom still makes him banana cream pie. If this example doesn't prove the seductive powers of pie, I don't know what does.

I tried to use my mom's method to snag a guy. I spent my college years in the fruit-fertile state of Washington, where I made apple pies for God-knows-how-many potential boyfriends. The one who stands out most was Scott, the swashbuckling, dark, curly-haired modern-day Tarzan. Tarzan because he lived in a treehouse, a two-story lair built in a stand of tall cedars. He came over to my dorm room to ask out my roommate Lisa, an exotic blue-eyed beauty from South America, but she wasn't home so I got the date instead. (There were no hard feelings. Aloof and highly sought after, Lisa swears she wouldn't have gone out with him anyway. And I didn't care if I was his second choice. He was…he was Scott!)

I followed up on our date by making Scott an apple pie. This was back when my pie-making skills were rough—back when I hadn't yet learned how to be gentle with my dough, and therefore my crusts were always hard to roll and even harder to chew. I didn't know how bad my pie was and I didn't care, especially when the response I heard repeatedly was one of appreciation: "Wow! No one's ever made me a pie before," they all said.

In anticipation of being invited up to Scott's famed treehouse—where many an eager coed had preceded me—I kneaded that dough, sliced those apples, sprinkled a little extra of that most seductive of spices, cinnamon, and for the final touch I carved a smiley face on top for the vent holes. I drove the pie out to his forest penthouse and pulled on the dangling string to ring the bell attached to his wooden abode about 40 feet up in the sky. He poked his head out the door and flashed his smile at me. My heart raced, my knees weakened.

As lithe as an orangutan, he scrambled down on his rope ladder to greet me and then whisked back up carrying the pie, with me following behind. "No one's ever made me a pie before," he predictably declared. I smiled to myself, smugly, knowingly.

After devouring half the pie, we made it to the futon mattress, which was surrounded by lit candles. As we slept, the house swayed in the wind and the scent of pine—and apple pie—filled the little room. The night was a romantic dream come true; the sex, however, was, well, mediocre at best. I saw him a few more times after that, but eventually we both moved on.

Fast-forward ten years, and it turns out sexy Scott became very famous. Not for his numerous female conquests (well, that too), but for his bank-robbing skills. He achieved the status of "most prolific bank robber in the history of the United States" and was known as the "Hollywood Bandit," so dubbed by the news media for his use of makeup and prosthetics as disguises during his heists. He was eventually cornered in a backyard trailer in Seattle, where he was found dead after a shoot-out with the police. (He was 42.)

No more pie for Scott.

I did finally land not just a boyfriend, but a husband, Marcus. He was even sexier than Scott, with dark hair, green eyes, strong cheekbones, a British accent, impeccable manners, and a great derriere. He was German and during my first trip to visit him in Stuttgart I brought him an apple pie. I had long since honed my baking skills after spending an entire year baking pies at a gourmet take-out café in Malibu, California. This time I made the extra effort of weaving a lattice crust. (Present-day note: If you ever receive a lattice-crust pie from me, you can be sure it means I like you.) Marcus didn't propose immediately upon biting into the pie, the way my dad did to my mom, but he took so many pictures of the thing before cutting into it I started to get impatient. We did eventually get married, and I do credit that pie in some ways. Over the years I made him many other pies: blackberry, blueberry, pecan, pumpkin, and more. But Marcus's story has an ending as tragic as Scott's, minus the bank robberies. Six years after we got married, Marcus died of a ruptured aorta due to a congenital heart condition. He was 43. (I wrote about Marcus in "Pies to Heal" on page 40.)

Four years since losing Marcus, I've tried getting out there in the dating scene again. I met a tall and handsome guy with a deep voice through a dating website and after a few dates I made him a strawberry pie. With a plain top crust though, not lattice. It was an extra-large, deep-dish pie, so it took a while to eat it all. I made the mistake of not refrigerating it. After sitting on the kitchen table for a few hot, late-August days, the red strawberries turned green and grey, covered in hairy tentacles of mold. Omen? Probably, because shortly afterward I discovered the boyfriend trolling the Internet for other women. Still, he kept a photo of that pie as his screen saver on both his phone and computer. I guess he was more in love with that pie than he was with me.

I also had a flirtation with a man who was slender, smart, and fun. He had a great smile. And, as I discovered later, a wife. He let it be known that his favorite pie was pecan, so I made him one and, given my rural location, I drove 90 miles just to buy the pecans. My oven at the time was old and the numbers had worn off the knobs, so I couldn't determine the temperature setting. That pie burned to a petrified crisp, the filling resembling lava rock rather than the gooey, luscious sweetness it should have been. The house filled with a black cloud of smoke that made my eyes burn for hours. Omen? Obviously. That guy is still pie-deprived—and still married. The strawberry pie guy is still serial dating. And I'm still looking for love.

It's clearly time to try a new kind of pie, and I have just the recipe in mind. A recent study by Dr. Alan Hirsch, director of Chicago's Smell and Taste Treatment and Research Center, found that the scent of pumpkin pie combined with lavender ice cream increased male arousal by 40 percent. That is a convincing statistic. Now I just need to find someone to bake for.

Pie Recipes to Seduce

Strawberry with Double Crust

Pecan

Pumpkin with Gingersnap Crust

Lavender Ice Cream

Coconut Cream

French Silk

Chocolate Cream

Banana Cream

Black Bottom Banana Cream

Chocolate Chess

Nutella

STRAWBERRY
WITH DOUBLE CRUST

In spite of the fate of this pie in my story, it really is a juicy, vibrant pie that spans the season of spring well into summer. Just because my relationship with the tall and handsome guy didn't work out, that doesn't mean the pie didn't still work its seductive magic. And if nothing else, I did learn an important lesson. (No, it's not "Never attempt online dating again.") It's that a strawberry pie needs to be refrigerated if you don't finish eating it the first day.

CRUST
Basic Pie Dough for double-crust pie
(see page 28)

FILLING
6 to 7 cups (2 to 3 pints) whole fresh
strawberries
1 cup sugar
¼ cup instant tapioca
Pinch of salt

1 tbsp butter, to pat on top of filling
1 beaten egg, to brush on top crust

GLUTEN-FREE SUPERHERO:
Tapioca, the Super Power of thickeners, is gluten-free. If you don't have minute tapioca, you can grind any size tapioca in a (clean) coffee grinder to get smaller granules.

Prepare the Basic Pie Dough for a double-crust pie (see page 28).

Prepare the Filling: Soak the strawberries in water to wash off any sand residue (strawberries grow in sandy soil), then rinse and drain.

Cut out stems (see Tip for efficient de-stemming), then slice in halves or quarters.

In a large bowl, mix together strawberries, sugar, tapioca, and salt, then let sit for 20 minutes to activate the tapioca.

Pour mixture into the pie shell, then place the pat of butter on top.

Cover with top crust. Trim and crimp edges, brush with beaten egg, and poke vent holes on top.

Bake at 425 degrees for 20 minutes or until top crust begins to brown. Reduce heat to 375 degrees and bake for another 20 to 30 minutes, until fruit bubbles up through the top and juice thickens.

BETH'S TIP:
To de-stem (some say "hull") strawberries, dig the tip of your paring knife in as close to the stem as possible, holding the knife at a vertical angle and cutting closely around the stem. Don't slice off the top of the strawberry as you'll waste precious fruit.

PECAN

It's just as well I burned that pecan pie I made for the married man. It saved me from getting myself into trouble. But under normal circumstances, when baking with integrity—meaning that both my oven dials and my moral compass are operating properly—this is a tried-and-true recipe for which I constantly receive praise. The funny thing is, the recipe is just from the Karo corn syrup bottle. I just add extra vanilla and extra pecans. Because sometimes more is better.

CRUST
Basic Pie Dough for a 9-inch single-crust pie (see page 28), crimped

FILLING
1 cup corn syrup
3 beaten eggs
1 cup sugar
2 tbsp butter, melted
2 tsp vanilla
2 cups pecans, whole or pieces

Prepare the Basic Pie Dough for a 9-inch single-crust pie (see page 28).

Prepare the Filling: Mix all ingredients together in a large bowl. Pour into the unbaked pie crust.

Bake at 425 degrees for 20 minutes, then turn heat down to 375 degrees and bake for another 30 to 40 minutes. You can tell if the pie is done by jiggling the pie plate a little. If the filling doesn't jiggle too much, then it's done. The top might rise a little too, which helps indicate the filling has cooked.

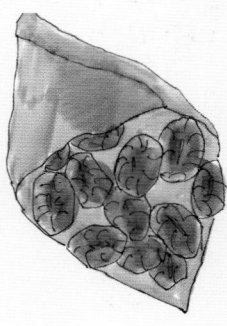

PUMPKIN
WITH GINGERSNAP CRUST

I know the study I cited called for "regular" pumpkin pie, but why not take it up a notch by adding a zing of ginger? I mean, hello, ginger is an aphrodisiac, used in ancient Chinese medicine. So, yeah, go with a gingersnap crust—and a scoop of lavender ice cream (see page 153) on the side—and you are just asking for a walk on the wild side. And you'll probably get it. Better get your hiking boots on for this one.

CRUST
2½ to 3½ cups gingersnaps (at least one whole box)
6 tbsp (¾ stick) butter, melted

FILLING
¾ cup sugar
1 tsp cinnamon
½ tsp salt
½ tsp ground ginger
¼ tsp ground cloves
2 eggs
1 can (15 ounces) pumpkin purée
1 can (12 ounces) evaporated milk

BETH'S SHORTCUT: Instead of the canned pumpkin, you can bake a pumpkin yourself (look for baking pumpkins like the "sugar" variety) and scrape out the flesh. However, I've tried it and any advantage of taste is not worth the effort. I am a huge advocate for all-things-fresh-not-canned, but honestly, with all the spices and the custardy texture of pumpkin pie, it's almost impossible to taste the difference between fresh and canned.

Prepare the Crust: Crush the gingersnaps by placing them in a ziplock bag and grinding over them with a rolling pin until they are a fine, crumbly texture. (That's how I do it, but if you *must*, use a blender or—I choke on the words—a *food processor*.)

Mix cookie crumbs with melted butter.

Pat the mixture into your pie plate as evenly as possible, pressing the crumbs up onto the sides of the dish as well.

Prepare the Filling: Mix sugar and all the spices in a small bowl and set aside.

In a large bowl, beat the eggs with a fork or whisk. Add the pumpkin and sugar-spice mixture, then whisk in the milk.

Bake at 425 degrees for 15 to 20 minutes, then turn temperature down to 375 degrees and bake for another 30 minutes or until done. Do the "jiggle test" to see if liquid filling has firmed. Sticking a knife in it also helps for determining doneness; knife should come out clean. If the custard cracks, it is done—though preferably get it out of the oven before cracks appear.

REMINDER:
Not all ovens bake alike. Some bake hotter than others. If the crust edges are getting too brown, or the top of the pie gets too brown, there is a simple solution: Turn the oven temperature down!

LAVENDER ICE CREAM

This makes a big batch so you can cut it in half if you want. But why go to all that trouble when you can have extra on hand? Of note: You will need an ice-cream maker for this. Electric or hand crank. If you're feeling lazy, you might be lucky enough to find lavender ice cream in your local store instead.

---

3 cups milk
1½ cups heavy cream
1½ cups sugar
½ cup fresh or dried lavender flowers,
    or 2 stems of fresh lavender
6 egg yolks
1 tsp vanilla

In a saucepan over medium heat, bring milk, cream, sugar, and lavender to almost boiling. Remove from heat and let sit for at least 15 minutes to "steep" (like you would a teabag). Strain lavender.

Beat egg yolks in a separate bowl. Whisk about ½ cup of hot milk mixture into your beaten egg yolks to "introduce" the heat without curdling the eggs, then pour egg mixture back into saucepan. Whisking is a good idea. So is stirring constantly.

Cook for at least 10 minutes, stirring. It should start to thicken to the consistency of, say, buttermilk, but will still be liquid.

Refrigerate until cold, then pour into your ice-cream maker and start cranking. But make sure you save some energy for the "dessert after the dessert," if you know what I'm sayin'. Isn't that the whole point of this exercise?!

COCONUT CREAM

Coconut Cream Pie is my mom's favorite. I can't help but think if my parents had courted in today's day and age, my dad might have cooked dinner and baked my mom her favorite pie. I got this recipe from local Eldon, Iowa, resident, Pat Hancock, who has been making it so long she "doesn't know where she got the recipe."

CRUST
Blind-Baked Crust (see page 31)

FILLING
3 cups milk
3 egg yolks (save whites for meringue)
1 cup sugar
¼ tsp salt
3 tbsp flour
3 tbsp cornstarch
2 tbsp butter
1 tsp vanilla
1½ cups unsweetened shredded
  coconut

MERINGUE
6 egg whites (you will need to
  separate 3 additional eggs since
  the filling calls for only 3 yolks)
4 tbsp powdered sugar
¼ tsp cream of tartar
1 tbsp cornstarch
Dash of salt

Prepare the Blind-Baked Crust (see page 31).

Prepare the Filling: In a heavy saucepan, combine all ingredients except butter, vanilla, and coconut, constantly stirring with a whisk (this helps the egg yolks blend better). Cook over medium heat until boiling and thick.

Remove from heat and stir in butter, vanilla, and coconut. Pour into pre-baked pie shell.

Prepare the Meringue: Using an electric beater, whip all the meringue ingredients in a clean bowl until stiff peaks form.

Cover the top of the pie with the meringue and bake at 375 degrees for 10 minutes.

BETH'S TIP:
To turn this into a chocolate pie, skip the coconut and add 3 tablespoons cocoa powder instead. To turn this into banana cream, slice 2 or 3 bananas instead of the coconut. On the other hand, life is short. Go ahead and throw everything in to make a choco-banana-coconut creation.

PAT'S TIP:
Pat claims the powdered sugar and cornstarch help prevent the meringue in her recipe from "weeping."

FRENCH SILK

If you read my memoir, Making Piece, *then you will recognize this recipe. It's from pie-maker extraordinaire Lana Ross of Indianola, Iowa. It's the pie I judged at the Iowa State Fair and, convinced it should have won first place, I tried persuading the other judges by telling them, "This is a pie I would like to rub all over my body and have a man lick it off." You want a pie to seduce? You can't go wrong with this one.*

CRUST
⅓ cup lard (see note below)
1 cup flour
½ tsp salt
⅓ cup ice water

FILLING
1 cup (2 sticks) butter
1½ cups sugar (Lana uses extra-fine sugar, I don't)
4 ounces (4 squares) unsweetened baking chocolate, melted
1 tsp vanilla
4 eggs

TOPPING
2 cups heavy whipping cream
4 tbsp powdered sugar
1 tbsp vanilla
Chocolate shavings, for garnish (optional)

Prepare the Crust: Cut the lard into the flour and salt.

Gradually add water until moist.

Roll out the dough and place in a 10-inch pie plate.

Blind-bake the crust (see page 31), then let cool.

Prepare the Filling: Beat butter and sugar until light and fluffy.

Blend in melted chocolate and vanilla.

Add eggs, one at a time, beating at medium speed for 5 minutes after each addition. (Of course, impatient me doesn't beat that long.)

Pour into cooled pie shell. Chill at least 4 hours.

Prepare the Topping: When pie is ready to serve, whip the cream, sugar, and vanilla until thick. Spread over cooled pie.

Garnish with chocolate shavings.

NOTE: If you don't want to use lard, replace with the fat of your choice: butter, shortening, or both.

BETH'S TIP:
People are squeamish about eating raw eggs these days because of food-borne illness risks. To ease your concerns, look for pasteurized eggs..

CHOCOLATE CREAM

This was one of my favorites to make at Mary's Kitchen in Malibu. I used to make moaning noises while stirring the pudding over the stove. My pleasure was so obvious, the staff teased me about it. About a year after I left my pie-making job, I got a note from Mary in the mail. The card read: Sending you this chocolate pie recipe. After the "performance" at the store whenever you made it, it is sure to be a hit with any new male friends you may have. Keep stirring. Love, Mary. *Oh, believe me, I'm still stirring.*

CRUST
Blind-Baked Crust (see page 31)

FILLING
3 ounces (3 squares) unsweetened
    baking chocolate
1½ cups sugar
¾ cup flour
1 tsp salt
3 cups whole milk
5 egg yolks (save whites for meringue
    topping)
3 tbsp butter
1 tbsp vanilla

MERINGUE
5 egg whites
½ tsp cream of tartar
½ cup sugar

Prepare the Blind-Baked Crust (see page 31).

Prepare the Filling: In a heavy saucepan, mix together all filling ingredients except for eggs, butter, and vanilla, and cook over medium to low heat until thickened.

Remove from heat and beat in the egg yolks thoroughly. Cook again until thickened.

Remove from heat and stir in butter and vanilla.

Mix well and pour into pre-baked pie crust.

Prepare the Meringue: In a clean bowl, beat egg whites at high speed until frothy.

While still beating, add cream of tartar and gradually add sugar. Continue beating until stiff peaks form.

Spread meringue on top of pudding, making sure to take it all the way to the edges to "seal" the top. Jab at the meringue with the back of a large spoon, pulling back with each stroke to create curlicue peaks.

Bake at 375 degrees until meringue turns golden, about 10 minutes.

BANANA CREAM

This book would not be complete without my mom's "famous" recipe. This is the pie that landed her a marriage proposal from my dad. Talk about the ultimate seduction pie! If not for this pie, I would not have been born. After 54 years, my parents are still married and banana cream is still my dad's favorite, a testament to the power of this recipe.

CRUST
Blind-Baked Crust (see page 31)

FILLING
1 cup sugar
¼ cup cornstarch
2 tbsp flour
¼ tsp salt
3 cups whole milk
5 egg yolks (save whites for meringue)
3 tbsp butter
1 tsp vanilla
4 sliced bananas

MERINGUE
5 egg whites
½ tsp cream of tartar
½ cup sugar
½ tsp vanilla

Prepare the Blind-Baked Crust (see page 31).

Prepare the Filling: In a heavy saucepan, whisk together dry ingredients, then gradually whisk in milk.

Stirring constantly, cook over medium heat until thick and bubbling. Once it bubbles, cook for another 2 minutes. Remove from heat.

In a separate bowl, beat the egg yolks. Add about a cup of the hot mixture to the yolks, stirring quickly so the eggs don't curdle. Then add this egg mixture back to the saucepan, stirring constantly.

Bring to a gentle boil and cook for another 2 minutes.

Remove from heat and stir in butter and vanilla.

Fill bottom of blind-baked pie shell with sliced bananas, then pour hot pudding on top.

Prepare the Meringue: In a clean mixing bowl, beat egg whites and cream of tartar at high speed for several minutes, until frothy.

Gradually add sugar, a little at a time, then add vanilla.

Continue beating on high speed until stiff peaks form.

Spread meringue over warm pudding until it covers the entire pie, sealing the crust edge. With the back of a large spoon, dab at the meringue, lifting the spoon high as you pull back to create a curlicue effect.

Bake at 375 degrees for 10 minutes, until meringue looks toasted. Watch carefully so as not to burn.

BLACK BOTTOM BANANA CREAM

Adding a layer of chocolate can only make an already seductive banana cream pie even more seductive. Of note, this recipe comes from Milwaukee, Wisconsin, where my parents met and courted, and where my mom made her "seduction pie" and got engaged. Thank you to the adorable and hardworking Valeri Lucks of Honeypie Café for sharing this recipe. If you're ever in Milwaukee, be sure to eat at Honeypie Café. I recommend Sunday brunch there. The Bloody Marys have so many veggies as a garnish, you might not need a meal. But make sure you save room for pie. They have so many tempting (some might say sinful) pie choices, you could just skip the main course altogether. Hotel rooms not provided.

CRUST

1½ cups graham cracker crumbs
½ cup sugar
½ tsp cinnamon
½ tsp salt
½ cup (1 stick) butter, melted

FILLING

½ cup sugar
4 egg yolks
½ tsp salt
¼ cup cornstarch
2½ cups whole milk
2 tbsp butter
1 tbsp vanilla
½ cup chopped dark chocolate
3 bananas

TOPPING

2 cups heavy whipping cream
Grated chocolate, for garnish

Prepare the Crust: Whisk dry ingredients together in a large bowl.

Pour the melted butter over graham cracker mixture. Stir together until butter is incorporated (mixture should feel like wet sand).

Press cracker mixture into a deep 9-inch pie pan. Use the bottom of a glass or a measuring cup to press crust firmly into the pan. Bake at 350 degrees for 10 minutes.

Prepare the Filling: In a large saucepan, whisk together sugar and egg yolks, then whisk in salt and cornstarch until smooth.

Pour in milk and whisk to combine thoroughly.

Cook over medium-high heat until thickened and bubbles form, whisking constantly. Remove from heat and add butter and vanilla.

Divide mixture in half. Mix chocolate into one half; leave the other half plain.

Pour the chocolate half of the mixture into the bottom of pre-baked pie crust.

Slice the bananas and distribute over the chocolate mixture.

Pour the vanilla mixture over the banana layer to fill the pie crust.

Cover with plastic wrap and refrigerate until cool, about 4 hours.

When you're ready to serve, top with whipped cream and decorate with grated chocolate on top.

CHOCOLATE CHESS

During the course of writing this cookbook I was dating someone new. It struck me as the perfect time to test the seductive powers of this recipe. I already knew Mr. Wonderful liked my chess pie (he had been a customer at my Pitchfork Pie Stand), and I knew he was addicted to chocolate, so what the heck? Why not sock it to him with a double dose of his favorite things? So did it work? Oh, yes. Every time he came over, he rummaged through my refrigerator hoping to find a secret stash of chocolate chess pie in there for him. Sometimes he got lucky.

CRUST
Basic Pie Dough for single-crust pie
   (see page 28), crimped

FILLING
1½ cups sugar
3 beaten eggs
1 can (5 ounces) evaporated milk
   (or substitute ½ cup whole milk)
¼ cup butter (½ stick), melted
¼ cup cocoa powder (or 2 squares
   unsweetened baking chocolate,
   melted)
1 tbsp cornmeal (see tip below)
1 to 2 tsp vanilla (I always use extra)
Dash of salt

Whipped cream, for garnish (optional)

Prepare the Basic Pie Dough for a single-crust pie (see page 28).

Prepare the Filling: Beat the sugar and eggs in a large bowl until blended.

Add the milk, butter, cocoa powder, cornmeal, vanilla, and salt and continue beating until smooth. (Or, if you bake like me, just throw everything into the mixing bowl at once and blend.)

Pour into the unbaked pie shell, then bake at 375 degrees for about 40 minutes. Filling will still be a little jiggly, but will set as it cools.

Serve with whipped cream for an extra touch.

NOTE: Also see page 92 in "Pies of the Pitchfork Pie Stand" for Granny Heck's Chess pie recipe, which inspired this chocolate version.

BETH'S TIP:
Cornmeal is not essential, but I like it for the texture and its nod to this pie's Southern heritage.

NUTELLA®

Really, is it possible to seduce yourself? Because let me tell you, I love Nutella® so much I don't even need a man in my life. It's pleasurable enough to spread this chocolate-hazelnut spread on my toast, but to put Nutella® in a pie? There are just no words for that. Unless you count moaning as words.

CRUST
Chocolate Cookie Crust (see page 32) or
　　Basic Pie Dough for single-crust pie
　　(see page 28)
(I prefer the basic pie dough so the
　　Nutella® flavor stands out more)

FILLING
1 package (8 ounces) cream cheese,
　　softened
¾ cup Nutella® (or any brand of
　　chocolate-hazelnut spread)
½ cup sugar
1 egg
½ cup toasted chopped hazelnuts
　　(optional, but gives it some crunch)
Pinch of salt

TOPPING
1 cup heavy cream
¼ cup sugar
1 tsp vanilla

Prepare the Chocolate Cookie Crust (see page 32) or the Basic Pie Dough for a single-crust pie (see page 28).

Prepare the Filling: In a large bowl, beat cream cheese, Nutella®, sugar, and egg until well blended.

Stir in hazelnuts (if using), then pour into pie crust.

Bake at 350 degrees for about 30 minutes or until the filling looks set. Let cool.

Prepare the Topping: Beat cream, sugar, and vanilla until peaks form. Serve whipped cream as a dollop on the side or on top.

 # Pies for Teaching

When I was 22, I took a career interest test. I had always wanted to be a writer, but my parents didn't consider writing a real job. But if not a writer then what would I be when I grew up? Desperate to find out, I consulted a career counselor. The test results suggested I become a beautician or a florist. Huh?! While I recognized the value of these jobs and the fact that these high scores showed I possessed a strong sense of aesthetics, I was, at the time, insulted. Further, I was advised by the career counselor, "Whatever you do, don't ever plan on becoming a teacher. You scored at the bottom of the charts for that."

Which is why, 28 years after taking that career test, I found it miraculous to be standing in a classroom in front of 26 high school students at Cardinal School in Eldon, Iowa, teaching them how to make apple pie. Me, a teacher?

I was originally invited to speak to the Literature Enhancement class about my career as a writer. After trying on many other salary-earning pursuits—sales, public relations, coffee entrepreneur, web producer, and a summer as a forest ranger—I finally mustered up the courage to defy my parents regarding my career path. I had had a lot of practice defying them for everything else, but my professional life was somehow the last stand I took against them. I officially became a writer after my Grandma Genny died and left me just enough of an inheritance to buy my first computer and pay for a college extension class called "How To Write for Magazines." I was 30.

Now, at 50, I have accumulated a portfolio with articles published in magazines including

Real Simple, Elle, Shape, Fitness, and—don't tell my mother—*Playboy*. But it was because of my blog, *The World Needs More Pie*, that the teacher, Patti Durflinger (or "Ms. D," as she is called), asked me to come to the class.

Me, a teacher?

I prefer hands-on learning to book learning, active participation as opposed to passively listening to a lecture, which, I suppose, explains why I experienced a temporary lapse of sanity and suggested to Ms. D that instead of just talking, I teach a pie class.

The day arrived and in spite of my best intentions, I dreaded going to school. School to me had always felt akin to being locked in a cage—too confining and so contrary to my free-spirited nature that I spent most of my own high school years plotting ways to escape. As it was, I was often tardy. But for this pie class at Cardinal School, I made it through the door well before the final 8:15 bell. After all, I was a responsible adult now! And I was no longer a student, but a teacher!

I carried my tubs of pie supplies into the Culinary Arts room (it was called Home Ec in my day) and laid out all the rolling pins, bowls, measuring cups, and pastry brushes, and awaited the onslaught of hormone-raging teenagers.

They filtered in, coming in waves, dressed in sweatshirts and jeans, backpacks slung over their shoulders and with cell phones in hands. Ms. D kept count, so when I heard her say "26" I knew it was show time.

I have taught many people how to make pie over the years, but I usually keep class size limited to 10. Because I insist that everyone leave with their own baked pie, the size of my pie classes is contingent on available oven space. The Home Ec department at Cardinal had five ovens and, based on capacity of eight pies per oven, it was easy to accommodate this large group. Well, the ovens could accommodate. I wasn't sure how *I* would do.

I can be bossy, opinionated, and when I get set on an idea there is no getting me to back down. I put these personality traits to work in my new role as schoolteacher. I greeted the class, briefly introducing myself as world traveler, writer, widow, pie baker, Native Iowan, and resident of the American Gothic House, and then immediately engaged the kids by having them wash their hands and choose an apron from my personal collection of the most hideous, old-fashioned aprons one can find. Aprons are a great icebreaker for students of any age, but the ensuing laughter and teasing when offering my frilliest aprons to the young and macho football players got us off to a good start.

After that, the next three flour-and-sugar-filled hours were a blur. It was as if I entered an altered state, a place where my focus was so extreme that nothing else outside of the present moment existed. I wondered: Is teaching always like this? Is it the kind of job where you're so engaged you not only don't watch the clock, you're not even aware if there's a clock in the room? And if it is, could this be a good job for me?

Everyone was spread out around six long tables. I had to stand on a chair to be seen, and from my elevated perch I talked loud and fast, enunciating every word, to keep everyone's attention. When it came time for mixing and rolling the dough, I raced around the room in my sneakers from student to student to student to offer my assistance or approval on their pie progress. I gave apple-peeling instructions while standing on a table in my overalls, wielding a paring knife. It was like being

part schoolmarm, part stand-up comedian. Did the students think I was bitchy or funny? I couldn't tell and I didn't have time to care. We had 26 pies to get in the ovens.

I used a portion of the 50 minutes of baking time to tell the group about my life, and I took the opportunity to convey a few lessons I've learned:

1. Good communication skills, including proper grammar and ability to write, provide the foundation for everything else.

2. Learn a foreign language while you're young. It's harder to learn as you get older.

3. Exercise. A strong body is a strong mind and a good confidence builder.

My little lecture was interrupted by smoke billowing out of the ovens. Pie filling overflowed onto the bottom of the ovens and choked the air with a thick gray haze, a consequence of packing so many pies in at once. The teachers raced to open the windows while I unloaded the finished—and unharmed—pies from the ovens.

What a sight to behold. Twenty-six pies lined up on a table, surrounded by 26 beaming, bouncy teenagers who couldn't wait to cut into their works of art. Every single pie looked perfect. Perfect in that homemade, no-two-are-alike kind of way. They weren't allowed to cut their pies until after lunch, giving the pies time to cool, which also gave the students time to think about sharing their pie with someone. Given that my life's mission is conveying how pie can heal, I had set a mandate that they give away at least one slice to someone in need, someone who might be going through a hard time or having a bad day, someone who needed cheering up, someone they wanted to thank or express their love to.

They really liked this idea of giving pie away to make others happy, and they took it seriously. This impressed me, along with everything else they did during the course of the three-hour class. They went from not wanting to get their hands dirty in the dough, to not wanting to put the dough down. They were very flexible when told we were short on rolling pins and that some were going to have to roll their pie dough with plastic sports drink bottles borrowed from the athletic department. They listened, they participated, they asked good questions, they jumped right in to do the work, they asked for help when they needed it, and they helped each other. If the dough was stuck to the table, extra apples needed peeling, or a pastry brush was in demand, I watched and smiled inside as they came to each other's aid.

When I got home, instead of being drained after the chaos and constant motion, I was energized. I was as beaming and proud of the students' efforts and outstanding results as they were. Maybe even more so. To quote a Swedish proverb: "Joy shared is joy doubled." If joy shared is joy doubled, then what is joy shared times 26? While baking pie makes me happy, I've never been as fulfilled as I was giving birth to 26 new pie bakers.

I'm not sure how I would do as a full-time teacher, but I'm just sorry it's taken me so many years to discover the results of that career test were wrong. Very wrong. Now I look forward to spending a lot more time in…yes, in school.

Pie Recipes for Teaching

Triple Berry

Blueberry Crumble

Peanut Butter

Chocolate-Chip Cookie

Harvest

Pecan Oatmeal

Spaghetti

TRIPLE BERRY

When I teach classes to young kids, this is the pie I make with them. First of all, there are no knives involved, and secondly, the berries are colorful, making for some artistic-looking pies. I also "cheat" when making this pie, buying my berries in bulk from—okay, I'll admit it—the frozen food section. I thaw the berries, but only partially, so they don't drown in their own watery juices.

CRUST
Basic Pie Dough for double-crust pie
　　(see page 28)

FILLING
6 to 8 cups berries, partially thawed
　　and drained
1 cup sugar (or less)
¼ cup cornstarch (or flour)
Dash of salt
Dash of cinnamon (optional)

1 tbsp butter, to pat on top of filling
1 beaten egg, to brush on top crust

Prepare the Basic Pie Dough for a double-crust pie (see page 28).

Prepare the Filling: In a bowl, mix all filling ingredients and pour into bottom pie crust.

Place pat of butter on top of the fruit mixture, then cover with top crust.

Trim edges, crimp, brush with beaten egg, then poke vent holes.

Bake at 425 degrees for 15 to 20 minutes, then turn oven down to 375 degrees and bake for another 20 to 30 minutes, until fruit filling is bubbling.

BLUEBERRY CRUMBLE

This pie just screams childhood. It's an easy pie to make, and even easier to eat. Simple as that.

CRUST
Basic Pie Dough for single-crust pie
    (see page 28), crimped

FILLING
3 pints blueberries (I pile them high!)
1 cup sugar (I usually use less)
¼ cup cornstarch
Dash of salt

CRUMBLE TOPPING
1 cup flour
½ cup (1 stick) butter, chilled and cut
    into large chunks
½ cup brown sugar, packed

Prepare the Basic Pie Dough for a single-crust pie (page 28).

Prepare the Filling: Rinse and drain blueberries.

While they are still slightly damp, toss them in a large bowl with sugar, cornstarch, and salt, coating the berries.

Pour into single, crimped pie crust.

Prepare the Crumble Topping: In a large bowl, rub ingredients together until texture resembles marbles. (**NOTE:** Not enough rubbing and your crumble topping will be too powdery and fine. So keep rubbing. Too much rubbing and it will become one big melted, sticky glob. In which case you can add a little more flour, or refrigerate until it gets cold and break it apart into manageable crumb size.)

With both hands, distribute the crumble topping over the top of the pie. Do not press down on it, as you don't want your crumbs to look flat. Bake this one on top of a cookie sheet or oven liner, as some of the crumbs may roll off in the oven.

Bake at 425 degrees for 15 to 20 minutes to brown the top, then turn oven down to 375 degrees and bake until the berries are bubbling.

PEANUT BUTTER

The hardest thing about making this pie is scraping the peanut butter out of the jar. In fact, it's so easy to make, it almost shouldn't qualify as learning experience. But then there are all kinds of students, with all levels of experience and ranges of tastes. And since peanut butter is the food of my childhood—and my adulthood—I feel it deserves a place here.

CRUST
Chocolate Cookie Crust (see page 32) or
  Graham Cracker Crust (see page 32)
  (I like the chocolate!)

FILLING
1 cup peanut butter (preferably creamy,
  but hey, it's your pie)
1 package (8 ounces) cream cheese,
  softened
½ cup sugar
2 cups heavy cream
4 tbsp sugar (to mix with heavy cream)
1 tsp vanilla

Chocolate peanut butter cups,
  chopped, for garnish

Prepare the Chocolate Cookie Crust (see page 32) or Graham Cracker Crust (see page 32).

Prepare the Filling: Blend the peanut butter, cream cheese, and ½ cup sugar in a large mixing bowl until smooth.

In a separate bowl, beat cream, 4 tbsp sugar, and vanilla with an electric mixer until fluffy. Fold half of the whipped cream into the peanut butter–cream cheese mixture.

Spoon into pie crust and chill for several hours.

Cover with remaining whipped cream before serving.

Garnish with chopped-up chocolate peanut butter cups.

BETH'S TIP:
If a little chocolate garnish isn't enough to satisfy, get a jar of hot fudge, melt it slightly, and pour it on the bottom crust for a chocolaty layer. Cool before adding the peanut butter.

• CHOCOLATE-CHIP COOKIE •

Before I became a pie baker, I was known for my cookies. I made lots of them in high school and my mom reminds me of how mad I would get when my three brothers devoured them as soon as they came out of the oven. Yeah, I was mad, because I never got to admire—let alone even see—the finished product. After all these years, I have found the perfect solution: Make a cookie pie, then they have to wait to eat it! Still, I recognize that people wanting to devour your baked goods is a compliment. Anyway, given that I got my start with cookies, I consider this a good starter pie. Hell, I consider it a good pie, period. (This is the same chocolate-chip cookie recipe I've been using since I was 14.)

CRUST
Basic Pie Dough for *two* single-crust
    pies (use double-crust recipe on
    page 28), crimped

FILLING
2¼ cups flour
1 tsp baking soda
1 tsp salt
1 cup (2 sticks) butter, softened
¾ cup sugar
¾ cup brown sugar, packed
1 tsp vanilla
2 eggs
1 package (12 ounces) chocolate chips
1 cup nuts (pecans or walnuts),
    chopped (optional)

Prepare the Basic Pie Dough for two single-crust pies (see page 28). (You'll still make the double-crust recipe, but for two separate pies.)

Prepare the Filling: Mix flour, baking soda, and salt in a small bowl and set aside.

In a large bowl, beat butter, sugars, and vanilla until creamy. Beat in eggs.

Stir in flour mixture, then add chocolate chips and nuts, if using.

Spread into pie shells and bake at 375 degrees for 50 minutes. If pie starts getting too brown, turn oven down to 350 degrees.

BETH'S TIP:
For a moister pie, cut back on the flour.

HARVEST

This is the pie that can be anything you want it to be—sweet, savory, or even both. I always liked a pie from the Seattle Pie Company (now operating as "Pie Bar" in Seattle) called "Everything But The…" It was some seemingly random combo of apples, blackberries, strawberries, and God-knows-what-else. And it was decidedly good. Harvest pie is a similar free-for-all in that you can just throw in whatever is in season. Be prepared to be amazed. If not, surprised. If it's a disaster (but it won't be), just serve it with ice cream.

CRUST

Basic Pie Dough for double-crust pie
(see page 28)

FILLING

4 to 5 apples (any kind, try mixing
varieties), peeled and sliced
2 pears, peeled and sliced
1 cup cranberries
½ cup raisins
½ cup walnuts or pecans, or both
¼ cup flour, to thicken
1 to 2 tsp cinnamon
½ tsp salt
½ tsp nutmeg (optional)
¼ tsp ginger (optional, but then again
everything in this pie is optional!)

1 tbsp butter, to pat on top of filling
1 beaten egg, to brush on top crust

Prepare the Basic Pie Dough for a double-crust pie (see page 28).

Prepare the Filling: Mix everything together in a large bowl, then pour into pie crust.

Place pat of butter on top of fruit, then cover with top crust.

Trim, crimp, brush with egg, then poke vent holes.

Bake at 425 degrees for 15 to 20 minutes, then turn oven down to 375 degrees and continue baking for another 30 minutes or more, until fruit softens and bubbles inside.

BETH'S TIP:

In general, a 10-inch pie can hold 3 pounds of fruit and 1 cup of sugar. So if you come up with your own Harvest fruit combo, just keep this ratio in mind and you will have a well-balanced pie.

PECAN OATMEAL

If there is such a thing as a soul mate in pie, then mine is Kathy Knapp, who runs the Pie-O-Neer Café in Pie Town, New Mexico. Kathy inherited this recipe from her grandmother, Rosie, who owned the Cozy Corner Cafe in Rochelle, Illinois, where many a pie sat cooling on the windowsill. This is Kathy's version of her grandma's pie. She calls it "Pie-O-Neer Pecan Oat" and it's the most requested recipe at her Pie-O-Neer Café. I want to be the pie student for a change and get a lesson from her. New Mexico, here I come.

CRUST

Basic Pie Dough for *two* single-crust pies (use double-crust recipe on page 28)

FILLING

½ cup (1 stick) butter, softened

½ cup sugar

½ tsp cinnamon

½ tsp salt

¼ tsp ground cloves

2 cups corn syrup (Kathy uses 1 cup dark and 1 cup light; I use only light)

6 eggs

1 cup old-fashioned oats (I doubled this from her recipe)

1½ cups toasted pecan pieces

Prepare the Basic Pie Dough for two single-crust pies (see page 28). (You'll still make the double-crust recipe, but for two separate pies.)

Prepare the Filling: Cream butter and sugar together in a medium-sized bowl.

Add spices and mix well. Blend in corn syrup.

Add eggs, one at a time, stirring—not beating—into the mixture (see note below).

Gently stir in oats.

Sprinkle bottom of pie crusts with most of the pecan pieces.

Pour filling into crusts and sprinkle additional pecan pieces on top.

Bake at 350 degrees for 45 to 50 minutes or until tops are browned. Do not overbake. It's okay if center jiggles a little when pie is moved. Eat it warm!

NOTE: If too much air is beaten into the mixture after eggs are added, this will turn into a cake, so go easy on the beating.

SPAGHETTI

This one is pretty clever. I first had it when an old boyfriend, a single dad who is not much of a baker, let alone a cook, wanted to impress me with a pie. I had to stop myself from laughing when I saw it. The pasta makes the "crust," the tomato-meat sauce is the "filling," and the cheese mimics a "top crust." Proof that pie comes in many forms. Sometimes surprising and humorous ones.

CRUST
6 ounces (⅓ box) spaghetti
½ cup grated Parmesan cheese
2 tbsp olive oil
2 beaten eggs

FILLING
1 small onion, diced
1 lb ground meat (beef or turkey)
Salt and pepper, to taste
2 cups tomato-based pasta sauce,
    from a jar or homemade
1 cup ricotta cheese (or cottage cheese)
6 to 8 fresh basil leaves, cut up
½ to 1 cup shredded mozzarella
    cheese

Prepare the Crust: Boil the spaghetti according to directions on pasta package.

Drain and mix with Parmesan cheese, olive oil, and beaten eggs.

Line a 10-inch deep-dish pie plate with this "crust."

Prepare the Filling: In a skillet over medium heat, sauté the onion then add the meat, cooking until it's browned.

Add salt and pepper to taste.

Stir in the tomato pasta sauce and simmer for 15 minutes or so.

Spoon the ricotta (or cottage) cheese onto the spaghetti crust (I shake my head every time I picture it).

Next, pour on the meat sauce, distributing evenly.

Bake at 350 degrees for 20 minutes.

Throw on fresh basil leaves for some nice flavor, sprinkle with mozzarella, then bake for another 5 minutes, until the cheese melts.

Cut into pie-shaped wedges, serve, eat, enjoy, and laugh.

Novelty Pies: Pies to Say Thank You

While sharing your homemade pie is perfect for celebrating birthdays, easing others' grief as well as your own, saying "I'm sorry," and, yes, sometimes luring lovers, I cannot understate the positive impact of using pie to say thank you.

I try to keep a supply of pies in my freezer, because you never know when you might need one to use as a token of thanks, a tip to the plumber, a hostess gift when you're invited to a last-minute dinner party, and sometimes an acknowledgment to the FedEx delivery person when he makes his third delivery of the week. (What can I say? My FedEx guy looks like Bradley Cooper, so I order online more often.)

Pies may come in all shapes and sizes, but you can scale the size of the pie gift according to the situation and the person. A small pie can go a long way. And it's the thought that counts, right? If you have a big pie on hand, maybe just wrap up a slice in waxed paper and tie it with a ribbon. My freezer supply contains a variety of sizes and flavors—mainly, the 5-inch mini pies I sell at my pie stand and a few pies-in-a-jar. Incidentally, these baby sizes make a nice, portion-controlled treat for your own gratitude-deserving self.

Also, when I freeze these small pies, I like to stockpile varieties like blueberry, peach, and Shaker Lemon, because it's like sharing a taste of summer sunshine in the middle of, say, a snowy day in April. (For more on that, see page 112 in "Pies to Lift Your Spirits.")

A mini pie or a slice is usually just enough to get your message through without overwhelming someone with the gesture. For example, if I thanked the FedEx man with a pie big enough to feed all 18 kids in the Duggar Family (see Slab pie on page 196), he might get the wrong idea.

You also may want to be mindful that your gesture—and your pie—isn't so outstanding that it outshines you. For example, one time I gave a whole apple pie as a thank you, following up after a job interview. I was so determined to outdo my competition for the position that I wanted to send something more impressive than a standard thank-you note. I was applying for a public relations job in Beverly Hills, during the year of my "pie sabbatical" at Mary's Kitchen in Malibu. (As much as I loved working at Mary's, I couldn't survive on minimum wage.)

The day after my PR interview, I was back in the Malibu kitchen, which, for the record, was only slightly larger than an office cubicle, only hotter.

And yet much more fun. After my baking shift ended that afternoon, I boxed up one of the apple pies I'd just made and drove through L.A. rush-hour traffic to Beverly Hills to hand-deliver it. If you know what L.A. traffic is like, that should tell you how determined I was to get this job! The pie was still so hot I had to leave the lid propped open so it didn't get soggy from its own steam.

I rode up in the elevator and several office workers, lured by the cinnamon scent, leaned in toward me to get a glimpse of what was in the box. "Sorry. It's not for you," I chirped, proud and confident that my pie would be a huge hit with my prospective new boss, Paul.

Well, Paul wasn't in, so I didn't get the satisfaction of seeing the surprised and happy look on his face upon seeing the heaping-high pie. Instead, I left the pie with his secretary and practically made her sign an affidavit stating that she wouldn't eat it. "And please don't

drool on it either," I called over my shoulder as I was leaving.

I phoned two days later to confirm that Paul got his pie. Oh yeah, he got his pie. And this is what he said: "That pie was incredible. I kept cutting into it. I couldn't stop. I ate the whole thing. My wife said, 'You don't even like pie.' Your pie was so good you should open a bakery."

My hopes for a bigger paycheck plummeted. "Sure, if you want to finance it," I muttered. I knew from his comment that he wasn't going to hire me.

Like I said, sometimes you just need to keep it small. Then again, because I didn't get that job, I took a road trip to Oregon a few weeks later and it was there I met my husband, Marcus. And even though my time with Marcus was cut short (we spent eight years together), the adventure of being married to him was far better than any PR job that would have confined me in a hermetically sealed high-rise. Who do I thank (with the hugest possible pie) for that?!

Pie Recipes for Novelty Pies

Mini Pies

Pies in a jar

Hand Pies

Cobblers & Crisps

Crumble Topping

Freeform Pies

Slab Pies

MINI PIES

I had to shop around to find these small 5- to 6-inch tins, but they're out there. If nothing else, search for them online. I also have an oven-proof, shallow ceramic cereal bowl that works well. And sometimes I use a ramekin. The point is, small is beautiful. Small is adorable. Small is irresistible. At the pie stand, I always sell out of my mini pies first. They are perfect for one or two people.

There is no science to making a mini pie. And I never make just one. I make several at a time and, if it's outside of my pie-stand season, I freeze them or give them as gifts. Follow the recipe for any of the pies in this book. Just roll out your dough to the shape and size of your pie dishes and divvy up the filling into your dishes. The crust-to-filling ratio should even out, regardless of what size dishes you're using.

Crimping can be a little trickier on these baby pies. You have much less room to pinch your fingers around the rim. But take your time, dip your fingers in flour when you need to keep the dough from sticking to them, and you can make a fluted edge that will have everyone gushing over the cuteness of your little pie.

PIES IN A JAR

If you thought the mini pies were popular, you should hear people gush over pies in a jar. Again, there's no science to this. Just remember: Any recipe can be made into any shape. You can find these darling squatty little canning jars in variety stores, hardware stores, and even drug stores. Pies made in them can be frozen in an unbaked state and go straight from the freezer to the oven (but do remove the lids first). They can also be baked first and then frozen. If freezing, however, stick to fruit, custard, savory, and ice-cream pies. Meringue-topped cream pies do not freeze well.

To make the jar pies, roll your dough thinner than usual. Cut out a circle larger than the jar, accounting for the jar's depth and width. Place the dough gently into the jar and press it into the sides with your fingers, pushing the gaps of air space out from the bottom corners. With a knife, scrape any excess dough off the rim of the jar so the lid can screw on tightly and get a clean seal. Add your filling (dice your apples to accommodate the small size). Berries and custards work especially well for this style of pie.

For variety, decorate the top with a lattice crust (cut and weave mini strips of dough—it's adorable!) or use a cookie cutter and place cutout shapes of dough on top. Crumble topping also works well.

HAND PIES

Small is trendy these days. You see mini pies popping up everywhere, including little pies-on-a-stick, a.k.a. "pie pops." Why bother with a stick when you're going to eat the pie in four quick bites? Per my usual style of eliminating steps and nonessential doohickeys, I just go for the hand pie, a.k.a. "turnover." This portable pie shouldn't be considered a trend, given that it is a staple food in many other cultures. The Jamaican patty, Italian calzone, British pasty, Indian samosa, Mexican empanada, Austrian strudel...I could go on, but you get the idea.

You can go rectangle (think Pop-Tarts) or round or even cutout shapes like hearts. Either way, just start with the Basic Pie Dough for a double crust (see page 28) and instead of forming your dough into two disks, reduce the size and make a bunch of mini disks. For the pie stand, I use a scale—though trust me, if I weren't making them in such huge bulk, I wouldn't bother with the precision! But to give you an idea, my little hand pies (and mini pies too) use 2½ ounces of dough. Just experiment and you will figure out the weight and size you need. Maybe you have bigger hands and thus want bigger pies.

Roll out your little dough disks to either your rectangle or round shapes. (Remember the horseback-riding analogy on page 26). *You control the direction that dough is going to roll.*)

Place a few spoonfuls of your pie filling (sweet, savory, whatever) in the middle of your dough shape.

If rectangle or cutout shape, cover with a matching-size piece for a top crust, then press the edges together with a fork to seal and crimp them. If round, fold the dough in half to encase the filling, making a half moon shape, then seal the edges together and crimp by pressing down with a fork. And by fork, I do mean the tines.

Brush with a beaten egg, and poke a few small vent holes in the top (a few perforations with the fork prongs will suffice).

Bake at 425 degrees to brown the crusts, about 10 minutes. Then turn oven down to 375 degrees and continue baking until they look done. Translation: Filling may start to ooze out.

NOTE: These little guys bake *much* faster than big pies, so stay close to your oven.

COBBLERS & CRISPS

Technically, the definition of pie states that it must have a crust to get the "p" label. But who cares? Sometimes you want to save a little time, in which case you can make your pie without the encasement. Prepare your fruit (or savory) filling as usual (note, we are not talking cream pies here!), then either whip up some baking-powder biscuit dough or make crumble topping to cover the top. You can make this in any shape deep-dish pan or pie plate you like. Bake at 350 degrees, since you won't need the high heat to set the crust.

BISCUIT TOPPING
1 cup flour
2 tsp baking powder
¼ cup sugar
¼ tsp salt
¼ cup (½ stick) butter
¼ cup milk (add more if needed)
1 beaten egg

Mix dry ingredients in a bowl and cut in butter (with hands or, ahem, metal tools of your choice).

Mix in milk and egg. Batter should be moist.

Drop spoonfuls on top of fruit filling (will be in "blobs" and not smooth).

Bake at 350 degrees for about 30 minutes, until topping is browned and filling bubbles.

CRUMBLE TOPPING

1 cup flour
½ cup (1 stick) butter, chilled and cut
   into large chunks
½ cup brown sugar, packed

In a large bowl, rub ingredients together until the texture resembles marbles. (NOTE: Not enough rubbing and your crumble topping will be too powdery and fine. So keep rubbing. Too much rubbing and it will become a melted, sticky glob. In which case you can add a little more flour, or refrigerate until it gets cold and break it apart into manageable crumb size.)

With both hands, distribute the crumble topping over the top of the filling. Do not press the crumbs down, as you want your topping to look robust, not flat.

FREEFORM PIES

You can make pie in virtually any kind of ovenproof dish. Then again, you don't even need a dish. You can just use the dough as a container for the filling, folding the excess edge in on top of the innards. You can do this round, rectangle, square, triangle...any shape you like. Just roll out your dough to the desired size and shape, and place it on a cookie sheet (on top of a piece of parchment paper or silicone baking mat, if you have on hand). Scoop pie filling into the middle, leaving a few inches of edge showing, then fold the edges inward to cover the filling. You can fold it in all the way so the top is closed, or leave some of the filling exposed. There will be wrinkles in the dough, giving your pie a "rustic" look, which is, of course, a euphemism for "messy." As I like to say, "Pie should look homemade."

SLAB PIES

This isn't a very nice name for what is simply a super-size pie made on a cookie sheet (the large kind with a lip, known as a jelly-roll pan). You can also use a casserole dish. Just as you use the same dough-to-filling ratio for mini pies, the same applies for the slab. You are feeding a crowd, so double the recipe for this one. Maybe even triple it. You may not be able to get your oversized dough into the pan without breaking it. If this is the case (and it probably will be), use a paring knife to cut the dough into manageable pieces and arrange them evenly in the pan. I like making this pie with a lattice top. Use extra-wide strips of dough to save time.

Above (left):
American Gothic by Grant Wood, 1930
Oil on Beaver Board
Friends of American Art Collection
1930.934
The Art Institute of Chicago
Photography © The Art Institute of
Chicago

Above (right): A view from the
famous second floor window
of the American Gothic House
(view is from the inside of the
house looking out).

Right: The front of the American
Gothic House which inspired
Grant Wood's famous painting.

About the American Gothic House

★ Grant Wood painted "American Gothic" in 1930. The original painting hangs in the Art Institute in Chicago.

★ The "couple" in the painting is actually supposed to be a father and daughter. The "father" was Grant Wood's dentist, Byron McKeeby, and the "daughter" was Wood's sister, Nan Wood Graham. The two never posed together in front of the house and Wood didn't set up an easel in front to the house; he painted his masterpiece in his studio in Cedar Rapids, Iowa.

★ The house appears tiny from the outside but whenever people step inside they always say, "It's bigger than it looks." The total square footage, including the finished basement, is 1,440 square feet.

★ There is a Gothic-style window on the backside of the house, identical to the famous one on the front. The back one, however, swings open on a hinge and that is how the furniture gets moved in and out of the top floor as the winding staircase is too narrow.

★ The house was built in 1881. Though it did not originally have a bathroom or central heating, it now has both. The wood plank floors are holding strong, but require occasional hammering of the square-headed nails that poke up.

★ Placed in the National Register of Historic Places in 1974, the house was privately owned until 1991, when it was donated to the State Historical Society of Iowa. It has always been a private residence and is not open to the public.

★ It takes a special kind of person to live in this house. Besides having tourists peek in the windows, there are other "intrusions." Given its rural location, some of the challenges include infestations of Boxelder bugs and Japanese beetles, the occasional field mouse, and a few too many snakes. Fortunately, no snakes have been found in the bedroom.

There is a visitor center and museum next door to the house that offers free costumes to dress up like the people in the painting. Volunteers are on hand to take your photo. Check their website for hours: www.americangothichouse.net

Dedication

This book is dedicated to my pie mentor, Mary Spellman. She not only taught me how to make pie, she restored my spirit at a time I needed it. I am forever indebted and grateful for her lessons that sustained me during my darkest days, lessons I have subsequently been privileged to share with others.

And to my parents, Tom and Marie Howard. I so greatly admire their love and devotion to each other, to our family, to me—and to banana cream pie.

My Mom

Acknowledgments

Trying to organize a list of people I want to thank turned out to be more difficult for me than writing a pie recipe. So I decided to approach the list the way I approach pie making—just throw everything—or everyone—in the bowl in no certain order and it turns out just fine in the end.

THE CRUST:

A crust is the foundation for a pie and the vessel that holds the filling in place. Thank you to the team at Race Point Publishing for being that foundation: my editor Jeannine Dillon, art director Jacqui Caulton, photographers Kathryn Gamble and Rick Lozier, illustrator

Melissa Wood, copy editor Lindsay Herman, food stylist Mandy Mack, publicist Dalyn Miller, and marketing manager Katie Fawkes.

THE FILLING:

There were a whole lot of people who contributed to this book, many of them offering more than one ingredient. The thanks for this filling, the sustenance of the book, goes to people who contributed recipes, tested recipes, proofread the manuscript, loaned pie plates for the photo shoot, brought ingredients to my backdoor, helped at the pie stand, offered a place to write, and provided guidance, support, love, and inspiration in Eldon, Iowa and far beyond.

Alan Marks, the Aldi staff in Ottumwa, Iowa, Allen and Rosie Morrison, Angie Klock, Ashlyn Martin, Bev Sloan, Bill Smith, Billye Jo Burnett, Bob and Iola Thomas, Carol Barnett, Carole Permar, Carolyn Agner, Catherine Gewertz, Christina Montalvo, Christine Buckley, Cindy Molitor of Retro Revival Biz (I'm wearing her apron in the cover photo), Colleen Sommers, Connie Sherman, Corey Irion, Dakota McElderry, Dave Pittman, David Sloan, Diana Harness, Diane Phillips, Don and Shirley Eakins, EllynAnne Geisel, Erin Margenau, Esther Tweedy, Hattie Peck, Holly Hollingsworth, Jayne Jordan, Jerome Thompson and the State of Iowa Historical Society, Jessi May, Joan Borel. Joan Posch, Joanne Maynard, Kathleen Beebout, Kathy Knapp, Kimberley Cetron, Kristi McDowell, Lana Ross, LeAnn Luedke, Leea Ostrander, Marie Zoromski, Mark Fisher, Mary Spellman, Nan Schmid, Nancy Moffat (with an added dash of love), Natalie Galatzer, Neal and Dianne Rhinehart, Pat Hancock, Patti Durflinger (an extra heaping spoonful of gratitude to you), Priscilla Coffman, Sue Sesko, Tom and Marie Howard, and Valeri Lucks.

THE TOPPING:

Just like a slice of pie is not complete without a dollop of whipped cream or a scoop of ice cream on the side, I want to give a generous topping of thanks to my many pie class students; Pitchfork Pie Stand customers and volunteers; the volunteers and staff at the American Gothic House Center; my Facebook, Twitter, and blog followers; and readers of *Making Piece* and of this book, *Ms. American Pie*. Your enthusiasm and support has been so helpful. Thank you, also, to the many journalists who have discovered and promoted my story—and more important, my message. Last but not least, a special nod to the lovely people of Newtown, Connecticut, for so graciously accepting and appreciating the healing powers of pie.

I'm sorry if I left anyone out. It happens sometimes, just like how I occasionally forget a pie ingredient. But please know I am still grateful for your help.

About the author

Beth Howard is a journalist, author, and an accidental cookbook author. Accidental, she says, because she has a hard time following recipes or any kind of rules. (She credits four years of Catholic high school for helping her hone her rebellious nature.) She is also the accidental resident of the American Gothic House. During the summer of 2010, she was planning on moving back to Los Angeles when a road sign led her on a six-mile detour in her beloved RV ("The Beast") to the tourist attraction. When she saw the little white farmhouse, it was love at first sight. Smitten but reluctant to commit to rural living (Eldon's population is 900 and the nearest Starbucks is 100 miles away), she asked the landlord for a three-month lease. He said no. Four years later she is still living in the famous one-bedroom cottage and loving it. Even her friends and family are shocked by this.

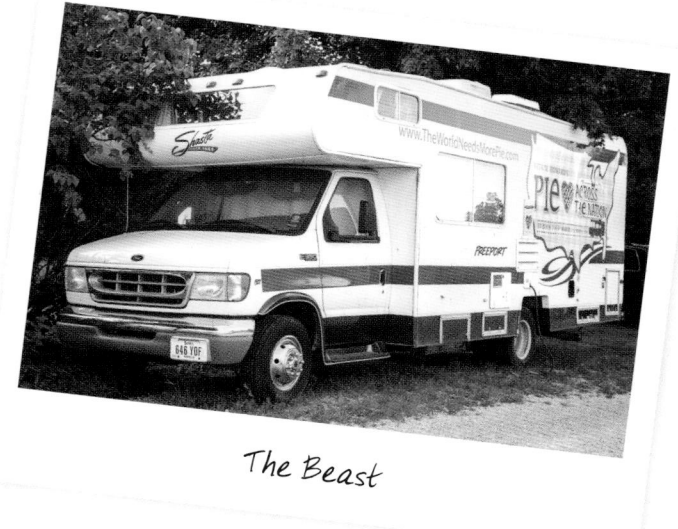

The Beast

Permissions

Recipes or images identified by page number are either reproduced or adapted with the kind permission of the following:

Page 54, *Cinnamon.* Printed with permission from Diana Harness.

Page 61, *Peach Pie with Lard Crust.* Printed with permission from Carole Permar.

Page 62, *Toffee Pecan.* Printed with permission from Kathleen Beebout.

Page 64, *Fresh Apricot.* Printed with permission from Kathleen Beebout.

Page 65, *Black Raspberry.* Printed with permission from Lana Ross.

Page 72, *Pulled Pork Hand Pies.* Printed with permission from Priscilla Coffman.

Page 92, *Chess.* Printed with permission from Holly Hollingsworth.

Page 95, *Shoofly.* Printed with permission from Sue Sesko.

Page 105, *Lemon Meringue.* Printed with permission from Mary Spellman.

Page 110, *BLT.* Printed with permission from Marie Zoromski.

Page 118, *Shaker Orange.* Printed with permission from Natalie Galatzer.

Page 122, *Atlantic Beach.* Printed with permission from Bill Smith.

Page 136, photo of Frank Barnett and Carol Barnett reproduced with permission from Carol Barnett.

Page 137, *Amish Funeral.* Reprinted with permission from Andrews McNeel Publishing. From the book *The Amish Cook at Home: Simple Pleasures of Food, Family and Faith* by Lovina Eicher with Kevin Willilams. Copyright © 2008 by Lovina Eicher with Kevin Williams.

Page 138, *Sour Cream Raisin.* Printed with permission from Joanne Maynard.

Page 144, *Shepherd's.* Printed with permission from Melissa Wood.

Page 155, *Coconut Cream.* Printed with permission from Pat Hancock.

Page 156, *French Silk.* Printed with permission from Lana Ross.

Page 159, *Chocolate Cream.* Printed with permission from Mary Spellman.

Page 162, *Black Bottom Banana Cream.* Printed with permission from Valeri Lucks/Honeypie Café.

Page 178, *Pecan Oatmeal.* Printed with permission from Kathy Knapp.

Page 198, *American Gothic* by Grant Wood, 1930. Image licensed from the Art Institute of Chicago/Friends of American Art Collection, 1930.934.

Special thanks to Libby's® Pumpkin and Karo® Syrup for their pumpkin pie and pecan pie recipes, and to Christina Montalvo for inspiring me with her Chai-Spice Pumpkin pie.

Index